EVERYMAN'S LIBRARY

911

POETRY

Everyman, I will go with thee, and be thy guide,
In thy most need to go by thy side

HEINRICH HEINE was born some time between 1797 and 1801 at Düsseldorf. Studied law at Bonn and after his graduation visited London, Munich, and Italy. In 1831 made Paris his home. Contracted spinal disease in 1848 and was an invalid until his death in 1856.

HEINE'S
PROSE AND POETRY

INTRODUCTION BY
ERNEST RHYS

LONDON   J. M. DENT & SONS LTD
NEW YORK   E. P. DUTTON & CO INC

INTRODUCTION

'*The wind of the Paris Revolution blew about the candles a little in the dark night of Germany, but the old watchmen are already bringing out the fire-engines and will keep the candles closer snuffed in future. Poor, fast-bound German people, lose not all heart in thy bonds!*' So Heine wrote near a century ago. What would he say if he could rise from his grave in his New Jerusalem at Montmartre and look upon Germany now, long after his death? For with all his despair of the new order he looked forward to the day of deliverance until the very end. He was born in 1797 at Düsseldorf when the echoes of the French Revolution were still reverberating. His father was a little Jewish tradesman—not exactly the fine figure he pictured, a bit of a dandy, an officer who arrived in the town with a train of horses, for in truth Samson Heine was looked on with suspicion at first by the Düsseldorf Jewish community. But he was extremely good-looking like the rest of the Heines, and he must have had a touch of his son's humour, for when the boy asked him about the family pedigree, he said: 'Your grandfather was a little Jew with a big beard!'

The grandfather's name was Chajjim Bückeburg, which had been adroitly cut down—from Chajjim to Heymann, Heymann to Heinemann, and from that to Heine. The name over the draper's shop at Düsseldorf in the Bolkerstrasse was plain Samson Heine. The shop did not prosper, for Samson in spite of his name was not the strong man of the family—that was his brother Salomon, who became a millionaire. But he was lucky in picking up a wife of better family than himself, Piera or Betty van Geldern, daughter of a Jewish physician. Heine was fond, very fond, of his mother, and made the most of her comeliness and even her culture; but in fact she spelt badly, and though said to be a reader of Goethe, she never cared much for her son Harry's poetry. Harry he was called after an English business friend of the family—a name he afterwards converted into the Heinrich by which he became famous.

Düsseldorf was in those days a little country town with the river Rhine running by and a pleasant countryside within easy reach, and Heine always spoke and thought of himself in his

vii

German moments as a true Rhinelander. The family was not too well off for him to play with the little street-boys in the town, and he picked up from them, no doubt, the bits of folk-lore that helped afterwards to colour his verse. Poets' mothers often have much to do with the real nurture of their sons, but Betty Heine, though she wished her Harry to become famous, had no notion of his turning poet. She did not like to see him reading story-books, would not let him go to see folk-plays, and was angry if the maids told him ghost-tales.

It seems odd to think of his being trained for a business life in Düsseldorf—he even once set up shop, happily without success. His rich uncle Salomon, who was settled in Hamburg, and his pretty cousin Amalie, who inspired him with his first boyish passion, bring that city vividly into the record after the Düsseldorf days. He stayed three years at Hamburg, and then, his father having failed and being unable to keep him, he went with his uncle's help to the University of Bonn. There Schlegel, who was a professor, widened his ideas and gave impetus to his poetry; there he translated poems of Byron, began a tragedy, wrote ballads and *Lieder*, and projected a first book of poems. From Bonn he went on to Göttingen, but only stayed six months, because of a duel fought against the rules. Besides his uncle Salomon and the lovely cousin Amalie, there was another member of his family group on the mother's side, his uncle Simon von Geldern, who strangely affected his boyish imagination. A great traveller, von Geldern had been an Arab chief in Africa, and Heine was so impressed by his romantic story that he thought of himself as his uncle's *Doppelgänger*. He never travelled into the East, but he dreamt of it, and the wanderer's instinct was in his blood. The holiday described in his *Harzreise* falls within his early student days—a delightful vagabond book which deserves to be a hiker's classic.

His third University was Berlin, and at Berlin he met a remarkable woman, Rahel Varnhagen von Ense, a rich and cultured Jewess whose house became a poet's haven to him. There he found a brilliant intellectual circle, in which homage to Goethe was an article of faith. One summer he went to Weimar to visit the Olympian poet, to whom he had already sent his first volume of poems, though Goethe does not appear to have been much impressed. The account Heine gave of his Weimar visit is in his most Heinesque vein. On getting there, he forgot all the fine things he had thought of saying. 'I was very near addressing Goethe in Greek,' he said, 'but when I found he understood German, all I was able to tell him was that the plums along the road between Jena and Weimar were very good.'

He did not like Berlin any more than he loved the Prussians, and thence he went back to Göttingen where he wrote, besides some of his loveliest lyrics, a remarkable prose book, the *Rabbi von Bacharach*, of which unluckily the greater part was destroyed in a fire. He took his degree of Doctor-of-Laws there, but instead of following up that career, his student days over, he entered upon a much more congenial period of *Wanderjahre* at home and abroad in which Uncle Salomon was still the chief, if at times a grumbling almoner. He went to the island of Norderney one autumn and made friends with the fisher-folk and the sailors—he always had a liking for the folk-life reflected in his poems. We find him later crossing the North Sea to the Thames, as an outcome of which he wrote his *Englische Fragmente*, a book by no means flattering to England or the English. 'Send a philosopher to London, but for heaven's sake, no poet,' he said in one of his proverbial asides. When in London he stayed in Craven Street, Strand, at No. 32. A tablet marks the house, which is little changed from his day, and on a moody dusky evening it is still possible to picture the narrow street of 1827 through which he came and went, not always in the best of humour.

All the while he was growing more disaffected towards his fatherland, where the anti-Jewish feeling and the stifling political atmosphere made the freedom he loved impossible, and he turned his eyes longingly to his New Jerusalem—Paris. But though he felt himself spiritually an outlaw in Germany, his fame was growing there. His book, *Lyrisches Intermezzo*, had won over the younger critics and gained him a place among the mastersingers, and a right to be ranked as Goethe's successor.

Before he had decided the plans for his Paris-exile, he made a journey to Italy, where he spent two prodigal years. Though he did not know Italian, he enjoyed at the Baths of Lucca what was for him, even allowing for some extravagance in the account, one of the halcyon times of his life. While there he shed the last mortifying shreds and rags of his Jewish gaberdine. The Latin and Hellenic sense of beauty drove out what he called the Spirit of the Nazarene—that sense for

* 911

which he afterwards found a formula in the Saint-Simonian creed of his New Gospel.

In 1831 he left Germany for Paris, in May, the month in the year when it is gayest. He revelled in the life of the boulevards and the theatres, the sense of being freed from the stigma of the Jew. He said that even the fishes in the sea, if they asked one another how they were feeling, would say, 'Like Heine in Paris!'

He wrote hard there, however, did much journalism, and though not the best his pen could do, he took endless pains over it. A friend, Hiller the composer, who saw some of his MSS., noticed there was hardly a line that had not been corrected and recorrected. He told Hiller: 'I worked like a goldsmith finishing a chain, link by link, one after another, one within another.'

He had begun in 1844 a series of volumes called the *Salon* —after the picture-gallery of that name—in which appeared some of his later poems and his comic masterpiece: the *Memoiren des Herrn von Schnabelewopski*, a delicious malicious extravanganza. In it the Jews came in for a deadly mixture of pity and satire, seasoned with impropriety; their Jehovah is the butt of the deadliest irony of all. Yet, immersed as he had become in the current of international politics, he confessed to being tired of it all — tired of politics, patriotism, public affairs, and journalism. He secretly longed to give himself up to his own art, write poems, and follow the bent of his genius. He was poetry's prodigal, who wished to return, but was tied to his land of exile by close strands, more binding than that Hegelian knot he had contrived to cut.

His campaign still went on against the reactionaries in France and Germany. But his attitude was bound to change in his Paris exile; even the tenets of his New Gospel gave way and grew more *convenable*. That did not mean any loss of his provocative powers, and now as if to rouse his critics, he turned Royalist, he, who had so often attacked the kings regnant—just as before he had renounced his Jewish birthright. That gave fresh zest to the deadly charge against him as a renegade and apostate; and he retaliated in kind. His old friend and fellow-exile, Börne, a Jew like himself, had led the attack, and as before in his quarrel with the poet Platen, Heine did not mind how he struck back. Unluckily in this case he waited till after Börne's death to take his revenge.

By the side of Börne, who was honest and loyal to his republican flag, Heine must have seemed turncoat, a moral coward to his old associates. But it was in his temperament to be mercurial and recalcitrant. Every formula he had used he was bound eventually to turn inside out. His most brilliant revoke is to be found in his lyric satire, *Atta Troll*, which he called 'the last free forest-song of Romanticism.' Atta Troll is a dancing bear, droll personifier of the Tendency-poets Heine was out to rout and destroy with his singing rapier. The poem is written in fluent quatrains, some of them as full of echoing consonances as a Welsh englyn:

> Andre Zeiten! andre Vögel!
> Andre Vögel, andre Lieder!
> Sie gefielen mir vielleicht,
> Wenn ich andre Ohren hätte.

Atta Troll he wrote in 1841, during a summer visit to Cauterets in the Pyrénées, with his beloved Mathilde, whom he married on his return to Paris that August. He had come to know her years before when a girl of nineteen—a shop-girl in her aunt's shoe-shop—and fallen passionately in love with her. Mathilde was his name for her; her real name was more imposing—Crescentia. She was a pretty creature, simple, uneducated, who knew and could know nothing of his poetry. For some time, though they lived happily together, he did not think of marrying her, and only decided on it when, his health failing, he was afraid she might be left unprovided at his death; Mathilde, no more than he, knew how to be saving of money, and he had to drive his pen late and early to keep the house going.

When at last they were married, he only asked to the wedding those friends who were living in irregular unions like his own, and at the wedding breakfast he made a humorous speech inviting them all to get married like him. He took Mathilde once to Germany with him, where, not knowing the language, she was extremely bored and unhappy, poor girl; on another visit, when he went over for the last time to see his old mother at Hamburg and his uncle Salomon, he left Mathilde behind and was torn with anxiety and jealousy while they were apart. His mother, whom he had always loved with the profound affection the sons of his race have so often shown, he last saw in 1844—and that was his final good-bye to Germany. He went back to Paris with the seeds of his fatal and prolonged illness already menacing his health.

To turn again to his books, his *Neue Gedichte* appeared that same year, 1844, a volume in which his lyric powers were, if less impulsive, not a whit abated. Before it appeared, he had been writing the series of critical and political articles that make up the prose volume, *Lutetia*. In these he poured out again, all hot, his hatred for the soi-disant Nationalist Party in Germany: 'Howl, ye Nazis: the day will come when the giant's foot will grind you into dust.' The giant's foot was Communism. There again we read, as so often in Heine's pages, a signal anticipation of the later play and counterplay of liberty and reaction in Germany.

He entered on the writing of his *Memoirs* with undiminished wit and almost savage humour when his illness at last made him a prisoner. His eye had all but given out, he suffered from endless excruciating headaches; he was so weak, his body had so dwindled, that he had to be lifted out of bed by a nurse, a negress, his poor legs hung down like those of a doll—when he took to what he called his 'mattress-grave.' There he lay eight years, and during them went on writing with invincible spirit, turning out poem after poem, article after article, book after book. Sometimes he had even to raise up an eyelid with one hand while he wrote with the other; but his latest work was dictated to a secretary.

In the last year of all, he had one alleviation—the coming of Camille Selden, who had long been a reader and admirer of his poems;—*La Mouche* he called her, after the fly engraved on her signet ring. His passion for her was beyond control, and poor Mathilde could not understand his love for this frail *petite* creature who was such an utter contrast to herself. He would have liked to keep 'La Mouche' at his side always. A song of Mendelssohn's kept haunting his ear as he wrote his last *Lieder* to her, and from them we learn how, too late, he felt here was the one woman who could have given him the love and latent sympathy he had longed for all his life.

He died at four o'clock on Sunday morning, the 17th February 1856. His friend, Meissner, said he looked in death more beautiful than any one had seen him in life, and *La Mouche* that his face was like an antique mask, marble-pale, whose lines recalled a Greek statue. His last illness was due to a decay of the spinal marrow, which he himself thought to be an inherited malady: but there is a doubt about the exact nature of the disease. He was buried at Montmartre, and over his grave now is a monument of the Danish sculptor

Hasselriis. I remember going one hot June afternoon to
Montmartre to look for it among those melancholy graves
and immortelles, and reading the lines engraved on it!

> Wo wird einst des Wandermüden
> Letzte Ruhestätte sein?
> Unter Palmen in dem Süden?
> Unter Linden an dem Rhein? . . .

This volume of Heine gives the reader as near an idea of his
work, verse and prose, as can be provided in selection and in
English translation. His *Lieder*, his exquisite songs and
lyrics, are admittedly all but untranslatable, as any one
knows who has tried to put them into English. The mingled
subtlety and simplicity of his verse, the deceptive mixed
innocence and irony of his prose—how can one hope to capture
them in any other tongue? Only the musicians who have set
his songs, Schumann, Schubert, Wolf and others, have by their
kindred art contrived to interpret, or even add to, his magic.
Their settings have indeed tended to mislead the English
public into thinking Heine only a *Lieder* writer, while much
of his most characteristic work, even in poetry, lies outside
the familiar lyrics and love-songs of his early books, and you
must turn to the *Nordsee* cycle, to *Atta Troll*, and his later
poems, to arrive at the full measure of his art, individual and
inimitable. Not only that, you must not be content to read
him only in English. This mixed anthology of his work
would fail of its purpose if it did not send its readers to the
original German. For no other writer so informed with charm
and pliancy of style, with Gallic lightness and Hebrew imagination, his old mother-tongue. Long ago, Matthew Arnold, who
was the first English critic to reveal Heine in his full power
to the British public, ended his tribute with some telling words
that may well be added to the record.

No account of Heine is complete which does not notice the Jewish
element in him. His race he treated with the same freedom with
which he treated everything else, but he derived a great force from
it, and no one knew this better than he himself. . . . He himself had
in him both the spirit of Greece and the spirit of Judea; both these
spirits reach the infinite, which is the true goal of all poetry and all
art—the Greek spirit by beauty, the Hebrew spirit by sublimity.
By his perfection of literary form, by his love of clearness, by his
love of beauty, Heine is Greek; by his intensity, by his untamable-
ness, by his 'longing which cannot be uttered,' he is Hebrew. Yet
what Hebrew ever treated the things of the Hebrews like this?—

'There lives at Hamburg, in a one-roomed lodging in the Bakers' Broad Walk, a man whose name is Moses Lump; all the week he goes about in wind and rain, with his pack on his back, to earn his few shillings; but when on Friday evening he comes home, he finds the candlestick with seven candles lighted, and the table covered with a fair white cloth, and he puts away from him his pack and his cares, and he sits down to table with his squinting wife and yet more squinting daughter, and eats fish with them, fish which has been dressed in beautiful white garlic sauce, sings therewith the grandest psalms of King David, and rejoices with his whole heart over the deliverance of the children of Israel out of Egypt. . . . I can tell you, the man is happy, he sits contented in his green bed-gown, contemplates with satisfaction his candles, which he on no account will snuff for himself; and I can tell you, if the candles burn a little dim, and the snuffers-woman, whose business it is to snuff them, is not at hand, and Rothschild the Great were at that moment to come in with all his brokers, bill discounters, agents, and chief clerks, with whom he conquers the world, and Rothschild were to say: "Moses Lump, ask of me what favour you will, and it shall be granted you"; —Doctor, I am convinced, Moses Lump would quietly answer: "Snuff me those candles!" and Rothschild the Great would exclaim with admiration: "If I were not Rothschild, I would be Moses Lump."'

There Heine shows us his own people by its comic side.

He shows us the serious side in his beautiful poem on Jehuda ben Halevy, a poet belonging to 'the great golden age of the Arabian, Old-Spanish, Jewish school of poets,' a contemporary of the troubadours . . . who makes his pilgrimage to Jerusalem; and there, amid the ruins, sings a song of Sion which had become famous among his people:

'That lay of pearled tears is the wide-famed Lament, which is sung in all the scattered tents of Jacob throughout the world,

'On the ninth day of the month which is called Ab, on the anniversary of Jerusalem's destruction by Titus Vespasianus.

'Yes, that is the song of Sion, which Jehuda ben Halevy sang with his dying breath amid the holy ruins of Jerusalem.

'Barefoot, and in penitential weeds, he sate there upon the fragment of a fallen column; down to his breast fell,

'Like a gray forest, his hair; and cast a weird shadow on the face which looked out through it—his troubled pale face, with the spiritual eyes.

'So he sate and sang, like unto a seer out of the foretime to look upon; Jeremiah, the Ancient, seemed to have risen out of his grave.

'But the bold Saracen came riding that way, aloft on his barb, lolling in his saddle, and brandishing a naked javelin;

'Into the breast of the poor singer he plunged his deadly shaft, and shot away like a winged shadow.

'Quietly flowed the Rabbi's life-blood, quietly he sang his song to an end; and his last dying sigh was Jerusalem!'

Nor must Heine's sweetest note be unheard—his plaintive note, his note of melancholy. Here is a strain which came from him as he lay, in the winter night, on his 'mattress-grave' at Paris, and let his thoughts wander home to Germany, 'the great child, entertaining herself with her Christmas-tree.' 'Thou tookest,' he cries to the German exile:

'Thou tookest thy flight towards sunshine and happiness; naked and poor returnest thou back. German truth, German shirts—one gets them worn to tatters in foreign parts.

'Deadly pale are thy looks, but take comfort, thou art at home! one lies warm in German earth, warm as by the old pleasant fireside.

'Many a one, alas, became crippled, and could get home no more! longingly he stretches out his arms; God have mercy upon him!'

God have mercy upon him; for what remain of the days of the years of his life are few and evil. 'Can it be that I still actually exist? My body is so shrunk that there is hardly anything of me left but my voice, and my bed makes me think of the melodious grave of the enchanter Merlin, which is in the forest of Broceliand in Brittany, under high oaks whose tops shine like green flames to heaven. Ah, I envy thee those trees, brother Merlin, and their fresh waving! for over my mattress-grave here in Paris no green leaves rustle; and early and late I hear nothing but the rattle of carriages, hammering, scolding, and the jingle of the piano. A grave without rest, death without the privileges of the departed, who have no longer any need to spend money, or to write letters, or to compose books. What a melancholy situation!'

He died, and has left a blemished name; with his crying faults— his intemperate susceptibility, his unscrupulousness in passion, his inconceivable attacks on his enemies, his still more inconceivable attacks on his friends, his want of generosity, his sensuality, his incessant mocking — how could it be otherwise? . . . But on the negative side of one's criticism of a man of great genius I, for my part, have no pleasure in dwelling. I prefer to say of Heine something positive. He is not an adequate interpreter of the modern world. He is only a brilliant soldier in the war of liberation of humanity. But, such as he is, he is (and posterity too, I am quite sure, will say this), in the European literature of that quarter of a century which follows the death of Goethe, incomparably the most important figure.[1]

ERNEST RHYS.

SELECT BIBLIOGRAPHY

WORKS. *Gedichte*, 1822; *Tragödien* ('Almansor,' 'William Ratcliff') *nebst einem lyrischen Intermezzo*, 1823; *Reisebilder*, 1826–31; *Buch der Lieder*, 1827; *Epistel an Deutschland*, 1832; *Zur Geschichte der neueren schönen Literatur in Deutschland* (later reprinted as *Die Romantische Schule*), 1833; *Französische Zustande*, 1833; *Der Salon*, 1834–40; *Zur Geschichte der Religion und Philosophie in Deutschland*, 1835; *Heine über Ludwig Börne*, 1840; *Neue Gedichte*, 1844; *Atta Troll*, 1847; *Der Doktor Faust*, 1851; *Romanzero*, 1851; *Briefe*, edited by Steinmann, 1861; *Briefe von Heine an seinen Freund M. Moser*, 1862; *Aus dem Nachlass Varnhagens von Ense*, 1865; *Letzte Gedichte und Gedanken*, 1869; *Memoiren und neugesammelte Gedichte, Prosa und Briefe*, 1884.

[1] *Critical Essays* by Matthew Arnold: Everyman's Library.

Collected editions of his works are: *Sämmtliche Werke*, 6 vols., 1856–7; *Sämmtliche Werke*, 21 vols., edited by Adolf Strodtmann, 1861–6; *Gesammelte Werke*, 9 vols., edited by G. Karpeles, 1887; *Sämmtliche Werke*, 7 vols., edited by Ernst Elster, 1887–90; *Werke*, 10 vols., edited by Oskar Walzel, 1910–15.

In English the most comprehensive—and effectively the best—edition is that issued by Heinemann in 12 vols., 1892–1905. It contains the prose and poetry and was translated by C. G. Leland, T. Brooksbank, and Margaret Armour. Translations of the verse include a complete edition translated by John Payne in 3 vols., 1911; *Book of Songs*, translated by John Todhunter, 1907; *Poems selected from Heine*, by Kathe Freiligrath-Kroeker and others, 1887; *Translations from Heine and Goethe*, 1912, and *More Translations from Heine*, 1920, by Philip G. L. Webb; *Translations from Heine*, by Monica Peveril Turnbull (first included in *A Short Day's Work*, 1902). Prose translations include *The Prose Writings of Heinrich Heine*, translated by Havelock Ellis, 1887; *Italian Travel Sketches*, translated by E. A. Sharp, 1892; *Heine in Art and Letters*, translated by E. A. Sharp, 1895; *Travel Pictures* and *The Romantic School*, translated by Francis Storr, 1887.

BIOGRAPHY AND CRITICISM. W. Sharp, *Life of Heinrich Heine*, 1888; H. G. Atkins, *Heine*, 1929; H. Walter, *Heinrich Heine*, 1930; Antonina Vallentin, *Poet in Exile* (Eng. trans.), 1934; F. H. Wood, *Heine as a Centre of his own Work*, 1934; H. Spaeth, *La Pensée de Heine*, 1946; L. Marouse, *Heinrich Heine*, 1951.

ACKNOWLEDGMENTS

The Editor and Publishers alike are particularly indebted to the courtesy of Messrs. Heinemann and Mrs. Macdougal (Margaret Armour) who have allowed them to make very liberal selections from their edition of Heine's works. Also to Mr. Havelock Ellis who has allowed them to make free use of his Camelot volume. Other copyright owners who have generously given permission for the use of various translations are: Mrs. Phyllis A. Turnbull for the work of Monica Peveril Turnbull, The Clarendon Press for the work of John Todhunter (from his version of *The Book of Songs*), Mr. Humbert Wolfe, and the executors of the late P. G. L. Webb. The Publishers regret they have been unable to get into touch with the representatives of John Payne and W. G. Waters, and trust that they will be pardoned for the liberty they have taken in including these authors' translations.

A final word is due to the editorial and critical services of Miss M. M. Bozman, in collating and revising the text, both verse and prose.

CONTENTS

CONTENTS

CONTENTS

ROMANCERO

LAST POEMS

PART II—THE PROSE

PART I

THE POEMS

BOOK OF SONGS

Lo, 'tis the fairy-forest old
With lime-tree blossom scented!
The moon had with her wondrous light
My soul and sense enchanted.

On, on I roamed, and as I went
I heard a high sweet strain:
It was the nightingale—she sang
Of love and lovers' pain.

She sang of love and lovers' pain,
Hearts blest and hearts that break;
So sad her mirth, so glad her sob,
Dreams long forgot awake.

And still I roamed, and as I went
I saw before me lie
On a wide lawn a lofty pile
With gables peaked and high.

Shut were its windows, everywhere
A silence and a gloom:
It seemed that stilly death did dwell
Within each empty room.

Before the doorway lay a Sphinx,
Hybrid of fears and lusts,
A lioness in body and claws
A woman in face and breasts.

A woman fair! The wan aspect
Spoke of consuming passion;
The mute lips curvèd in a smile,
Of wordless invitation.

The nightingale she sang so sweet
I yielded to their wooing—
And as I kissed that lovely face
I sealed my own undoing.

The marble image thrilled with life—
The stone began to move—
She drank my kisses' burning flame
With a fierce and thirsty love.

She almost drank my breath away
And then, voluptuous, bending
She clasped me close, her lion claws
My hapless body rending.

Delicious torture, rapturous pang!
O pain and bliss unbounded!
Her lips, her kiss were heaven to me,
Her talons, how they wounded!

The nightingale sang, 'Lovely Sphinx,
O Love, what meaneth this—
That with the anguish of Death itself
Thou minglest all thy bliss?'

O lovely Sphinx, interpret now—
This riddle strange make plain,
For I have mused upon it still
A thousand years in vain!

DREAM PICTURES

Mir träumte einst

I DREAMED long since of love's warm ecstasies,
Of myrtles, mignonette, and ringlets' glitter,
Of rosy lips most sweet, and words most bitter—
Of sad songs matched with saddest melodies.

Faded those dreams, swept by the winds of time,
Vanished is even my dearest Dream-desire!
Nothing remains save that in passion's fire
I cast and fix 't in matrix of soft rhyme.

Thou, orphaned song, yet stay'st! Away with thee!
Seek thou for me that vanished Vision fleeting
And, when thou 'st found, deliver this my greeting—
To airy Shade my airy fantasy!

Ein Traum, gar seltsam Schauerlich

A DREAM of fearful mystery
Delighted and appallèd me.
Strange forms of terror haunt me still,
And heart and bosom wildly thrill.

I saw a garden wondrous fair,
And I was fain to wander there;
Uncounted flowrets glistened bright,
And filled my senses with delight.

The birds from many a leafy spray
Sang many a loving roundelay;
The sun with golden splendour glowed—
A thousand tints the flowrets showed.

Balsamic odours everywhere
Came floating on the summer air;

5

And all was smiling, all was bright,
As eager to rejoice the sight.

And, 'mid the flower-bespangled glade,
Limpid a marble fountain played;
And there I spied a maiden bright—
She stooped, and washed a robe of white.

Her eyes were mild, her cheeks were fair,
Like pictured saint with golden hair;
And as I gaze, methinks I trace
A strange and yet familiar face.

Her task with haste the maiden plies,
And chants a song in wondrous wise:
'Flow, flow, water flow,
Wash the linen white as snow.'

With lingering step her side I seek,
And in a low-toned whisper speak:
'O gentle maid! so wondrous fair!
Say, who the robe of white shall wear?'

'Be ready soon,' swift answered she,
'Thy dying shroud I wash for thee!'
And scarcely had the words been said—
Like wreaths of mist the vision fled.

The trance continued, and I stood
Deep in a wild and gloomy wood;
Huge trees their arms above me crossed,
I stood beneath, in musings lost.

When hark! a sullen echo woke,
Like far-off woodman's heavy stroke;
Through brake and thicket swift I pace,
And gain, at length, an open space.

There in a clearing of the wood,
A mighty oak-tree towering stood;
And lo! my wondrous maid I see—
She hews the knotted old oak-tree.

Stroke follows stroke, as, swift and strong,
She swings her axe, and sings her song:
'Blade, blade, broad and bright,
Hew the oaken plank aright.'

With lingering step her side I seek,
And in a low-toned whisper speak:
'For whom, O maid, so wondrous fair,
Dost thou the oaken plank prepare?'

'Thy time is short,' swift answered she;
'A coffin this—and meant for thee!'
And scarcely had the words been said,
Like wreaths of mist the vision fled.

A dreary waste, without a bound,
A barren heath lay all around;
In helpless wonder there I stood,
And secret terror froze my blood.

Aroused, at length, I wander on
Where something faintly glimmering shone;
And hastening up, I see once more
The lovely maid I saw before.

Upon the bare heath the fair maid
Was digging with a sexton's spade;
I scarce dared gaze at what I saw,
She looked so fair, yet full of awe.

Right swift her task the maiden plies,
And chants a song in wondrous wise:
'Spade, spade, sharp and strong,
Dig the grave both deep and long.'

With lingering step her side I seek,
And in a low-toned whisper speak:
'Tell me, tell me, maiden dear!
What the grave betokens here.

'Be still,' she swift did answer me,
'The grave I dig is dug for thee!'

And even as she thus replied,
The yawning chasm opened wide.

I gaze adown the fearful steep,
Cold shudderings o'er my heartstrings creep;
And, while the dark abysses quake,
I plunge in headlong—and awake.

In nächtigen Traum hab' ich mich selbst geschaut

I FELL asleep and dreamed at eventide:
I saw myself, as for some festive day,
Decked in silk vest, white shirt, and best array;
And then I saw my love stand by my side:
I bowed and said: 'My dear, are you a bride?
Then I 'll congratulate you if I may!'
But the cold speech half choked my breath away,
And in my throat the words had almost died.
Then bitter tears began to flow apace
From my love's eyes, and in a mist of tears
Was wellnigh hid from me her gentle face.
—O tender eyes! though you have lied to me,
Both waking and in dreams these many years,
Yet I believe you all too readily.

Da hab' ich viel' blasse Leichen

WITH words of might that wake them,
    I 've called up many a sprite:
Now will they not betake them
    Back to their native night.

The master-word compelling
    Forgot have I for awe;
And now to their cloud-dwelling
    Myself mine own ghosts draw.

Hands off, ye demons darkling!
    Press on me not!   For me
Here in life's rose-light sparkling
    Yet many a joy may be.

Still must I aim at gleaning
  The flower all flowers above.
What were my whole life's meaning,
  If her I should not love?

Would her I once but clip might
  And strain her to my heart!
But once on cheek and lip might
  Kiss off love's sweetest smart!

One loving word but might I
  By her sweet mouth hear said!
Ghosts, follow you forthright I
  Would to the place of dread.

Grim nod the ghosts. Full well me
  They apprehend; and see,
Sweet love, here am I, tell me,
  Sweet love, then, lov'st thou me?

SONGS

Morgens steh' ich auf und frage

RISING with the sun I cry,
  'Comes my love to-day?'
To my bed at eve I sigh,
  'Still she stays away!'

All the night long with my sorrow
  Wide awake I weep,
And I dawdle through the morrow
  Dreaming, half asleep.

Schöne Wiege meiner Leiden

FAIR cradle of my sorrow,
  Fair tomb of peace for me,
Fair town, my last good-morrow,
  Farewell I say to thee!

Farewell, thou threshold holy,
  Where my lady's footsteps stir,
And that spot, still worshipped lowly,
  Where mine eyes first looked on her!

Had I beheld thee never,
  My bosom's beauteous queen,
Wretched now, and wretched ever,
  I should not thus have been!

Touch thy heart?—I would not dare
  Ne'er did I thy love implore;
Might I only breathe the air
  Thou didst breathe, I asked no more.

Yet I could not brook thy spurning,
  Nor thy cruel words of scorn:
Madness in my brain is burning,
  And my heart is sick and torn.

So I go, downcast and dreary,
  With my pilgrim staff to stray,
Till I lay my head aweary,
  In some cool grave far away.

Mit Rosen, Cypressen und Flittergold

WITH roses, cypress and gold-leaf bright,
Fain would I cover, soft and light,
This my book, for a coffin fair
To bury all my verses there.

Oh might I therewith my love enclose!
The flower of quiet on love's grave grows;
All may gather it—all but I
Until with love in the grave I lie.

Here then are my verses: once they pressed
Wild as a torrent from Etna's crest,
A lava-stream of my soul's desire
Shooting lightnings and sparks of fire.

Now they lie mute and still as death;
Now white and chill as winter's breath;
Yet a flame as of old from their ashes would leap
If the spirit of love should o'er them sweep.

Yea, deep in my heart I presage feel
That the spirit of love shall o'er them steal:
Some day this book shall reach thy hand,
Sweetheart mine, in a distant land.

Then from the spell shall my song be free,
The pallid letters shall gaze on thee,
In thy beautiful eyes shall look their prayer,
And whisper of love and sorrow there.

Romances

The Voice of the Mountain

ALL sadly through the valley wild
    Rode slow a warrior brave:
'Ah, draw I nigher my sweetheart's arms,
    Or nearer the silent grave?'
    The mountain answer gave:
        'The silent grave!'

The warrior rideth a league, a league,
    A sigh breaks from his breast:
'And must I find the grave so soon?
    Ah well, in the grave is rest!'
    Came the voice from the mountain's crest:
        'In the grave is rest.'

The warrior's brow is troubled,
    A tear rolled down and fell:
'Is there then no rest in the world for me?
    Then the rest of the grave shall be well.'
    The voice from the mountain fell:
        'The grave shall be well!'

The Two Grenadiers

NACH Frankreich zogen zwei Grenadier',
Die waren in Russland gefangen.
Und als sie kamen ins deutsche Quartier,
Sie liessen die Köpfe hangen.

Da hörten sie beide die traurige Màr:
Dass Frankreich verloren gegangen,
Besiegt und zerschlagen das grosse Heer—
Und der Kaiser, der Kaiser gefangen.

Da weinten zusammen die Grenadier'
Wohl ob der kläglichen Kunde.
Der eine sprach: Wie weh wird mir,
Wie brennt meine alte Wunde!

Der andre sprach: Das Lied ist aus,
Auch ich möcht' mit dir sterben,
Doch hab' ich Weib und Kind zu Haus,
Die ohne mich verderben.

Was schert mich Weib, was schert mich Kind,
Ich trage weit bessres Verlangen;
Lass sie betteln gehn, wenn sie hungrig sind—
Mein Kaiser, mein Kaiser gefangen!

Gewähr' mir, Bruder, eine Bitt':
Wenn ich jetz sterben werde,
So nimm meine Leiche nach Frankreich mit,
Begrab mich in Frankreichs Erde.

Das Ehrenkreuz am roten Band
Sollst du aufs Herz mir legen;
Die Flinte gib mir in die Hand,
Und gürt' mir um den Degen.

So will ich liegen und horchen still,
Wie eine Schildwach', im Grabe,
Bis einst ich höre Kanonengebrüll
Und wiehernder Rosse Getrabe.

Dann reitet mein Kaiser wohl über mein Grab,
Viel' Schwerter klirren und blitzen;
Dann steig' ich gewaffnet aus dem Grab—
Den Kaiser, den Kaiser zu schützen!

Two grenadiers were returning to France from imprisonment in Russia. When they reached the German frontier they hung their heads, for there they heard the sad story how France was lost, the Grand Army defeated, and cut to pieces, and the Emperor, the Emperor, taken!

At these woeful tidings the two grenadiers wept together. One said: 'It goes ill with me—how my old wound burns!' And the other said: 'The song is sung. I too would gladly die with you, but I have at home a wife and child, and they would be undone without me.' 'What care I for wife or child? I cherish nobler longings. If they are hungry let them beg their bread—my Emperor, my Emperor, is taken! Grant me one prayer, brother! As soon as I am dead take up my body and

B 9¹¹—8 m

carry it to France with you, and bury me in French earth.
Lay my Cross of Honour with its red ribbon upon my heart, put
my musket in my hand and buckle my sword about me.   Then
I will lie in my grave and listen quietly, like a sentry, until the
day comes when I hear the roar of cannon and the trotting and
whinnying of horses.   My Emperor shall ride over my grave,
a myriad swords shall flash and ring, and I shall rise fully armed
from my grave, my Emperor, my Emperor to guard!

The Wounded Knight

I KNOW an ancient legend,
A sad and cheerless tale:
A knight by love lies smitten,
But his lady's faith is frail.

For false he needs must scorn her
His heart's delight and dole,
Must hold as base and shameful
The pang that rends his soul.

Fain in the lists he'd bear him
And challenge all that came—
'Let him for fight prepare him
That dares impeach her fame!'

Yet he knows that none would answer
Save his own soul's clamorous smart;
His lance he must couch and level
'Gainst his own accusing heart.

SONNETS

To my Mother

(1)

I HAVE been wont to bear my head on high,
   Haughty and stern am I of mood and mien,
   Yea, tho' a king should gaze on me, I ween,
I should not at his gaze cast down my eye.
But I will speak, dear Mother, candidly:
   When most puffed up my haughty mood hath been,
   At thy sweet presence, blissful and serene,
I feel the shudder of humility.

Does thy soul all unknown my soul subdue,
Thy lofty soul that pierces all things through,
And speeds on lightning wings to heaven's blue?
Or am I racked by what my memories tell
Of frequent deeds which caused thy heart to swell—
That beauteous heart which loved me, ah! too well.

(2)

Thee had I once in a mad dream forsaken,
   And then I longed to roam the wide world over
   To see, perchance, if I might Love discover,
And, with embraces loving, Love awaken!
   I made my search for Love thro' all the ways,
Before each door with outstretched hands implored,
Like any beggar, alms from Love's rich hoard.
   Men sneered, and froze me with their scornful gaze,
But in my love-search never ceasing, ever
For Love, still Love, I sought and found it never;
   Then turning once more homeward, sick with care,
Thou didst come forth to meet me—was I dreaming?
For oh, behold! in thy deep eyes lay gleaming
   Love, the long sought-for, sweetest Love, was there.

(1822–3)

Im wunderschönen Monat Mai

IM wunderschönen Monat Mai,
Als alle Knospen sprangen,
Da ist in meinem Herzen
Die Liebe aufgegangen.

Im wunderschönen Monat Mai,
Als alle Vögel sangen,
Da hab' ich ihr gestanden
Mein Sehnen und Verlangen.

In the lovely month of May, when all the buds were opening,
love sprang up in my heart.
In the lovely month of May, when all the birds were singing,
I confessed to her my longing and my desire.

Aus meinen Thränen spriessen

A THOUSAND flowers open
    Beneath my teardrops' rain,
And in the sighs I utter
    The nightingales complain.

And if you love me, darling,
    To you the flowers I 'll bring,
And underneath your window
    The nightingales shall sing.

Die Rose, die Lilie, die Taube, die Sonne

THE rose, the lily, the sun and the dove,
I loved them all once in the rapture of love.
I love them no more, for my sole delight
Is a maiden so slight, so bright and so white,
Who, being herself the source of love,
Is rose and lily and sun and dove.

Wenn ich in deine Augen seh'

DEAR, when I look into thine eyes,
My deepest sorrow straightway flies;
But when I kiss thy mouth, ah, then
No thought remains of bygone pain.

And when I lean upon thy breast,
No dream of heaven could be more blest;
But, when thou say'st thou lovest me,
I fall to weeping bitterly.

Lehn' deine Wang' an meine Wang'

OH, let your tears with mine bedew
    The cheek you lay your cheek on,
And let the flames of heart on heart
    Blaze in a single beacon.

And when that fiery signal must
    To tidal tears surrender,
Oh, then I 'll hold you to my heart,
    And die of love's mere wonder.

Es stehen unbeweglich

FOR many thousand ages
    The stars in heaven above
Stand stirless, and each other
    Regard with grief and love.

So rich, so fair the language
    They speak is, each with each;
But never yet was linguist
    Might understand their speech.

Yet I, forsooth, have learnèd
    Nor e'er forget shall it—
In my love's eyes of heaven
    I found its grammar writ.

Auf Flügeln des Gesanges

ON wings of song, heart's dearest,
   I 'll bear thee, soft and light,
To a grove I know, the fairest
   By Ganges' waters bright.

In a rose-red garden burning
   'Neath the silent moonbeams there
The lotus-flowers are yearning
   To greet their sister fair.

Violets, laughing and lisping,
   Look up to the stars above;
Softly the roses, whispering,
   Tell perfumed legends of love.

There leap the gazelles, and listen,
   Innocent-eyed and grave,
And Ganges' waters glisten,
   And ripples his sacred wave.

There will we lie together
   Under the tall palm's crest,
And drink of love, and rest there,
   And dream the dreams of the blest.

Die Lotusblume ängstigt

THE lotus-flower feareth
The splendour of the sun:
With drooping head she tarries,
Dreaming, till day be done.

The moon, he is her leman—
She wakes beneath his rays,
Gladly to him unveiling
Her still, adoring face.

She blooms, she glows, she lightens,
Mutely she gazes above,
She trembles, weeps, and is fragrant
For love and the pains of love.

Du liebst nicht, du liebst mich nicht

You do not love me, sweet one? Why,
    That is a trifling thing;
Let me but see your face, and I
    Am happy as a king.

'I hate you, hate you!' even this
    The little mouth has said;
Yet give me but that mouth to kiss,
    Child, and I 'm comforted.

O schwöre nicht und küsse nur

O SWEAR me not, but only kiss!
I trust no woman's promises.
Sweet is your word, but sweeter far
My unindentured kisses are.
For I shall keep, when oaths are air,
The kiss for ever everywhere.

Nay! I 'll recant. Swear as by right,
Love, and I 'll be your acolyte,
To suffer, sinking on your breast,
The absolution of the blessed,
In faith eternal that you will
Love while I trust—and longer still.

Ich grolle nicht, und wenn das Herz auch bricht

ICH grolle nicht, und wenn das Herz auch bricht,
Ewig verlornes Lieb! ich grolle nicht.
Wie du auch strahlst in Diamantenpracht,
Es fällt kein Strahl in deines Herzens Nacht.

Das weiss ich längst. Ich sah dich ja im Traum,
Und sah die Nacht in deines Herzens Raum,
Und sah die Schlang', die dir am Herzen frisst,
Ich sah, mein Lieb, wie sehr du elend bist.

I 'll bear no grudge, although my heart should break, eternally
lost love, I 'll bear no grudge! Though thou shinest, radiant
with diamonds, not a ray pierces the night in thy heart.

I 've known it long; for I saw thee in a dream, and saw the
night that fills thy heart, and saw the serpent that gnaws thy
heart; I saw, my love, how very wretched thou art.

Und wussten 's die Blumen, die kleinen

AND if the little flowers could see
    How pierced my heart with grief,
Then surely they would weep with me
    To bring my pain relief.

And if the nightingales could tell
    How sick I am, and sad,
Their merry songs would fill the vale,
    To make my heart more glad.

And if the golden stars on high
    My sorrow could but guess,
They would come down from out the sky,
    To comfort my distress.

Yet none of these can ever know;
    One knows, but only one.
Herself she pierced my heart—and so
    She knows, and she alone.

Ein Fichtenbaum steht einsam

ON a bare northern summit
A pine-tree stands alone.
He slumbers; and around him
The icy snows are blown.

His dreams are of a palm-tree
Who in far lands of morn
Amid the blazing desert
Grieves silent and forlorn.

Seit die Liebste war entfernt

SINCE my love now loves me not,
How to laugh I have forgot;
Jests no more my griefs beguile,
For I cannot, cannot smile.

Since my love now loves me not,
How to weep I have forgot;
Broken is my heart with woe,
But my tears refuse to flow.

Aus meinen grossen Schmerzen

FROM pain wherein I languish
My little songs I utter,
And their rustling wings they flutter
And bear her my tale of anguish.

They find her heart, but stay not:
They come again with sighing,
They come again with crying,
Yet what they have seen they say not.

Ein Jüngling liebt ein Mädchen

A YOUNG man loves a maiden
That longs for another lad;
But that lad loves another
And none but her will wed.

The maiden marries to spite him
The first man, good or ill,
Who happens to cross her pathway,
And her true love's heart grows chill.

An old and outworn story—
As old and as new as May:
The latest of its heroes—
His heart broke yesterday.

Hör' ich das Liedchen klingen

WHEN to the songs you sang me
I listen once again,
My heart is nigh to breaking
With wild and bitter pain.

By some dim longing driven,
I bring the woods my grief,
And find in tears of anguish
My burdened heart's relief.

Sie haben mich gequälet

THEY have tormented me
    Early and late
Some with their love,
    Some with their hate.

The wine I drank,
    The bread I ate,
Some poisoned with love
    Some poisoned with hate.

Yet she who has grieved me
    Most of all,
She never hated
    Nor loved me at all.

Es liegt der heisse Sommer

THE rosy glow of summer
    Is on thy dimpled cheek,
While in thy heart the winter
    Is lying cold and bleak.

But this will change hereafter,
    When years have done their part,
And on thy cheek be winter
    And summer in thy heart.

Wenn zwei von einander scheiden

THE last farewell of lovers
    Is whispered as they stand
With tears they cannot conquer,
    And hand in trembling hand.

But when we two were parted
    We did not sigh nor moan.
We had all life before us
    In which to weep alone.

Sie sassen und tranken am Theetisch

WE drank our tea and chattered
    Of love about the table.
The men were strong and silent,
    The women sweetly feeble.

'The only love 's Platonic,'
    The public man professed.
Whereat his lady sniggered,
    And she, no doubt, knew best.

'Unless love is domestic,'
    The Dean was heard to vow,
'It ruins the digestion.'
    The schoolgirl asked him how.

'Love,' said my lady blushing,
    'Is savage as a sword,'
And passed, while she was speaking,
    His teacup to my lord.

There was a place left vacant,
    My love, and if you 'd come,
They would have learned what love was,
    Though both of us sat mum.

Vergiftet sind meine Lieder

MY songs are poisoned, say you—
    How should they wholesome be
When my young blood is tainted
    With a poison poured by thee?

My songs are poisoned, say you—
    How should they wholesome prove
When my heart is full of serpents—
    And of thee, my Lilith-love?

Nacht lag auf meinen Augen

NIGHT lay upon my eyelids,
    My lips were sealed with lead,
With heart and brain death-stiffened,
    I lay in the graveyard dead.

I cannot now remember
　How long I lay asleep,
I woke, and heard a footstep
　Over my grave-bed deep.

'Wilt thou not rise up, Heinrich?
　The nightless dawn breaks clear.
The dead folk have arisen,
　The endless joy is near.'

'I cannot rise, my true love,
　For I am blind as night,
And bitter tears and weeping
　Have reft my eyes of sight.'

'I will kiss away, dear Heinrich,
　The dark night from your eyes,
So you may see the angels,
　And radiance of the skies.'

'I cannot rise, my true love,
　My heart at every beat
Bleeds, for a word once stabbed it,
　A word of your own, my sweet.'

'Light on your heart, dear Heinrich,
　My loving hand I'll lay,
To stop the red blood flowing
　And take the pain away.'

'I cannot rise, my true love,
　My head bleeds piteously,
With fatal wound I pierced it
　When thou wast torn from me.'

Oh, let me bind, dear Heinrich,
　My soft hair round your head,
To heal its wounds and aching,
　And stanch the blood-stream red.'

She spoke so soft, so gently,
　I could not say her no.

My spirit bade me follow
  And to my true love go.

But ah, more dire, more fatal,
  Again the life-stream broke
From wounded head and bosom,
  And lo—from sleep I woke!

Die alten, bösen Lieder

THE evil dreams and bitter,
  Old lilts of wicked song,
To bury now, come, bring me
  A coffin deep and long.

I 'll lay therein things many,
  But what, I 'll tell to none;
This coffin must be bigger
  Than Heidelberg's great tun.

And bring a bier to match it,
  Each stout and mighty beam
Long as the bridge that crosses,
  By Mainz, the broad Rhine-stream.

And bring me eke twelve giants,
  Each stronger in the spine
Than stout St. Christopher's self in
  The minster at Köln on Rhine.

The twelve shall carry the coffin
  To sink it in the sea;
For such a mighty coffin
  No meaner grave should be.

But know ye why this coffin
  Is heavy and hard to move?
I 've laid therein my sorrow,
  I 've laid therein my love.

In mein gar zu dunkles Leben

ONCE a candle in the midnight
    Of my heart was briefly lit,
Beggared twice, and even darker
    After that gold benefit.

Children, when the lamp's extinguished,
    And their little hearts are cowed,
Often to restore the level
    Of their courage, sing aloud.

I, a baffled child, in darkness
    Sing, like them, to check the tears,
And my verse, however sullen,
    Does at least dispel my fears.

Ich weiss nicht, was soll es bedeuten

ICH weiss nicht, was soll es bedeuten,
Dass ich so traurig bin;
Ein Märchen aus alten Zeiten,
Das kommt mir nicht aus dem Sinn.

Die Luft is kühl, und es dunkelt,
Und ruhig fliesst der Rhein;
Die Gipfel des Berges funkelt
Im Abendsonnenschein.

Die schönste Jungfrau sitzet
Dort oben wunderbar,
Ihr goldnes Geschmeide blitzet,
Sie kämmt ihr goldenes Haar.

Sie kämmt es mit goldenem Kamme,
Und singt ein Lied dabei;
Das hat eine wundersame,
Gewaltige Melodei.

26

Den Schiffer im kleinen Schiffe
Ergreift es mit wildem Weh;
Er schaut nicht die Felsenriffe,
Er schaut nur hinauf in die Höh'.

Ich glaube, die Wellen verschlingen
Am ende Schiffer und Kahn;
Und das hat mit ihrem Singen
Die Lorelei gethan.

I know not what it should portend that I am so full of sorrow. A legend of olden days haunts me and will not leave my thoughts. The air is cool, dusk falls, and the Rhine stream flows in peace. A mountain-peak glitters in the rays of the evening sun, and O wonder! a maiden of surpassing beauty is seated there, decked in shining gold and combing her golden tresses. She combs them with a golden comb, singing the while a song with a strange, compelling melody. It grips the boatman in his little boat, filling him with a wild anguish. He does not look at the rocky reef, he looks at naught but the heights above him.

In the end, methinks, the waves devour both boatman and boat: that has the Lorelei done by her singing!

Mein Herz, mein Herz ist traurig

My heart, my heart is heavy,
 Though joyously shines the may,
As I stand 'neath the lime-tree leaning
 High on the ramparts grey.

The moat winds far beneath me;
 On its waters calm and blue
A boy in his boat is drifting,
 Fishing and whistling too.

Beyond, like a smiling picture,
 Little and bright, lie strewed
Villas and gardens and people,
 Cattle and meadows and wood.

The maidens are bleaching linen—
 They skip on the grass and play;
The mill-wheel scatters diamonds,
 Its drone sounds, far away.

A sentry-box is standing
  The old grey keep below,
And a lad in a coat of scarlet
  Paces there to and fro.

He handles and plays with his musket—
  It gleams in the sunset red,
He shoulders and presents it—
  I would that he shot me dead!

Wir sassen am Fischerhause

In the fisherman's cabin
  We sat and watched the sea
With the stealthy mists of evening
  Hidden gradually.

The lanterns in the lighthouse
  Were kindled light by high light,
And somewhere far to westward
  One ship wore through the twilight.

We spoke of storm and shipwreck,
  And how the sailor's path
Lies half a league to heaven
  And half a league to death.

We spoke of distant landfalls
  South and North the moon,
And of the peoples distant,
  And odd as Pantaloon.

The spices of the Ganges,
  The immemorial trees,
The lotus, and the comely
  Still folk upon their knees:

The Lapps—those dirty creatures—
  Broad faces smeared with blubber,
Who stew themselves, and fry their fish
  With shrill incessant jabber.

Entranced the women listened
  Till all was still, and we
In the deep night descending
  Saw neither ship nor sea.

Du schönes Fischermädchen

YOU lovely fisher-maiden,
  Shoreward set your sail
And let us dream together
  Where there is no more gale.

O hide your gentle forehead
  Against my heart, and be
Assured that it is safer
  Than your inconstant sea.

And though, sea-like, it suffers
  Both ebb and flow and storm,
It has its pearls, my sweet one,
  Hidden and deep and warm.

Der Mond ist aufgegangen

THE silver moon is risen
  And shines upon the sea;
I hold my love to my bosom,
  And our hearts beat fervently.

In the arms of my lovely maiden
  I lie alone on the strand:
'Why hear'st thou the wind that whispers?
  Why trembles thy white hand?'

'It is no wind that whispers,
  It is the mermaids' song,
And they that sing are my sisters,
  Drowned in the sea so long.'

Wenn ich an deinem Hause

WHEN day by day at morning
  I pass your window fair,
It gives me joy, sweet maiden,
  To see you standing there.

With dark-brown eyes of wonder
    You seem to question me—
'Who are you, pallid stranger,
    What is it aileth thee?'

I am a German poet,
    Renowned beyond the Rhine
Speak they of names—the greatest—
    Be sure they speak of mine.

In Germany 'tis common,
    The ill from which I pine;
Speak they of pains—the sorest—
    Be sure they speak of mine.

Sie liebten sich beide, doch keiner

THEY loved, but God forgive them!
    They would not tell their love,
With cold detachment hiding
    What they were dying of.

They parted at last, but sometimes
    Met in their dreams, those two
Lovers, who died of loving
    Long since, and never knew.

Mensch, verspotte nicht den Teufel

MORTAL! mock not at the Devil:
    Soon thy little life is o'er;
And eternal grim damnation
    Is no idle tale of yore.

Mortal! pay the debts thou owest:
    Long 'twill be ere life is o'er;
Many a time thou yet must borrow,
    As thou oft hast done before.

Mein Kind, wir waren Kinder

MY child, we two were children,
    Two children, small and gay;
We used to creep to the hen-house
    And hide beneath the hay.

We tried to chirp like chickens,
    And hoped the passers-by
Would hear us there and fancy
    They heard a chicken cry.

We built a lordly castle
    With boxes, in the court,
And set up house together,
    Quite grandly as we thought.

The old cat paid us visits
    As often as she could;
We used to bow and curtsy
    And 'hoped her health was good.'

We made her pretty speeches,
    And spoke of this and that—
Things we have since repeated
    To many a grave old cat.

We sat and talked as wisely
    As grown-up people may;
Complaining things had altered
    Most sadly since our day.

'Love, faith, and truth no longer
    Existed anywhere:
But coffee had grown dearer
    And money very rare!'

Those days are past, and all things
    Are passing by, in sooth:
Money, the world, the ages,
    And love and faith and truth.

Teurer Freund!   Was soll es nützen?

'WORTHY friend, how can it help you,
    Still the same old song to fashion?
Wilt thou sit for ever brooding
    O'er the addled eggs of passion?

'Why, it 's one eternal hatching!
　From the shells the chickens shake them:
And they chirp about and flutter,
　And straight in a book you bake them!'

Herz, mein Herz, sei nicht beklommen

HEART, my heart, yield not to sadness;
　Be submissive to thy fate;
And spring restoreth—only wait—
　All that winter steals from gladness.

Think but how much there still is left thee,
　Think but how fair the world is still;
Heart, my heart, befall what will,
　Love can never be bereft thee.

Du bist wie eine Blume

Du bist wie eine Blume,
　So hold und schön und rein;
Ich schau' dich an, und Wehmut
　Schleicht mir ins Herz hinein.

Mir ist, als ob ich die Hände
　Aufs Haupt dir legen sollt',
Betend, dass Gott dich erhalte
　So rein und schön und hold.

Thou art like a flower—so gentle, fair, and pure.　I gaze on
thee and sadness steals into my heart.　I feel as though I should
lay my hands upon thy head, praying that God would keep thee
so pure and fair and gentle.

Kind, es wäre dein Verderben

CHILD, indeed 'twould be thy ruin,
　And I strive right earnestly
Lest thy gentle heart should ever
　Feel the glow of love for me.

Yet it daunts me, I confess it,
　That my task should easy prove;
Many a time I fall a-musing—
　After all—if thou shouldst love!

Du hast Diamanten und Perlen

MY sweet, you have the jewels,
   And all that men go wrong for—
And the eyes beneath your eyelids—
   What else have you to long for?

And I, my sweet, have written
   Song after deathless song for
The eyes beneath your eyelids—
   What else have you to long for?

The eyes beneath your eyelids,
   My sweet, proved far too strong for
This broken heart—and therefore,
   What else have you to long for?

Wer zum ersten Male liebt

HE that loves the first time, even
Unrequited, is a god.
But he that loves a second time
Unrequited, is a fool.

Such a fool am I, I love
Once again, and am not loved.
Sun, moon, stars—all rock with laughter,
I too laugh with them—and perish.

Mir träumt' : ich bin der liebe Gott

I DREAMT I was the Lord Himself,
   Throned up in heaven so grandly,
With sweet young angels round my throne
   Who praised my verses blandly.

And cakes I ate, and comfits, too,
   By crownsworths, day by day there;
With cardinal I washed them down,
   And not a groat to pay there.

But sheer ennui it plagued me sore,
   I longed on earth to revel,
And were I not the Lord Himself,
   Had gone straight to the devil.

'Thou long-legged angel Gabriel,
    Put on thy boots directly;
Seek me my gossip dear, Eugene,
    But, mark me, circumspectly.

'Don't look for him in lecture-rooms,
    But where Tokay inspires;
Don't look for him in Hedwig's church,
    But snug at Mam'selle Meyer's.'

Swift he unfurls his pair of wings,
    And down from heaven he flings him,
Picks up my friend, my dear old pal,
    And back to heaven brings him.

'Ay, lad, I am the Lord Himself,
    The whole world owns my sway, man!
I always told thee I should turn
    Respectable some day, man.

'And every morn some miracle
    I 'll work for thy impressing;
And for thy sport I 'll pour to-day
    Upon Berlin my blessing.

'The paving-stones in every street
    Shall split, the town all over,
And lo! an oyster fresh and clear
    Shall every stone discover.

'A rain of fresh-squeezed lemon-juice
    Shall daintily bedew them,
The very kennels, rare old hock
    Shall run like water through them.'

How all Berlin comes out to browse,
    With hearts in joyous flutter!
The gentry of the county courts
    Lap wine from every gutter.

How gleefully the poets rush
    This feast of gods to eat up!

Lieutenants eke with ensigns troop
   To lick the very street up.

The ensigns and lieutenants, though,
   Are shrewdest in the mellay;
They know that every day can't work
   Such wonders for their belly.

Wir fuhren allein im dunkeln

WE took a chaise and posted
   Grandly as princes do,
And scudded through the darkness
   Privately, I and you.

Close and warm we travelled,
   But when the dawn-wind stirred,
We found, my love, between us
   The blind, immortal third.

Und bist du erst mein ehlich Weib

IF you would only be my wife
   We 'd teach old Time to measure
His moments with a golden rod
   Scaled to degrees of pleasure.

And you should scold without reproof,
   Provided that of course you
Knew that, unless you praised my verse,
   I 'd instantly divorce you.

Es blasen die blauen Husaren

THE Blue Hussars are riding,
   The bugles sound retreat,
And therefore I am bringing
   This wreath of roses, sweet.

My God, they kept us busy
   In camp, and field, and mart,
And some of them found quarters,
   Beloved, in your heart.

Der Tod, das ist die kühle Nacht

DEATH—it is still, cool night;
　　Life—it is sultry day.
　　Dusk falls, mine eyes grow heavy,
Weary am I of the light.

O'er my bed a tree leans near;
　　A nightingale sings on the bough.
　　She singeth only of love,
And even in dreams I hear.

Sag', wo ist dein schönes Liebchen

'SAY, where is the maiden sweet,
　　Whom you once so sweetly sung,
When the flames of mighty heat
　　Filled your heart and fired your tongue?'

Ah, those flames no longer burn,
　　Cold and drear the heart that fed;
And this book is but the urn
　　Of the ashes of love dead.

Donna Clara

IN the evening-shadowed garden
Walks the great Alcalde's daughter;
From the castle, darkly towering,
Roll the drums and blare the trumpets.

'I am weary of the dances,
Weary of the flattering speeches,
Weary of the knights who neatly
Match my beauties with the sunshine.

'All things are to me a burden
Since the moon's rays lighted for me
That same Knight, whose lute, spell-binding,
Nightly draws me to my window.

'As he stood there, slender, daring,
And his eyes shot fiery glances
From a face of noble pallor,
Almost a St. George I held him!'

Musing thus walked Donna Clara,
Eyes downcast and all unseeing,
Till she raised them to behold her
Unknown, handsome, knightly stranger.

Clasping hands and whispering passion
To and fro they move in moonlight;
Gently Zephyr comes to meet them,
Roses greet, speech-dowered by magic.

The enchanted roses greet them,
Liveried red, as Love's own heralds.
'Tell me, tell me, my Belovèd,
Why thy cheek so sudden flushes.'

''Twas the flies that stung, Belovèd,
And I hate these flies in summer
With a hate as deep as though they
Were a mob of long-nosed Hebrews.'

'Waste not words on Jews or midges,'
Spake the Knight in tones caressing.
From the almond trees there fluttered
Myriad hosts of snowy blossom.

Myriad hosts of snowy blossom
Poured their fragrance on the evening.
'Tell me, tell me, my Belovèd,
Is thy whole heart given to me?'

'Yea, I love thee, my Belovèd,
I will swear it by that Saviour
Whom the Jews, of God accursèd,
Once did slay in treacherous malice.'

'Waste not words on Jews or Saviour,'
Spake the Knight in tones caressing.
Far away, as in a vision,
Swayed white lilies, bathed in moonlight.

Gleaming lilies, bathed in moonlight,
Gazed upon the starry heavens.
'Tell me, tell me, my Belovèd,
Was thine oath not falsely sworn me?'

'Naught in me is false, Belovèd,
Even as in my breast there floweth
No blood-drop of Moorish tincture,
Nor the unclean blood of Hebrews.'

'Waste not words on Moors or Hebrews,'
Spake the Knight in tones caressing,
And towards a grove of myrtles
Leads he the Alcalde's daughter.

With love's soft and subtle meshes,
Secretly hath he ensnared her!
Short their words and long their kisses,
And their hearts were overflowing.

Sweet and melting is the bride-song
Sung by Philomel the gentle;
In the grasses close about them
Fireflies bear the bridal torches.

In the grove the silence deepens,
Naught is heard save furtive rustlings
Of the discreet myrtle-branches,
And the breathing of the blossoms.

Roll of drums and blare of trumpets
Ring out sudden from the castle.
Clara wakens and withdraws her
From her lover's arm encircling.

'Hark, they call for me, Belovèd,
Yet before we part, oh tell me,
Tell me thy dear name, Belovèd,
That so long thou 'st hidden from me!'

And the Knight, with merry laughter,
Kissed his lady's lily fingers,
Kissed her lips and kissed her forehead,
Ere he made her answer slowly:

'I, Señora, your Belovèd,
Am the son of the renownèd,
Famed, and scripture-learned Rabbi,
Israel of Saragossa!'

The Pilgrimage to Kevlaar

I

A MOTHER stood by the window,
  Her son in bed lay he.
'Wilt thou not rise up, Wilhelm,
  The pilgrim bands to see?'

'I am so sick, dear mother,
  I cannot hear nor see,
I think of my dead Gretchen,
  And my heart is sad in me.'

'Arise, we will to Kevlaar,
  Take rosary and book,
And the Mother of God with healing
  On thy sick heart shall look.'

They bear the Church's banners,
  They chant her hymns divine,
As winds the long procession
  Through Köln upon the Rhine.

The mother follows with them,
  Her sick son leadeth she,
And both sing in the chorus,
  'Hail Mary!   Praise to thee!'

II

The Mother of God at Kevlaar,
  Her best dress wears to-day;
She is busy indeed, for many
  Are the sick who come to pray.

The sick and crippled pilgrims
  Bring her as offerings meet
Limbs that of wax are fashioned,
  Many waxen hands and feet.

And he that a wax hand offers,
  Is healed of his hand's sore wound,
And he that a wax foot offers,
  His foot grows whole and sound.

To Kevlaar came many on crutches
    That dance the tight-rope now,
And many with crippled fingers
    That draw the fiddle-bow.

The mother took a taper,
    And from it moulded a heart.
'Take that to God's dear Mother,
    And she will heal its smart.'

Sighing her son did take it
    And as the shrine he nighs,
The words well from his sad heart,
    The tears well from his eyes.

'O Thou that art highly-favoured,
    O Virgin without stain,
O royal Queen of Heaven,
    To Thee I tell my pain!

'I dwelt at home with my mother,
    At Köln city fair;
Many hundred chapels,
    And many a church is there.

'And near to us lived Gretchen,
    But dead is Gretchen now—
Mary, I bring Thee a wax heart,
    My heart's deep wound heal Thou!

'Heal Thou my deadly heartache—
    Fervent my prayer shall be,
Each night and morning singing,
    "Hail Mary!   Praise to Thee!"'

III

The sick man and his mother,
    Lay in their lodging poor;
The Mother of God came to them,
    And lightly crossed the floor.

She bent above the sick man,
    And laid her hand upon

His wounded heart so gently,
  And softly smiled, and was gone.

In a dream the mother saw it,
  And more she might have seen,
But the dogs they bayed so loudly
  She started from her dream.

On his bed her son was lying
  Outstretched, and he was dead.
His wan and wasted features
  Glowed in the sunrise red.

Her hands his mother folded,
  A woman rapt was she,
Meekly she sang, and softly,
  'Hail Mary!   Praise to thee!'

FROM 'THE HARZ JOURNEY'

A Mountain Idyll

I

On the mountain stands a cabin,
   Where there dwells a miner old;
There the unfading spruces whisper,
   And the moon gleams bright as gold.

In the cabin stands a settle,
   Carven quaintly, curiously;
Who upon it sits is happy,
   And that happy man am I.

On the footstool sits a maiden,
   O'er my knees her arm she throws;
Eyes like twin blue stars of heaven,
   Little mouth a crimson rose.

And the dear blue stars gaze on me,
   Wide and sweet as heaven come close;
Roguishly her lily finger
   Lays she on the crimson rose.

No! the mother does not heed us,
   Spinning, spinning late and soon,
And the father plays the zither,
   Crooning o'er some old-world tune.

And the young one softly whispers,
   Softly, and with bated breath,
Trusting many a weighty secret
   Unto only me, she saith.

'Since aunt died,' she tells me, 'never
   Have we gone, no more can go,
To the rifle-range at Goslar,
   That's the jolliest place I know.

'While up here 'tis—oh, so lonely!
  On this chilly mountain height,
And we seem the livelong winter
  In the snow-drifts buried quite.

'Never girl so lived in terror,
  I 'm as frightened as a child,
For the wicked mountain spirits
  Work by night their witchcraft wild.'

Then she pauses, on a sudden
  Mute, my darling little maid;
With both hands her eyes she covers,
  As by her own words affrayed.

Louder moans the spruce outside there,
  And the wheel still whirs and brums,
While between rings out the zither,
  And the old tune the father hums:

'Fear not thou, my child, my darling,
  Fear no evil spirit's power!
Day and night, my child, my darling,
  Angels guard thee, hour by hour!'

II

Lightly on the lowly casement
  Taps the spruce with fingers green,
While the moon, a mute eavesdropper,
  Sheds her golden rays between.

Father, mother, gently snoring,
  In their room soft concert make;
While we two with happy prattle
  Keep each other wide awake.

'That you pray one bit too often
  I can hardly think that same,
For your lip curls in a fashion
  That from praying never came.

'Oh, that curl, so cold and wicked,
    Every time it shocks me so!
Though your eyes' good-natured shining
    Charms away the gloomy woe.

'Then about your faith I 'm doubtful,
    What is held true faith by most—
Don't you, really though, believe in
    Father, Son, and Holy Ghost?'

'Ah! my child, while yet I nestled
    In my mother's lap and love,
I believed in God the Father,
    Good and great, who reigns above!

'Who this goodly world created,
    And the goodly folk thereon,
Sun and moon, and stars set spinning
    Their predestined course upon.

'Then, my child, as I grew bigger,
    Things I mastered, more than one,
I began to use my reason,
    And believed in God the Son;

'On the Son beloved, who, loving,
    Love revealed, with us to abide,
And for guerdon, 'tis its custom,
    By the world was crucified.

'Now that I have grown to manhood,
    Read and travelled more than most,
Swells my heart, and I acknowledge
    With whole heart the Holy Ghost.

'He hath wrought the mightiest marvels
    Mightier works for suffering folk;
He cast down the baron's stronghold,
    Burst for aye the villein's yoke.

'Old and deadly wounds He healeth,
    And restores the ancient right;
All mankind are born His nobles,
    All are equal in His sight.

'Mists of evil scares He from us,
   Fancies dark on brains that prey,
Sickening us of love and gladness,
   Grinning at us night and day.

'Thousand knights in shining armour,
   Of the Holy Ghost inspired,
Chosen His will to do in all things,
   With great courage hath He fired.

'Now their blessed swords are flaming,
   Now their kindly banners wave!
Oh, my child, dost long to see them,
   Knights so noble and so brave?

'Well, my child, come—look upon me,
   Kiss me, boldly look, and boast
Thou hast looked on such a champion,
   Knight, child, of the Holy Ghost.'

III

Still the moon outside the window
   Lurks behind the unfading pine,
And our tiny lamp within-door
   Flickers low with fitful shine.

Yet my twin blue eyes are mingling
   With the dawn their brightest rays,
Glowing too the crimson roses,
   And the gentle maiden says:

'Tiny fairies, little elf-men,
   Steal our bacon and our bread,
Left at evening in the cupboard,
   In the morning, not a shred!

'Tiny fairies from the milk-pan
   Skim our cream, skim off the best,
And the milk-pan leave uncovered,
   And the cat laps up the rest.

'And the cat 's a witch, I 'm certain,
   For she slinks on stormy nights
Off to yonder haunted mountain,
   And the old ruin on the heights.

'There stood once a lordly castle,
   Full of mirth and armour's flare;
Shining knights and squires and ladies
   Flung through many a torch-dance there.

'Then on castle and retainers
   Laid her curse a wicked witch,
Nothing 's left of it but ruins,
   Owls have nests in every niche.

'But my aunt in heaven has told me
   If one speak the Word of Power,
In the fated place up yonder,
   In the night, at fated hour,

'Swift the ruins change to a castle,
   Lights a-shine at every loop,
And once more to merry dances
   Knights and squires and ladies troop.

'And who speaks that Word of Power,
   Castle, vassals, his must be,
Drums, and trumpets blown, do homage
   To his new-born seignory.'

Thus there bloom fantastic folk-tales
   From the rosebud mouth so small,
And the eyes their azure starlight
   Shed divinely over all.

Then the child with golden ringlets
   Winds my hands, to bind me fast,
Pretty names she gives my fingers,
   Kisses, laughs, is mute at last.

And in that still chamber all things
   Look on me like friends of yore;

Table, press, I seem to have seen them
    Half a hundred times before.

Grave, and friendly chats the house-clock,
    And, the ear scarce catches it,
Of itself the zither tinkles,
    And as in a dream I sit.

Here's the fated place for certain,
    And 'tis now the fated hour,
And methinks I feel it gliding
    From my lips, the Word of Power.

See, my child, how night already
    Feels the quickening dawn and quakes!
Brook and spruces murmur louder,
    And the hoary mountain wakes.

Clang of zithers, songs of kobolds
    From the mountain glen resound,
And, as in a madding springtime,
    Sprouts a grove of flowers around;—

Flowers of magic, boldly springing,
    Leaves more huge than fable saith,
Bright and odorous, swiftly trembling
    To the gale of passion's breath.

Roses, wild as crimson flamelets,
    From the coil flash suddenly;
Lilies, fair as crystal columns,
    Shoot aloft into the sky.

And the stars, like suns for glory,
    Gaze from heaven with longing glow;
Into giant cups of lilies
    Bright their streams of radiance flow.

But ourselves, my gentle maiden,
    Are transfigured more tenfold;
All about us gleam the torches,
    Shimmering gay on silk and gold.

Thou thyself art grown a princess,
　And this hut, as round I glance,
Turns a castle—lo! where gaily
　Knights and squires and ladies dance!

And for me, I have been seised of
　All things, castle, vassals—thee;
Drums, and trumpets blown, do homage
　To my new-born seignory!

(1825–6)

FIRST CYCLE

I

Coronation

Ho, songs! My own good songs and trusty!
Up, up! and don your arms!
Let blow the merry bugles,
And lift upon my shield
This fair young Maiden,
Who now alone shall rule
O'er all my heart as rightful Queen.

Hail, hail to thee, my fair young Queen!

From the sun above thee
I 'll snatch the beaming fiery gold,
And from it weave a diadem
For thine anointed head.
From the fluttering silk of the heaven's blue curtain,
Wherein the jewels of night are gleaming,
I 'll cut the richest piece,
And this, for coronation-mantle,
I 'll hang upon thy royal shoulder.
I 'll give thee a royal household
Of sonnets in starch and buckram,
Haughty terzains and courtierlike stanzas;
As running footman take my Wit,
As Court-fool, my Imagination,
As Herald, with laughing tears for his bearing,
My Humour will serve thee well.
But I myself, your Majesty,
I humbly kneel before you,
Presenting on crimson velvet cushion,

With my homage profound,
That morsel of sense
Which of her mercy she has left me still—
Your predecessor in the realm.

II

Evening Twilight

On the wan sea-strand
Lonely I lay, and in sorrowful brooding.
The sun sank lower and lower, and flung
His red rays, glowing, on the water,
And I watched the far white billows,
In the grip of the flood,
Foaming and roaring, nigher and nigher—
Strange medley of sounds! a whispering and wailing,
A laughing and murmuring, sobbing and sighing,
Low voices, the while, a strange lullaby singing.
Methought I heard long-forgotten legends,
World-old adorable folk-tales,
That long since in boyhood
From neighbours' children I learnt;
When, of a summer evening,
On the steps of stone by the house-door,
We squatted for quiet story-telling,
With small hearts eagerly listening
And young eyes keen for wonders;
While the fair grown-up maidens
Sat, 'mid balm-breathing pots of flowers,
At a window over the way there,
With rosy faces,
Smiling and lit by the moon.

III

Sunset

The red and glowing sun goes down,
Down into yon far-shuddering sea,
A world of waters, silver-grey;
Airy cloudlets tinted rosily
After him float; while, o'er against him,
From autumn's duskily-looming cloud-veils

With sorrowful death-pale visage,
Breaks the gentle moon,
And after her, tiny sparklers,
Shimmer the stars out of space.

Once through heaven went shining,
Wedded and one,
Luna the Goddess, and Sol the God,
And the stars in multitudes thronged around them,
Their little, innocent children.

But evil tongues came whispering discord,
And parted in anger
The august and radiant wedded pair.

Now, in lonely splendour, by day
The Sun-god on high goes his ancient round,
Still, for his majesty,
Blandly worship, and much belauded
By proud and fortune-hardened worldlings.
But all night long
Through heaven wanders Luna,
The wretched mother,
With all her orphans, her starry children,
And she gleams in silent sorrow,
And love-lorn maidens and gentle poets
Vow to her tears and songs.

Ah, tender Luna! with woman's heart
Ever she dotes on her beautiful spouse,
Still at even, trembling and pale,
Forth will she peer from her veil of cloud,
And after him aching she gazes,
And fain in her anguish would cry to him: 'Come!
Come! The children are pining for thee——'
Naught the implacable Sun-god heeds,
At the sight of his consort he flushes
His luridest crimson,
In wrath and pain;
And unrelenting he hastens down
To his widower's bed in the sea-waves cold.

Evil tongues with a whisper
Thus brought down such ruin and sorrow
Even on the gods, the immortals!
And the wretched gods, high-moving in heaven,
Wander in anguish
Comfortless ways without ending,
And die can they never,
But still drag with them
Their radiant sorrow.

But I, a mere man,
So lowly planted, of Death so favoured,
I 'll whine here no longer.

IV

A Night by the Strand

Starless and cold is the night,
Wide yawns the sea,
And over the sea, flat on his paunch,
Sprawls that uncouth lubber, the northwind,
And, quite at his ease, with hoarse, piping voice,
Like a peevish curmudgeon who grows good-humoured,
Chats to the water below;
And he spins mad yarns without number,
Slaughter-breathing tales of giants,
World-old Norwegian sagas;
And between-whiles, far-bellowing, laughs he, and
    howls he
The magic songs of the Edda,
And runic-spell rhymes,
So darkly defiant, and potent in glamour,
That the white sea-children
Leap their highest and cheer him,
Drunk with insolent glee.

Meanwhile, on the shore's flat margin,
Over the tide-washed, surf-wetted sand,
Strides a stranger, the heart within him
A wilder thing than wind or billows.
Where his feet fall
Sparks fly out, and crackle the sea-shells;
And he wraps him close in his mist-grey mantle,

And swiftly strides through the blustering night;
Surely led by the little candle
That pleasantly luring glimmers
From the fisherman's lonely cabin.

Father and brother are on the sea,
And all alone by herself is left
In the cabin the fisherman's daughter,
The strangely beautiful fisherman's daughter.
By the hearth she sits,
And lists to the humming kettle's
Bodeful, sweet, mysterious murmur;
And feeds the fire with sharp-crackling brushwood,
And blows it up,
Till the flickering ruddy blazes
Gleam again with magic beauty
On the face fresh and blooming,
On the tender, fair young shoulder,
So winsomely peeping
From the smock of coarse grey homespun,
And on the careful neat little hand,
As it binds the petticoat-skirt more tightly
Round her shapely haunches.

But on a sudden the door springs wide,
And at once walks in the night-wandering stranger;
Bold with love his eye reposes
On the fair and slender maiden,
Who trembling before him stands,
Aghast, like a terrified lily;
And he flings on the floor his mantle,
And laughs, and says:

'Behold, my child, I keep my word,
For I come, and with me there comes
The good old time when the gods out of heaven
Stooped in love to the daughters of men,
And, the daughters of men embracing,
Begot upon them
Kings, and races of sceptre-bearers,
And heroes famous on earth.
But gape there, my child, no longer

Over my godliness,
And I beg of thee brew me some tea with rum;
For outside 'twas cold,
And in such a night-wind,
Gods though we be, eternal, we shiver,
And easily catch the godliest of snuffles,
And even a cough that's immortal.

v

Poseidon

The sun's bright beams were playing
Over the rolling waste of the sea;
Far in the roadstead glittered the ship
That waited there to bear me homeward;
Only the waft of a fair wind failed us,
And I sat in peace on a silver sand-hill
On the lonely strand.
And I read the Song of Odysseus,
That old, that ever-youthful song,
From out whose leaves, where ocean murmured,
There joyously breathed on me
The breath of the gods,
And the sunny springtime of mortals,
And the burgeoning heaven of Hellas.

My noble heart still faithfully followed
The son of Laertes in wandering and danger,
Sat beside him, heavy in spirit,
By friendly hearth-sides,
Where queens were spinning purple linen;
And helped him to lie, and craftily vanish
From giants' caverns, and arms of sea-nymphs;
Followed him down through Cimmerian night,
And through storm and shipwreck,
Still suffering with him unspeakable sorrow.

Sighing I spoke: 'O cruel Poseidon,
Thy wrath is dreadful!
For myself I fear
In my homeward sailing.'

The words were scarce spoken,
When up foamed the sea,

And from the white-capt waves arose,
With sedge-crowned brows, the head of the Sea-god,
In scorn he bellowed:
'Keep a bold heart, my bardling!
I care not in the least to endanger
Thy wretched smack there,
Nor make thy life, so precious, a burden
With even a redoubtable tossing;
For thee, my bardling, I owe thee no grudge,
Thou never didst damage the tiniest turret
In Priam's citadel holy;
No tiniest eyelash didst thou e'er singe
In the eye of my son Polyphemus,
And thee hath never counselled and kept
The Goddess of Prudence, Pallas Athena.'

Thus roared Poseidon,
And into the sea plunged back;
While, over his vulgar sailor's joke,
Laughed under the water
Amphitrite, the buxom fishwife,
And the stupid daughters of Nereus.

VI

Declaration

Duskily fell the evening twilight,
Wilder blustered the tide,
And I sat on the shore, and gazed upon
The white dance of the billows,
And then my breast upswelled like the sea,
And longing seized me, and deep home-sickness
For thee, thou image sweet,
That hoverest ever o'er me,
Dost call me everywhere,
Everywhere, everywhere,
In the snore of the wind, in the roar of the sea,
In the sigh of my own fond heart.

With fragile reed I wrote in the sand:
'Agnes, I love but thee!'
But cruel billows came pouring in
Over the tender confession,

And blotted it out.
O brittlest of reeds, O sand so unstable,
O treacherous billows, I 'll trust you no more!
The heavens grow darker, my heart grows wilder,
And with strong right hand, from Norway's forests,
I pluck the tallest fir-tree,
And plunging it deep
Into Etna's glowing crater, and wielding
This for my fire-steeped pen titanic,
Write on the gloomy vault of heaven:
'Agnes, I love but thee!'

Night after night, blazing on high,
Shall burn the unquenchable scripture of flame,
And myriads to come, earth's unborn generations,
Read, rejoicing, the heavenly motto:
'Agnes, I love but thee!'

VII

A Night in the Cabin

The sea hath its pearls for treasure,
The heavens their starry jewels,
But ah! my heart, my heart,
My heart hath its own love.

Great are the sea and the heavens,
But greater is my heart,
And fairer than pearls or starlets
Beameth and gleameth my love.

Thou young and slender maiden,
Come to my mighty heart;
My heart, and the sea, and the heavens
Are dying for utter love.

.   .   .   .   .   •

On the dark blue vault of heaven,
Where the loveliest stars are twinkling,
Oh, that I might press my kisses,
Wildly press with stormy weeping!

Those bright stars in thousands twinkling
Are the eyes of my Belovèd,
Thousandfold their tender greeting
Shines from the blue vault of heaven.

To the dark vault of heaven,
To the eyes of my Belovèd,
I uplift my arms devoutly,
And beseech them and implore them:

Sweetest eyes, ye gracious candles,
Oh, possess my soul with blessing,
Let my spirit fly to inherit
You and your whole heaven of blisses!

.   .   .   .   .   .

From the eyes of heaven up yonder
Golden sparks fall trembling downward,
Through the night, as Love my spirit
Fills, expands through boundless heaven.

O ye eyes of heaven up yonder,
Weep yourselves into my spirit,
Till your starry tears with radiance
Flood and overflow my spirit!

.   .   .   .   .   .

Gently rocked by ocean-billows
And the tides of dreamy musing,
I lie quiet in the cabin,
In my dark berth in the corner.

Through the open hatchway gazing,
Bright I see the stars up yonder,
The belov'd sweet eyes in heaven
Of my sweet, my well-belovèd.

Those belov'd sweet eyes in heaven,
O'er my head their watch are keeping,
And they glimmer and they shimmer
From the dark blue vault of heaven.

Toward the dark blue vault of heaven
Blissfully I gaze long hours,
Till a wan white veil of sea-mist
Hides me from those eyes belovèd.

.　　　.　　　.　　　.

On the vessel's thin planking,
Where my dream-haunted head lies,
Batter the billows, the boisterous billows;
They welter and murmur
Aside in my ear:
'Thou dream-befooled fellow!
Thy arm is short, and the heavens are far,
And the stars up yonder are firmly fastened
With golden rivets—
In vain is thy longing, in vain is thy sighing,
'Twere better for thee to go to sleep.'

.　　　.　　　.　　　.

In dreams I saw a moorland vast and dreary,
All muffled thick with white and silent snow,
And under the white snow I lay deep-buried,
And slept the cold and lonely sleep of death.

But from the gloomy heaven above looked ever
The starry eyes upon my grave below,
Those gentle eyes! From heaven they shone victorious,
And calmly bright, and ever full of love.

VIII

Storm

Loud rages the Storm,
And he flogs the billows,
And the billows, foaming and combing,
Tower aloft, and in white water-mountains
Heave restless, for ever restless;
And the good ship upclimbs them,
Eagerly toiling;
Then, suddenly plunging, she sounds
The gloomy waves' wide-yawning abysses.

O Sea!
Mother of Beauty, the foam-born cruel one!
Grandmother of Love, have mercy upon me!
There comes hovering, scenting corpses,
That white apparition, the sea-mew;
And, whetting her beak on the topmast,
She lusts with greedy lust for the heart
That with praise of thy daughter resounds,
And which thy grandson, the little rogue,
Hath chosen for toy.

In vain are my pleading and prayer!
My call dies away in the rage of the storm,
In the noise of winds warring.
They howl, and whistle, and prattle, and roar,
Like a madhouse of sounds!
And in the lulls I hear distinctly
Siren wailing of harp-strings,
Wildest yearning of song,
Soul-dissolving and soul-lacerating;
Surely that voice I remember!

Far on the rocky coast of Scotland
Looms a castle, jutting and beetling
Grey o'er the shattering surge;
There, at a deep high-vaulted window,
Stands a woman, sickly and fair,
Ghostly fragile, and marble-pale;
And she sweeps her harp as she sings,
And the rough wind raves through her long locks
    rudely,
And bears her gloomy song
Over the raging waste of the sea.

IX

Calm

CALM the ocean lies, the sunbeams
Shimmering, dancing on the water,
And the ship through heaving jewels
Gently cleaves her green sea-furrow.

By the tiller lies the Pilot
On his belly, gently snoring.
Patching sails beside the foremast,
Cross-legged, squats the tarry ship-boy.

Red his cheeks beneath their griming
Burn; his wide mouth sadly twitches,
And his beautiful big eyes are
Piteously o'erbrimmed with sorrow.

For the Skipper stands before him,
Raging, swearing, roaring: 'Curse you,
You young rogue, you 've been and robbed me,
From the cask you 've stol'n a herring!'

Calm the ocean!   From the ground-swell
Boldly leaps a smart young spratling,
Warms his little head in sunshine,
Glad with tiny tail he splashes.

But from airy height a sea-gull
Darts like lightning on the spratling,
And, his hasty prey half-swallowed,
Soars again into the azure.

x

Ocean-wraith

BUT I, the while, leant over the gunwale,
With rapt eyes dreamily gazing,
Far down through the water clear as crystal,
Still gazing deeper and deeper—
Till, deep in the sea's abysses,
First like a glimmering dawn-cloud,
But ever growing clearer in colour,
Domes of churches and towers loomed upward;
And soon, as clear as day, a city entire,
Antiquated, Netherlandish,
And busy with folk.
There solemn burghers in sable mantles,
With prim white neck-ruffs and chains of honour,
And long in sword, and long in the visage,

Gravely stride through the swarming market
Tow'rd the Town Hall, high of stairway,
Where Emperors, marble phantoms,
Guard are keeping with sceptre and sword.
And near them, before long rows of houses,
With windows a-gleam like mirrors,
And quaint pyramidal pollard lindens,
Maidens walk with rustling of satin,
Slender-waisted, their flower-like faces
Framed demurely in coifs black-bordered,
Their golden tresses outrippling.
Gay attired gallants, in Spanish costume
Come swaggering to meet them, and bowing.
Aged women,
In sober old-fashioned garments,
With hymn-book and rosary in their hands,
Haste, with faltering footsteps,
To the great cathedral,
Impelled by the carillon's pealing
And muttering organ's tone.

Me too that far-off music grips
With its mysterious shudder!
An infinite longing, deepest sorrow
O'ersteals my heart,
My scarcely healèd heart;—
I feel as though its wounds were gently
Kissed open by belovèd lips,
And set once more a-bleeding—
Blood-drops, warm and crimson,
Fall slowly, slowly dripping fall
On a grey old house below there,
In the deep sea-city,
On an old and steeply-gabled house,
Tenantless now, and melancholy;
Save at the basement window
A maiden sits,
And leans her head on her arm,
Like a poor and forsaken child—
And I know thee, thou poor forsaken child!

So deep, so ocean-deep, then,
Thou hiddest thyself from me

In childish ill-humour,
And ne'er couldst again come up,
But strange must dwell in a land of strangers,
These centuries long;
And all the while, with soul full of grief,
O'er the whole wide world have I sought thee,
For ever have sought thee,
Thou ever-belov'd one,
Thou long, long lost one!
But now I have found thee—
Ay, now I have found thee again, and gaze in
Thy own sweet face,
Those eyes, so grave and loyal,
That smile so tender—
And never, never again will I leave thee,
And I come to thee, down to *thee*.
And with arms outstretched to enfold thee
Down will I plunge to thy heart!

Just in the nick of time here
The wideawake skipper gripped my foot,
And pulled me back from the bulwark,
And cried, maliciously laughing:
'Devil come for you, Doctor?'

XI

Purification

Bide thou in thine own deeps of ocean,
Delirious dream,
Thou who once for many a night
Didst wring my heart with bliss deceiving,
And now, as ocean-wraith,
In day's clear light hast come to ensnare me—
Bide thou below there for evermore;
And I fling, moreover, down to thee
All my old sins and my sorrows;
And the cap and bells of my folly,
That so long round my head have jingled;
And the cold, sleek-glistening serpent-skin,
Hypocrisy,
That all too long my spirit strangled,
The sickly spirit,

The God-belying, the angel-belying,
Unholy spirit—
Yoho! yoho! Here comes a breeze!
Up with the sails! They flutter and fill!
O'er the calm treacherous plains of ocean
Speeds the good ship,
And 'Hurrah!' cries the soul set free.

XII

Peace

High in heaven the sun was riding,
Round him white billowy clouds.
The sea was calm,
And musing I lay in the stern of the vessel,
Dreamily musing—and, half in waking
And half in slumber, I saw the Christ,
The Saviour of men.
In white and flowing raiment
He walked, a giant shape,
Over land and sea;
His head rose high into heaven,
His hands he stretched as in blessing
Over land and sea;
While, for the heart in his breast,
The sun he carried,
The golden fire-flaming sun;
And his golden fire-flaming sun-heart
Poured forth its beams of mercy,
And its kindly all-fostering light,
Illuming and warming,
Over land and sea.

Peals of bells rang, drawing festally,
As though swans with wreaths of roses
Towed her onward, the swift-gliding ship,
And drew her in play to the shore's green places,
Whereby men dwelt in their lofty-steepled
Sky-scaling town.

O peace mysterious! How still the town!
At rest were the rumble and roar

Of trade, with its chaffer and swelter;
And through the clean and echoing alleys
Wandered the townsfolk, clothed in white raiment,
Palm-branches bearing.
And where two met, with sympathy
Each looked on each, and read his bosom,
And, trembling for love and sweet self-abnegation,
Each on his brow kissed the other,
Uplifting their eyes
To the sun-bright heart of the Saviour,
That shed from the heavens his crimson blood
In glad atonement;
Then, thrice-redeemed, they cried aloud:
'Blessed be Jesus Christ!'

SECOND CYCLE

I

Greeting to the Sea

Thalatta ! Thalatta !
I hail thee, O Sea, thou Ancient of Days!
I hail thee, O Sea, ten thousand times
With jubilant heart,
Of yore as once hailed thee
Those Grecian hearts ten thousand,
Homestead-desiring, calamity-mastering,
World-renowned bold Grecian hearts.

The billows were heaving,
Were heaving and roaring,
The sun shed briskly from heaven
His quivering rosy sparklets,
In sudden scare the tribes of sea-birds
Rose on the wing, loud-shrieking;
O'er stamping of war-steeds and clang of shields
      smitten,
Far-pealed that shout, like a victor's cry:
'*Thalatta ! Thalatta !*'

I hail thee, O Sea, thou Ancient of Days!
Like speech of my homestead murmurs thy water,
Like dreams of my childhood shimmer before me
The heaving leagues of thy billowy realm,
As Memory, the grey-beard, remurmurs his stories
Of all those dear magnificent playthings,
Of all those glittering Christmas-presents,
Of all those branchy red trees of coral,
Gold-fishes, pearls, and shimmering sea-shells,
Which thou mysteriously dost guard
Down there in thy lucid crystal house.

Oh, how long have I languished in lonely exile!
Like a poor fading flow'ret

Shut in a botanist's tin for collecting
Drooped the sick heart in my breast.
Meseems I 've sat the livelong winter,
A sick man alone in his gloomy sick-room,
And now have suddenly left it;
And blindingly flashes upon me
The emerald spring by the sun awakened,
And the trees are a-whisper with snowy blossom,
And the fair young flowers gaze in my face,
Their bright eyes brimming with sweetness;
All 's odour and hum, and laughter and breeze,
And in heaven's blue deep the birds are all singing—
Thalatta ! Thalatta !

Thou valiant homing heart,
How oft, how bitter oft,
The northern she-barbarians have beset thee!
From great eyes, roving for conquest,
Shooting their fiery arrows;
With words ground crooked like sabres,
Threatening still to cleave my bosom;
With letters like clubs they battered to bits
My feeble and stupefied brain—
In vain I braced my buckler against them,
The shafts flew hissing, the blows fell crashing,
And by the northern she-barbarians
Down was I driven to the sea—
And, breathing freely, I hail thee, O Sea,
Thou kindly, rescuing Sea,
Thalatta ! Thalatta !

II

Thunderstorm

Dull tempest lies prone on the ocean,
And through the lurid wall of cloud
Darts the lightning with zigzags flare,
Swift-illuming, and swiftly vanished,
As a gleek from the brain of Kronion.
Over the waste of weltering water
Far the thunders go rolling,
And lustily leap the white sea-horses
That Boreas once in his might

Sired on the alluring mares of Erichthon;
And the sea-fowl anxiously o'er them hover,
Like shades that flit by the Styx,
Whom Charon repels from the night-coloured barge.

Woeful pinnace of pleasure,
Which there goes dancing the direst dance!
Aeolus sends her the briskest of partners,
Who strike up madly a rollicking round-dance,
And one doth pipe, and one doth blow,
A third on double-bass keeps brumming,
And the tottering steersman grips the tiller,
And with fixed eye looks down on his compass,
The shuddering soul of the vessel,
Then lifts his hands imploring to heaven:
'Oh, succour me, Castor, Tamer of Steeds,
And thou, valiant with fists, Polydeuces!'

III

Shipwreck

Hope gone, and Love gone!   All dashed to pieces!
And myself—most like a drowned body
That grumblingly the sea hath cast up,
Lie on the strand here,
The bald and desolate strand.
There heaves before me the waste of waters,
Nothing behind me but trouble and sorrow,
And over my head hurry the rain-clouds;
The grey and formless daughters of air,
Who from the sea, in cloudy pitchers,
Draw up the water,
And with labour lift it, and lift it,
But to pour it again in the sea,
A dull and most wearisome task,
And useless as my own vain life is.

The waves are murmuring, the sea-gulls crying,
Wafts of old memories over me steal,
Old dreams long forgotten, old visions long vanished,
Sweet and torturing, rise from the deep.

A woman dwells in the Norland,
A fairest woman, royally fair.

The amorous white folds of her gown
Clasp close her slender cypress-like form;
The dark wealth of her tresses
Falls, like a night of bliss,
From her head, with its garland of plaits, down-
    flowing
To curl itself dreamily sweet
Round a face sweet in its paleness;
And from that face, sweet in its paleness,
Large and intense her dark eye flashes,
Like a black sun from heaven.

O thou swarthy sun, how oft,
Witchingly oft, I drank from thee
The flames of a madness ecstatic,
And stood and reeled, as one drunk with fire—
Then hovered a smile of dovelike mildness
O'er the proud lips, ripe in their haughty curving,
And the proud lips, ripe in their haughty curving,
Sighed forth words more sweet than moonlight,
And tender as breath of roses—
And then my soul shook its pinions,
And soared, like an eagle, aloft into heaven!

Hush! ye billows and sea-fowl!
For all is over, hope and good-fortune,
Hope gone and Love gone! On earth I lie lonely,
A desolate shipwrecked man,
And bury my burning face here
In the wet sea-sand.

IV

Sunset

The sun in glory
Has paced serenely into the sea,
The wavering waters are softly tinged
With the gloom of night;
Yet still the afterglow
Strews them over with golden spangles;
And the might of the murmuring tide
Shoreward urges the white-capt billows,

That gambol as briskly and blithely
As woolly white flocks of lambkins,
At even, when, singing, the herd-boy drives them
From pasture home.

'How glorious the sun is!'
So said, long silence breaking, the friend
With whom o'er the strand I was wandering;
And half in jest, half in sad earnest,
Assured me he held the sun to be
A beautiful woman the hoary sea-god
Had married for mere convenience;
The livelong day she wanders in gladness
The heights of heaven, her purple robe
Ablaze with diamonds flashing,
Of all admired, of all belovèd—
All the wide world's fair creatures,
And gladdening all the world's fair creatures
With her bright face's warmth and radiance;
But in the evening, desolate, helpless,
Back must she come, like a slave,
To the damp sea-hall, and barren embraces,
Of her hoary spouse.

'Trust me'—further my friend went on,
And laughed and sighed, and again laughed dryly—
'They live down below there in tenderest wedlock!
For either they sleep, or wrangle so savagely
The sea above them foams with the strife,
And 'mid roaring of billows the sailor hears
How the greybeard miscalls his dame:
"All creation's bold strumpet!
Wanton of radiance!
The livelong day for others thou glowest,
At night for me thou art frosty and jaded!"
And after such curtain-lectures,
What wonder? into passionate weeping
The proud sun breaks, and bewails her fortune,
And wails so bitterly long, the sea-god
Springs from his couch there in sheer desperation,
And swiftly swims up to the sea's broad surface,
His wits and his wind to recover.

'I saw him myself, 'twas only last night,
Peering, breast-high, above the billows.
A jacket of yellow flannel he wore,
And on his head a lily-white nightcap,
And wrinkled and sere was his face.'

v

The Song of the Oceanids

Pallor of evening blanches the sea,
And lonely there, with his soul so lonely,
Sits a man on the bald sea-strand,
And stares with death-cold gaze aloft
At the far-off death-cold vault of heaven;
And stares o'er the waste of weltering sea—
Airy sailors, his sighs go soaring,
And back to him come in sorrow,
For barred to their entrance the heart they have found
Wherein they fain had anchored.
Then so loud he groans that the white-wing'd sea-gulls,
Scared from their sandy nesting-places,
In flocks around him circle,
And he speaks these words to them, strangely laughing:

'Poor, black-legg̀ed sea-fowl!
On snowy pinions ocean o'erhovering,
With crooked beaks the sea-water sipping,
And train-oily seal-blubber gobbling,
Your life is bitter as is your diet!
But I, happy mortal, I taste but of dainties!
I feed on the sweetest breath of roses,
The brides of the nightingale, fed by the moon;
I feed on yet sweeter confectioner's cates,
Filled full of rich cream thickly-clotted;
And the sweetest sweet I have tasted,
Love, sweet love, sweet being-belov̀ed.

'She loves me! she loves me! the sweetest maiden!
This morning at home, from her balcony leaning,
She looks through the gloaming away down the high
        road,
And listens, longing for me—yes, really!
In vain she peers all around her, then sighs she,

And sighing down she goes to the garden,
And wanders in balm and moonlight,
And speaks to the flowers, and fain must tell them
How I, her Belovèd, am oh, so dear!
And so worth her loving—yes, really!
In bed thereafter, asleep, in her dreams,
Her innocence plays with my image dear;
Next morning, even, at breakfast,
In her glistening bread and butter
Spies she my countenance smiling,
And she eats it up for love—yes, really!'

E'en so boasts he, and boasts he,
And ever the sea-gulls' wild screaming
Seems cold and ironical tittering.
The mists of gloaming rise from the sea;
From opalescent grey cloud looks weirdly,
Peering forth, the wan yellow moon!
Up surge, moaning, the ocean billows,
And deep from the surging and moaning sea,
As mournful as whispering breezes,
Sounds the Song of the Oceanids,
The beautiful, pitiful water-wives,
And loveliest the voice, o'er the others outringing,
Of Peleus' consort, the silver-footed,
And they sing to him, sighing:

'O fool, thou fool, thou hectoring fool!
Thou tortured of sorrow!
Thy hopes behind thee lie slaughtered most wretchedly,
Poor babes of the heart fondly dandled,
And ah! thy heart, like Niobe,
Grows marble through grief!
Black night sinks down o'er thy brain,
And there flash through the gloom the lightnings of
    madness,
In thy grief-wrung boasting!
O fool, thou fool, thou hectoring fool!
Stiff-neckèd art thou, like thy forbear,
The Titan so haughty who stole from Jove's children
The heavenly fire, and gave it to men,
And plagued by the vulture, nailed to the rock-wall,
Defied Olympus, defying and groaning

Till we could hear in our green sea-deeps,
And came to him with comforting song,
O fool, thou fool, thou hectoring fool!
Thou art in sooth yet feebler than he,
And 'twere mere common sense that the gods thou
    shouldst honour,
And patiently bear thy misery's burden,
Ay, patiently bear it for ages and ages,
Till Atlas' self shall his patience lose,
And the heavy world shall pitch from his shoulders
Into endless night.'

So sounded the song of the Oceanids,
The beautiful, pitiful water-wives,
Till waves growing louder quite over-roared it—
Into the clouds went plunging the moon,
Night over me yawned,
And I sat long, long, in the darkness weeping.

VI

The Gods of Greece

O moon in full bloom! in thy soft light
The sea is a-shine like flowing gold;
With noonday clearness, yet glamour of gloaming,
It rests in peace on the strand's broad bosom;
Through the starless azure of heaven,
Huge the white clouds go sailing,
Like forms of gods colossal, moulded
In glimmering marble.

Nay, in good sooth, no clouds are those yonder!
These are themselves, the gods of old Hellas,
Who once in gladness the world o'erlorded;
But now, defunct and supplanted,
Like monstrous ghosts make spectral procession
Through midnight spaces of heaven.

Awed, and mysteriously dazzled, I gaze on
The airy Pantheon,
Dumb-moving, majestic, dreadfully moving,
Giants in stature.
He there is Kroníon, the King of Heaven,
Snow-white gleam the curls on his brow,

Those curls so renowned that made tremble Olympus;
And cold in his hand are his thunders extinct,
And in his visage dwell sorrow and care,
Though there sits ever his ancient pride.
Those times were better, far better, O Zeus,
When thou divinely didst gloat on
Fair boys, and fair nymphs, and hecatombs also!
But e'en the gods may not lord it for ever,
The younger still drive out the elder,
As thou thyself o'er thy hoary father,
And over thy Titan uncles usurpedst,
Jupiter Parricida!
Thee too I know, thee too, proud Juno!
In spite of thine anguish of jealous care,
Another the sceptre has won from thy keeping,
And thou art no more the Queen of Heaven,
And thy great ox-eyes have grown dull,
And power from thy lily-white arms has vanished,
And never more thy wrath shall swoop on
The virgin filled with the godhead,
And the wonder-working strong son of Zeus.
Thee too, I know thee, Pallas Athena!
With shield and wisdom hadst thou no skill
To turn from the gods this destruction?
Thee too I know, even thee, Aphrodite!
Once the golden, and now the silvern!
But certés the zone of desire still decks thee,
Though creeps my spirit before thy beauty;
And me wouldst thou bless with thy body so fair,
Like other heroes, of dread I should die—
As pale corpse-goddess thou seem'st to me,
Venus Libitina!
No more with love upon thee there
Gazes thy terrible Ares.
How mournfully looks Phoebus Apollo,
The youthful!   Dumb is his lyre
That gladdened the gods at Olympian feasts.
Yet mournfuller looks Hephaistos,
And truly the Limper shall never more
Play the Hebe in heaven,
And serve with zeal to the gods assembled
The genial nectar.—And long is extinguished
The gods' inextinguishable laughter.

Ye gods of Greece, I have never loved you!
For Greeks I hold in distinct aversion,
And even Romans I frankly hate;
Yet sacred compassion and shuddering pity
O'erflow my heart,
When thus I see you there above me,
Ye gods long forsaken,
Dead, night-wandering phantoms,
Weak as clouds that the wind scares by!
And when I bethink me what quaking wind-bags
Are these new gods who have overcome you,
These new sad gods who are now the fashion,
The malice cloaked in the sheepskin of meekness—
Oh, my heart swells with gloomiest rage,
And I would batter the modern temples,
And battle for *you*, ye gods of Hellas,
For you and your genial ambrosial right,
And before your altars majestic,
Rebuilded once more, and a-smoke with sacrifice,
I myself would kneel to you, praying,
And lift to you arms beseeching—

For always, ye old gods of Hellas,
Have ye of old in the battle of mortals
Stood by the side of the conqueror stoutly;
But man is magnanimous rather than ye,
And I stand here now in the battle of gods
Firm on your side, ye old gods, though vanquished

Thus I spake, and above me visibly
Blushed those pallid and cloudy spectres,
And gazed at me even as the dying,
Transfigured by pain—and suddenly vanished.
The moon just then had hidden
Under the clouds, which drove on her darkly;
Loudly murmured the sea,
And bright paced forth, victorious in heaven,
The stars eternal.

VII

Questions

At night by the sea, the desolate sea,
Doth a young man stand,

His head full of doubt, his heart full of anguish,
And with livid lips he questions the billows:

'The Riddle of Life, oh, read me,
That world-old tormenting riddle,
O'er which have been addled heads without number,
Heads in strange hieroglyphic bonnets,
Heads in turbans, and barret-caps black,
Heads in perukes, and a thousand other
Plagued and perspiring heads of mortals—
Tell me now the meaning of man!
Whence comes he coming? Where goes he gone?
Who dwells up there in the golden starfields?'

The billows but murmur their murmur eternal,
Still blows the wind, the clouds still go sailing,
The stars go on twinkling, indifferent and cold,
And a fool waits for the answer.

VIII

The Phoenix

There comes a bird flown out of the west,
And eastward flies he,
To his home in an eastern garden,
Where groves of spice are breathing and growing,
And palm-trees whisper, and cool springs bubble—
And flying sings the bird of wonder:

'She loves him! she loves him!
In her little heart she enshrines his picture,
And keeps it sweetly, secretly hidden,
And knows not 'tis there!
But in her dreams he stands before her,
She weeps and implores, and his hand she kisses,
And his name she utters,
And uttering it wakens, and lies affrighted,
And rubs in her wonder her beautiful eyes—
She loves him! she loves him!'

At the foot of the mast I was leaning on deck,
Where as I stood I could hear the bird's song.
Like dusky green coursers with manes of bright silver,

Tossing their foam-crests, bounded the billows;
Like swans in flight sailed over the ocean,
With glimmering canvas, the Heligolanders,
The nomads bold of the North Sea!
Over me, in the eternal blue,
Hovered the white-wingèd clouds,
And sparkled the sun eternal,
The rose of the heavens, that blooms so fierily,
And laughed on the ocean that mirrored him;—
And heaven, and sea, and my own swelling heart
Resounded in echo:
'She loves him! she loves him!'

IX

Sea-sickness

The afternoon clouds droop downward,
Greyly they sag o'er the breast of the sea,
Which heaves to meet them in sullen gloom,
And the ship scuds fast between.

Sea-sick, ever I sit by the mainmast,
And there on myself make reflections full many,
Primeval ashen-grey reflections,
That Father Lot made long ago,
When pleasant things he 'd enjoyed too freely,
And found himself after in evil case.
I think, too, sometimes of other old stories:
How pilgrims marked with the cross in the old-time
Devoutly would kiss, in their stormy sea-faring,
The Blessed Virgin's comfortful picture;
How sea-sick knights, in as dire sea-trouble,
Each one the cherished glove of his lady
Would press to his lips, and straight gat comfort—
But here I 'm sitting and chewing morosely
An old red-herring, that salty consoler
When you 're sick as a cat, and down as a dog.

All the while the good ship fights
With the wild and buffeting tide;
Like a war-horse uprearing poises she now
On her shuddering stern, till the rudder creaks,
Then downward she plunges, heels over head,

Into the bellowing water-gulf;
Anon, as one reckless, faint with love,
Fain would she gently nestle
On the gloomy breast of the giant billow,
That, mightily roaring,
Comes tumbling aboard her, a sea-waterfall,
And drenches myself with foam.

Oh, this heaving, and swaying, and rocking
Is past all bearing!
In vain my eyes go peering to seek
The German coastline.   Alas! but water!
For ever but water, unstable water!

As the winter traveller at evening will yearn
For a warm, heart-comforting cup of tea,
So yearns my heart even now for thee,
My German Fatherland!
Though evermore thy pleasant soil be encumbered
With madness, hussars, and wretched verses,
And pamphlets weak and small-beery;
Though evermore thy zebras
On roses go browsing instead of thistles;
Though for evermore thy noble monkeys
So lazily strut in superior splendour,
And think themselves better than all their brothers,
The vulgar herd of dull plodding cattle;
Though evermore thy worthy Snail-Council
May deem itself immortal,
It creeps along at such a snail-pace,
And day by day will vote on the question:
'Does the cheese to the tribe of the cheesemites
      belong?'
And consumes long years in profound debate
On modes of improving Egyptian hoggets,
And making their fleeces grow longer,
That the shepherd may shear them just like the others,
No favour shown—
Though for ever injustice and folly
May flourish, Germany, o'er thee,
For thee my bowels are yearning now:
For thou art at least still good firm dry land.

X

In Haven

Happy the man who has come to his haven,
And left the sea with its tempests behind him,
And cosy now and quiet sits
In the pleasant town-cellar at Bremen.

How kindly looks the world, and how cheery
Reflected in this brimming rummer,
And how the billowing *microcosmos*
Sunnily fathoms the thirst of my heart!
All things I see in the glass,
Ancient and modern histories of nations,
Turks and Greeks, and Hegel and Gans,
Groves of lemons, and guards parading,
Berlin and Gotham, and Tunis, and Hamburg;
But fore all else my belov'd one's image,
That angel's head on its Rhine-wine gold-ground.

Oh, how fair! how fair art thou, Belovèd!
Fair as a rose thou seemest!
Not like the Rose of Shiraz,
The Bride of the Nightingale, Hafiz-besung;
Not like the Rose of Sharon,
Whose holy crimson the Prophets have glorified;—
Thy peer is 'The Rose' in the Cellar of Bremen!
That is the Rose of Roses.
The older she grows the lovelier she blushes,
And her heavenly breath has made me thrice blessèd,
Her breath has inspired me, and made me so drunk,
That gripped he not fast the hair of my head,
Mine host of the Cellar of Bremen,
I'd turn topsy-turvy!

The honest man! We sat there together,
And drank like two brothers,
Discoursing on high mysterious matters,
We sighed and sank on each other's bosoms,
And his convert am I to the True Faith,—Charity—
I drank to the health of my bitterest foes,
And all bad poets forgave as freely

As I myself would fain be forgiven.
I wept most devoutly, whereafter
The Gates of Salvation opened to me,
Where the 'Twelve Apostles,' the holy big wine-casks,
Preach in silence, yet well comprehended
Of all the nations!

These are heroes!
Uncomely outside in their wooden jackets,
They are within more bright and beautiful
Than all the haughty Priests of the Temple,
And all King Herod's guardsmen and sycophants,
Beprankt with gold, and in purple raiment—
Well, I have always declared
That not among quite common people,
Nay, but the best society going,
Lived for ever the King of Heaven!

Hallelujah! how pleasantly breathe on me
The palm-trees of Beth-El!
How sweetly the myrrh breathes from Hebron!
How rushes Jordan and reels in his gladness!—
And I reel with him now, and reeling
Lugs me from stair unto stair to daylight
Mine excellent host of the Cellar of Bremen.

Mine excellent host of the Cellar of Bremen!
Behold, on the roofs of the houses sitting,
The angels, gloriously drunk, and singing;
Yon sun, all aglow up above them,
Is only the jolly red nose of a toper,
The World-Spirit's nose 'tis;
And round the World-Spirit's big red nose there
Circles, reeling, the drunken world.

XI

Epilogue

As in the cornfields the golden wheat-ears,
So wax and so wave in the spirit of man
Thoughts in thousands.
Ay, but ever the love-thoughts tender
Spring between them like happy corn-flowers,
Blue and scarlet flowers.

Blue and scarlet flowers!
The churl of a reaper rejects you as useless,
Clowns in dull scorn but thresh you to pieces,
And even the neediest vagrant,
Whom the sight of you comforts and cheers,
Shakes his wise pate,
And pretty weeds will call you.
But the fair maid of the village,
Her garland weaving,
Respects you and plucks you,
To twine with you her beauteous tresses;
And decked with you thus, she hastes to the dance-floor,
Where fiddles and flutes are merrily sounding,
Or to the silent beech-tree,
Where the voice of her lover sounds sweeter by far
Than flutes do or fiddles.

VARIOUS POEMS

Where?

WHERE shall I, of wandering weary,
 Find my resting-place at last?
Under drooping southern palm-trees?
 Under limes the Rhine sweeps past?

Will it be in deserts lonely,
 Dug by unfamiliar hands?
Shall I slumber where the ocean
 Crawls along the yellow sands?

It matters not! Around me ever
 There as here God's heaven lies,
And by night, as death-lamps o'er me,
 Lo, His stars sweep through the skies!

To Edom!

WITH each other, brother fashion,
Have we borne this many an age.
Thou hast borne with my existence,
And I borne have with thy rage.

Many a time, in days of darkness,
Wonder-strange hath been thy mood,
And thy dear and pious talons
Hast thou reddened in my blood.

Now our friendship groweth closer;
Nay, it waxeth daily now:
I myself begin to bluster
And am nigh as mad as thou.

With a Copy of 'The Rabbi of Bacharach'

BURST out in wailing riot,
  Thou darkling martyr-lay,
That in my soul, flame-quiet,
  I 've borne this many a day!

It thrills through every hearing
  And so the heart doth gain.
I 've conjured up, unfearing,
  The thousand-year-old pain.

Great, little, weep and even
  Cold hearts do tearful grow:
The small stars weep in heaven,
  The maids and flowers below.

The tears, still southward fleeting,
  To the still conclave go
And all, each other meeting,
  Into the Jordan flow.

NEW POEMS

Leise zieht durch mein Gemüt

SOFT, aloft, the bells do ring,
  Gentlest thoughts they sing me.
Ring and sing, my song of spring,
  Through the blue sky wing thee

To the house of budding flowers,
  Borne by Echo fleeting.
Shouldst thou chance to see a Rose—
  Say, I send her greeting!

Die Rose duftet

THE Rose is fragrant—yet if she doth know
  Her sweet scent's meaning, if the Nightingale
Herself feels aught that through Man's soul doth flow
  At sound of her enraptured madrigal,

I know not, I.   Yet often much offence
  We find in truth!   If Rose and Philomel
Do but pretend emotion, evidence
  We have enough that such lies profit well.

Wie des Mondes Abbild zittert

As the moon's fair image trembles
  In the troubled, tossing tides,
Though herself, serene and stately,
  O'er heaven's vaulted pathway glides,

Even so glidest thou, Belovèd,
  Still, serene; thine image taken
In my heart but seems to tremble,
  For my heart is tossed and shaken.

83

Es war ein alter König

THERE was an aged monarch,
  His heart was sad, his hair was grey;
Alas, poor fool, he took him
  A wife that was young and gay!

There was a handsome page-boy,
  Light was his heart and gold his hair;
The silken train he carried
  Of that queen so young and fair.

Dost thou not know my story,
  So sweet, so sad to tell?
Death was the lovers' portion
  Because they loved too well.

Durch den Wald im Mondenscheine

THROUGH the forest, in the moonlight,
  Late I saw the elfin train
Pass with hunting-horns resounding,
  Heard their horse-bells ring again.

Golden antlers, nobly branching,
  Crowned each little snow-white steed;
Like a flight of wild swans homing
  Through the glades they passed at speed.

Smiled the Fairy Queen upon me—
  Smiled, and looked, and passed me by.
Does her smile mean love's renewal?
  Does it mean that I must die?

Die holden Wünsche blühen

THE tender wishes blossom,
  And wither at a breath,
And bloom again, and wither—
  Until they cease in death.

'Tis knowing this that saddens
  For me the love most blest:
My heart has learned such wisdom
  That it bleeds within my breast.

From 'To Seraphine'

Wandl' ich in dem Wald des Abends

THROUGH the wood when I am wandering
  In the dusky eventide,
Goes a dainty form in silence
  Always closely at my side.

Is not this thy veil, the white one?
  This the gentle face I love?
Is it merely moonlight breaking
  Through the gloomy firs above?

Is that sound the sound of weeping
  From mine own eyes welling deep?
Or dost thou, Belovèd, truly
  Walk to-night by me and weep?

Es ragt ins Meer der Runenstein

THE Runic stone from the sea rears high
  Where I sit and dream and ponder;
The winds they pipe; the sea-gulls cry;
  The billows foam and wander.

Oh, many a maiden loved have I,
  With many a lad gone roaming—
Where are they now? The winds, they sigh—
  The billows wander foaming.

Tannhäuser
(*A Legend*, 1836)

I

GOOD Christians all, avoid the snare
    When Satan's guile entices!
I 'll sing you the Tannhäuser song,
    To warn from his devices.

Tannhäuser was a warrior bold,
    Who, love's delight pursuing,
Dwelt seven years in the Venusberg,
    Seven years to his undoing.

'O Venus, mistress fond and fair,
    My love, my life, farewell now!
For, with your leave, I fain would go—
    No longer here would dwell now.'

'Tannhäuser, noble knight, this day
    You have withheld your kisses.
Oh, kiss me quick, and tell me true,
    If aught in me amiss is.

'The wine that day by day I pour,
    Say, sweet have you not found it?
And day by day, with roses red,
    Your head, have I not crowned it?'

'O Venus, mistress fond and fair,
    Of your wine so sweet in flavour,
Of your kisses warm, my soul is sick—
    Some sourness I would savour.

'Jested and laughed too long have we,
    I yearn for weeping bitter;
I want no roses for my head—
    A crown of thorns were fitter.'

'Tannhäuser, good and noble knight,
   With cruel words you grieve me;
You have promised me a thousand times
   That you would never leave me.

'Come, let us to our chamber go,
   And taste again love's gladness;
My lovely body, lily-white,
   Will chase away your sadness.'

'O Venus, mistress fond and fair,
   Your charm will never perish;
As men have loved you in the past,
   They still will love and cherish.

'Yea, when I think upon the gods
   And heroes who have lusted
After your body lily-white,
   My soul recoils disgusted.

'Your lovely body lily-fair
   Wellnigh my soul affright will,
If I but think how many more
   Your beauty yet delight will.'

'Tannhäuser, noble knight and good,
   You shall not thus accuse me;
Oh, liefer were I beaten sore,
   As you were wont to use me.

'Yea, liefer were I beaten sore,
   Than that such words were spoken,
Or that by you, a Christian cold,
   My pride of heart were broken.

'Because I have too fondly loved,
   I hearken while you chide now;
Farewell, I give you leave to go:
   Myself the door throw wide now.'

II

In Rome, in Rome, in the holy town,
   They are tolling from every steeple;

The procession with ringing and singing goes
    The Pope in the midst of his people.

'Tis the pious Urban who passes along,
    The triple crown he's wearing;—
He is clad in his purple robe of state,
    The barons his train upbearing.

'O holy Father, Urban, hear!
    A sinful tale to tell is;
Thou shalt not move another step,
    Till saved my soul from hell is.'

The folk, they fall in a circle back,
    Hushed are the anthems holy;
'Who is the pilgrim wan and wild,
    That kneels to the Pope so lowly?'

'O holy Father, Urban, thou
    Canst bind and loose from evil;
Deliver me now from the pains of hell,
    And the power of the Devil.

'I am Tannhäuser, the noble knight,
    Who, love's delight pursuing,
Dwelt seven years in the Venusberg,
    Seven years to his undoing.

'A lovely woman Venus is,
    With many a grace to charm one;
Like sunshine and the scent of flowers,
    Her voice can soothe and warm one.

'As the butterfly, fluttering, sips from the cup
    Of the fragrant flower posies,
So flutters my soul for ever round
    Her lips as red as roses.

'Her blooming curls flow dark and free,
    Her noble face enwreathing;
Her great eyes, when they gaze on you,
    Will almost stop your breathing.

'Ah, if her eyes but gaze on you,
  A captive fond you languish!
To win away from the mount at last
  Has cost me bitter anguish.

'Yea, though I now am won away,
  Still shine her eyes and yearn there;
The eyes of the woman follow me,
  And beckon to return there.

'By day I am a sorry ghost;
  My life awakens nightly;
For by night I dream of my mistress fair:
  She sits by me laughing lightly.

'So whole of heart she laughs, and gay,
  Her teeth like pearls peeping!
If on her laughter I but think,
  I straight must fall a-weeping.

'I love her with a boundless love,
  Nothing will stay its urging;
'Tis like a swirling cataract,
  You cannot stem its surging.

'From rock to rock it leaps and foams:
  The thunder-voices roar on;
If it broke its neck a thousand times,
  The mighty flood would pour on.

'To Venus I would gladly give,
  Were it mine, the whole of heaven;
I would give her the sun, I would give her the **moon**,
  And all the stars of even.

'I love her with a mighty love,
  With flames that burn and consume me—
Are these already the quenchless fires
  To which I feared to doom me?

'O holy Father, Urban, thou
  Canst bind and loose from evil;

Deliver me from the pains of hell,
　And the power of the Devil.'

In sorrow the Pope has raised his hands,
　In sorrow he has spoken:
'Tannhäuser, thou unhappy man,
　The spell may not be broken.

'The devil that is Venus named,
　Of all the fiends the worst is;
The man she holds in her lovely claws
　For evermore accurst is.

'For the lust of the flesh thy soul must pay,
　Must pay the bitter cost now;
Thou art damned to hell's eternal woe:
　Thou art for ever lost now.'

III

Tannhäuser, the knight, he walked so fast,
　That his wounded feet were bleeding;
'Twas midnight when, at the Venusberg,
　He stayed at last his speeding.

Venus awakened from out her sleep,
　And blithe from her couch upspringing,
Round her lover she threw her milk-white arms,
　·　And held him, closely clinging.

Down from her nose the red blood ran,
　Her eyes with tears gushed over;
The tears and blood besmeared the face,
　And wet the cheek of her lover.

The knight awearied sank on the bed
　Ere a single word was spoken;
To cook in the kitchen Venus went,
　That his fast might straight be broken.

She gave him soup and she gave him bread;
　Herself his wounds washed featly;
His matted hair she brushed and combed,
　And laughed the while full sweetly.

'Tannhäuser, noble knight, 'tis long
  Since you left me, and wandered forth, now;
Oh, where have you been this weary while—
  In what land of the south or the north, now?'

' 'Twas in Italy, my Venus fair,
  That business made me tarry;
From Rome I have returned as fast
  As hasting feet would carry.

'Oh, Rome is built on seven hills,
  Beside the Tiber River.
I saw the Pope, who mentioned you,
  And said, "My greetings give her."

'Through Florence I passed on my homeward
        way,
  And Milan.   Then I started
To climb the heights of Switzerland,
  Light-footed, eager-hearted.

'Over the Alps I toiled apace,
  And there the snow was falling;
The lakes of azure laughed to me,
  The eagles hoarse were calling.

' 'Neath the care of six-and-thirty kings
  Lay Germany, like a dotard,
Snoring in happy peace below
  Where I stood, on the Mount Saint Gothard.

'I saw the Swabian poet-school—
  That set of darling ninnies;
They sat in a row with guards on their heads,
  So careful each of his skin is.

'At Frankfort I stopped awhile at Schwabb's,
  And the famous dumplings ate there;
For religion the folk are far renowned,
  And the giblets are first-rate there.

'A dog, who was once of the better sort,
  I saw at Dresden, sadly;—
Too aged now to bark at all,
  His teeth he misses badly.

'At Weimar, the widowed muses' seat,
  A voice to sorrow giving,
They wept because Goethe, alas! was dead,
  And Eckermann was living.

'At Potsdam I heard a deafening din,
  And asked them what the cause was.
For Gans, who read them at Berlin
  Last century's tale, the applause was.

'At Göttingen learning blooms apace,
  Though scanty fruit 'tis bearing;
No light I spied as I passed it through,
  In the murky midnight faring.

'The bridewell I saw at Zell was used
  For Hanoverians purely.
O Germans, a national jail and whip,
  Were meet for Germany surely!

'At Hamburg I asked—I was fain to know—
  Why the streets so vilely stank there.
And Jews and Christians answered, both,
  'Twas the river was to thank there.

'In Hamburg, in the city good,
  Oh, many a rascal strange was!
I thought I was back in the jail at Zell,
  When it merely the Exchange was.

'From Hamburg I went to Altona:
  The neighbourhood is pleasant;
You shall hear of that another time;
  Let this suffice for the present.'

From 'Songs of Creation'

Warum ich eigentlich erschuf

THE reason why I made it all,
   This world so glorious, would you learn?
   Within my soul there seemed to burn
A flaming and resistless call.

'Twas sickness at the last which lured
   My hand to the stupendous deed.
   Creation satisfied my need;
Creation ended, I was cured.

From 'In Foreign Lands'

Ich hatte einst ein schönes Vaterland

OH, I had once a beauteous Fatherland.
   High used to seem
The oak—so high!—the violets nodded kind.
   It was a dream.

In German I was kissed, in German told
   (You scarce would deem
How sweetly rang the words) 'I love thee well!'
   It was a dream.

ROMANCES
(1839–42)

A Woman

THEY loved each other beyond belief;
She lived by her wits and he was a thief.
When he played his tricks on the crowd
She rolled on the bed and laughed aloud.

The day went by in joy and zest,
By night she lay upon his breast.
When they haled him to jail she vowed
It the best of jests, and laughed aloud.

He sent her a message: 'Oh, come to me!
Day and night I yearn for thee!
I cry to thee, for my heart is cowed'—
She shook her head and laughed aloud.

At six in the morning they hanged him high,
By seven he deep in the grave did lie;
He had scarce been an hour in his shroud
Ere she quaffed red wine and laughed aloud.

Anno 1839

O GERMANY, so far, so dear,
   Thy memory dims mine eye with woe!
This merry France seems sad and drear,
   Her lightsome folk a burden grow.

'Tis reason only, cold and bare,
   In witty Paris that is crowned—
O foolish bells! O bells of prayer!
   Yonder at home how sweet ye sound!

These men how mannerly! And yet
   Their courteous bow I take amiss.—

The rudeness that of old I met
   Where I was born, was joy, to this.

These smiling women! For their lives
   They chatter like a turning mill!
Give me the silent German wives,
   That go to bed demure and still.

Here round and round in frantic chase
   Things whirl as in a dream, and move!
There all seems nailed into its place,
   And glides along the ancient groove.

The watchman's horn, I hear it blow:
   Familiar, faint, from far it hails;
The watchman's song, I hear it grow
   And mingle with the nightingale's.

Those were the poet's golden times,
   'Neath Schilda's oaks of shadowy boon;
Where once I wove my tender rhymes
   From the violet's breath and the light o' the moon.

Sir Olave

I

By the door of the cathedral
Stand two figures scarlet-coated,
And the king himself the one is,
And the other is the headsman.

Says the monarch to the headsman,
'From the hymn the priests are singing
Seem the nuptials to be over—
Let thy goodly axe be ready.'

Peal of bells and roll of organ;
Stream of folk from out the minster;
Festal-robed in the procession
Move the lovers newly wedded.

Spectre-pale, and sad, and fearful,
Is the monarch's lovely daughter;
Bold and debonair, Sir Olave,
And his rosy mouth is smiling.

Gay he greets the gloomy monarch
With his smiling mouth and rosy:
'Father freshly won, good morrow;
Forfeit duly is my head now.

'Since to-day I surely perish,
Let me live—ah, live!—till midnight,
That, with feast and torchlight dancing,
I may celebrate my wedding.

'Let me live till drained and empty
Is the last of all the goblets;
Let me dance till dance is over—
Let me live and love till midnight!'

Spake the king then to the headsman,
'To our son-in-law a respite
Until midnight be accorded—
Let thy goodly axe be ready.'

II

At his wedding feast Sir Olave sups;
He drains the last of all his cups.
  Upon his shoulder lies
  His wife and sighs—
By the door the headsman is standing.

The dance begins; by the torches' blaze
Sir Olave clasps his bride, nor stays
  His foot till, wild and fast,
  They have danced their last—
By the door the headsman is standing.

The fiddles strike up so merry and glad,
The flutes, they sigh and grieve so sad!
  The watchers gaze with woe,
  As they come and go—
By the door the headsman is standing.

And, as they dance to the music's cheer,
Sir Olave stoops and whispers drear,
  'The half of my love is untold,
  And the grave is so cold'—
By the door the headsman is standing.

III

Sir Olave, 'tis the midnight hour;
  Thy life is sped and over!
Thou hast enticed a prince's child
  To take thee for her lover.

The priests, they murmur the funeral mass,
  The man in scarlet's ready;
He stands beside the sombre block,
  And holds his good axe steady.

Sir Olave steps to the court adown,
  Where the gleaming lights and swords are.
His rosy mouth is smiling gay,
  And gay as his mouth his words are:

'I bless the sun, I bless the moon,
  And I bless the stars of even;
I also bless the little birds
  That pipe in the blue of heaven.

'I bless the sea, I bless the land,
  And the flowers upon the meadow;
The violets too, for, like my bride's,
  Are their eyes of wistful shadow.

'Ye violet eyes of my bride, so blue,
  For your sake my life is over!
Yet most I bless the elder tree
  Where you took me for your lover.'

The Water Nymphs

THERE's a murmur of waves on the lonely strand,
  The moon o'er the deep has risen;
The warrior rests on the white sea sand,
  His dreams are a radiant prison.

The lovely nymphs in their filmy dress
　　Mount up from the waters under;
They fancy the youth is asleep, and press
　　Around him with stealthy wonder.

A marvelling finger the first one laid
　　On the plumes he wore in his bonnet;
With his woven armour another played,
　　And the bandolier upon it.

With gleaming eyes then laughed the third,
　　As she snatched from the sheath its treasure;
She leaned upon the naked sword,
　　And smiled on the knight for pleasure.

The fourth drew near with a merry dance,
　　And yearned till the words welled over:
'Fair mortal flower, sweet the chance
　　If thou hadst been my lover!'

The hand of the knight the fifth held fast,
　　And kissed it long and dumbly.
The sixth was coy, but she kissed at last
　　His mouth and his cheeks so comely.

To the wily knight it seemed far from wise
　　To wake, that the joy should miss him;
So motionless under the moon he lies,
　　As long as they care to kiss him.

Away!

THE day is in love with darksome night,
The spring's in love with winter;
Life is in love with death—
And thou, thou lovest me!

Thou lovest me—and shadows grim
Already close around thee;
Thy bloom and beauty fade;
Thy soul to death is bleeding.

Ah, let me be! and only love
The butterflies that gaily
Flit i' the scent and sunshine—
Forsake me and my sorrow!

Dame Mette

(*From the Danish*)

WITH Sir Peter at wine Sir Bender sat,
  Said Sir Bender, 'I wager securely,
Though your singing compel all the world beside,
  Dame Mette withstandeth it surely.'

To which Sir Peter: 'I 'll lay my horse
  Against your hounds, Sir Bender,
Dame Mette will hie to my hall this night:
  'Tis thither my song will send her.'

And lo! when the hour of midnight fell,
  Sir Peter began his singing;
Over the water, and over the wood
  His notes came sweetly ringing.

Hushed is the river, the listening pines
  Are mute where the forests darken,
The pale moon trembles above in heaven,
  The stars with their wise ears hearken.

Dame Mette has heard it; she starts from her sleep:
  'What singer without is wooing?'
She draws on her gown and forth she steps—
  She hastens to her undoing.

And through the water, and through the wood,
  She wanders far and fleetly;
'Twas Sir Peter who drew her for doom to his house,
  With the song he sang so sweetly.

And when she returned by the morning light,
  At his door Sir Bender sought her;

'Oh, where have you been, Dame Mette, this night?
　　Your kirtle is full of water.'

'I have been to the pool where the witches dwell,
　　Who the future dark uncover;
And there, by the teasing water-sprites,
　　I was wet and sprinkled over.'

'The sand by the witches' pool is soft,
　　Not thither, I ween, your going;
For wounded and bloody are both your feet,
　　And your face with blood is flowing.'

'I have been to-night to the elfin wood,
　　To watch the fairies dancing,
And there I wounded face and feet,
　　'Gainst boughs and brambles chancing.'

'The elves, they dance in the month of May
　　On the smooth and flowery meadows;
But the winds of autumn are blowing cold,
　　They howl in the forest shadows.'

'With Peter Nielson I 've been this night;
　　He sang a song of wonder,
And through the water, and through the wood
　　He drew me to him yonder.

'The notes he sang are as strong as death,
　　In my bosom they burn and sigh now;
They drew me to death and a doom of woe;
　　I know that I must die now.'

The minster door is hung with black,
　　There 's mournful music rolling;
For Dame Mette, who came to a pitiful end,
　　The passing bell is tolling.

Sir Bender he stood beside the bier,
　　And a sorrowful sighing made he:
'Alack! I have lost my faithful hounds,
　　And eke my lovely ladye.'

A Meeting

THERE is music beneath the linden trees,
  And a dancing of youths and maidens;
'Mid the dancers are two whom nobody knows;
  They gracefully move to the cadence.

And it's up and down, with a motion strange
  They foot it, glancing shyly;
Then they laugh to each other and shake their heads,
  And the maiden whispers slyly:

"'Tis a curious lily, my lovely youth,
  That trembles upon your bonnet;
It only grows i' the depth o' the sea—
  No son of Adam won it.

'You are the merman who comes to woo
  The village maids to your wishes.
As soon as I saw you I knew you well
  By your teeth like bones of fishes.'

And it's up and down, with a motion strange,
  They foot it, glancing shyly;
Then they laugh to each other and shake their heads,
  And the gallant whispers slyly:

'My lovely lady, I'm fain to know
  Why your icy hand so cold is;
And tell me why, of your garment white,
  The hem so wet i' the fold is.

'As soon as I saw you I knew you well,
  By your nods and curtsies tricksy,
I knew you were no child of earth,
  But my cousin, the water nixie.'

The fiddles give over, the dance is done,
  They part with a courteous greeting;
They know one another alas! too well,
  And crave for no further meeting.

King Harold Harfager

THE great King Harold Harfager
    Sits in the sea below,
Beside his lovely water-fay;
    The years, they come and go.

He cannot live, he cannot die,
    Bewitched in his magic tomb;
Already for two hundred years
    He has dreed his blissful doom.

The head of the king on the lovely lap
    Of the woman lies, and still
He gazes upward on her eyes,
    He cannot gaze his fill.

His golden hair grows silver-grey,
    And, from his face so pale,
The bones of his cheek, like a ghost's, stick out,
    His body is withered and frail.

And many a time from his dream of love
    On a sudden he starts, and shakes,
For the billows on high are raging wild,
    And his crystal palace quakes.

And oft in the wind he seems to hear
    The Norseman's battle-call,
And lifts his arms in gleeful haste;
    Then sadly lets them fall.

And ever the sailors he will hear,
    Who sing as they sail along,
And praise King Harold Harfager
    In a glorious hero-song.

And then the king from his inmost soul
    Will groan and sob and weep;
But the water-fay will quickly bend,
    And kiss his woe to sleep.

POEMS OF THE TIMES
(1839–46)

Geheimnis

WE do not sigh, our eyes are tearless,
    And if we laugh, we smile no more,—
Never shall our lips reveal it,
    The secret love kept, long before.

Ask of the babe within the cradle,
    Ask of the dead within the grave;
Perhaps you may get them to tell you,
    What love as secret to me gave.

The New Jewish Hospital at Hamburg

A HOSPITAL for sick and needy Jews,
For the poor sons of sorrow thrice accursed,
Who groan beneath the heavy, threefold evil
Of pain, and poverty, and Judaism.

The most malignant of the three the last is:
That family disease a thousand years old,
The plague they brought with them from the Nile
    valley—
The unregenerate faith of ancient Egypt.

Incurable deep ill! defying treatment
Of douche, and vapour-bath, and apparatus
Of surgery, and all the healing medicine
This house can offer to its sickly inmates.

Will Time, the eternal goddess, in compassion
Root out this dark calamity transmitted
From sire to son?—Will one day a descendant
Recover, and grow well and wise and happy?

I know not.   Let us praise and bless him meanwhile,
Whose tender heart so lovingly and wisely
Sought to allay such woes as can be softened,
Upon the wounds a kindly balsam dropping.

The dear, good man!   He builded here a refuge
For troubles that the art of the physician
(Or Death, at worst!) could heal, providing fully
For pillows, soothing draughts, and careful tendance.

He was a man of deeds and did his utmost:
Gave to good works, when life had reached its evening,
The wage of his laborious days, humanely
Finding refreshment after toil in mercy.

He gave with open hand—yet alms more costly
Fell from his eyes: tears fair and very precious,
With which he often wept the vast and hopeless
Incurable affliction of his brothers.

The Tendency

GERMAN bard! acclaim the glory
  Of our German freedom high;
Be your song a brand to fire us;
To heroic deeds inspire us,
Like the *Marseillaise* of story.

Turn from Werther and his cooing,
  For his Lotte let him cry.
Voice the message to your people
That has rung from every steeple—
Dagger, sword, and doughty doing.

Let the flute be trampled under,
  With the soul's idyllic sigh.
Be your nation's trump of battle,
Boom of cannon, musket rattle;
Blow and crash and kill and thunder

Loud with thunder let each day be,
  Till the tyrants all shall fly.
Take my counsel for your banner,
But be sure you keep your manner
Vague and general as may be.

Only Wait !

BECAUSE my lightnings never blunder,
  You fancy (but you fancy wrong)
That impotent must be my thunder!
  In thunder I am quite as strong.

In fear and dread you 'll find your error
  When dawns at last the day of harm;
Then shall ye hear my voice with terror,
  My voice of thunder and of storm.

That tempest many an oak will shiver,
  And, tottering at the awful sound,
Full many a palace proud will quiver,
  And many a steeple strew the ground.

Night Thoughts

WHEN on my land I think by night,
The boon of sleep forsakes me quite;
My burning eyes I cannot close,
And many a tear for sorrow flows.

The years they come, the years they pass!
Twelve years have vanished since, alas!
I saw my mother, and amain,
The longing strengthens and the pain.

My longing grows to such a pitch,
The woman surely is a witch!
My thoughts on her for ever dwell.
May God preserve and guard her well!

The dear old woman loves me so!
How tremulous her hand and slow,
How deep the mother's heart is moved,
Her every letter plain has proved.

My mother 's always on my mind.
Twelve weary years now lie behind,
Twelve weary years since last I pressed
My dear old mother to my breast.

My Germany will last for aye;
Sound to the core, it mocks decay;
Strong with its oaks and lindens, still
I 'll find it waiting when I will.

Thirst for my country I could bear,
But that my mother tarries there;
Germany will not fade nor fly,
But ah! my mother, she might die.

Since last my Fatherland I trod,
So many lie beneath the sod,
That once I loved; I count the roll,
And bleed within my very soul.

I count and count—the numbers grow
Until my heart is big with woe;
Dead men seem waltzing on my breast—
Thank God! they stop and give me rest.

Thank God! at last my window 's bright
With France's gay and cheerful light;
My wife comes in, like morning fair,
And smiles away my German care.

ATTA TROLL

A SUMMER-NIGHT'S DREAM

The Bear-Dance at Cauterets

WHERE the dark encircling mountains
Overtop each other proudly,
Lulled asleep by foaming torrents
Like a dream-begotten picture,

Cauterets, the haunt of fashion,
Nestles whitely in the valley;
On the balconies the ladies,
Lovely ladies, laughing loudly,

Watch a bear and she-bear dancing
To the music of the bagpipes,
In the market-place below them
Where the motley crowd is surging.

It is Atta Troll who dances
With his mate, the swarthy Mumma,
And the wondering Biscayans
Shout and cheer them to the echo.

Stiff and earnest, grave and solemn,
Dances noble Atta Troll;
But his shaggy spouse is wanting
Both in carriage and decorum;

There is even in her dancing,
To my fancy, a suspicion
Of the cancan, and the licence
Of the Grand'-Chaumière at Paris.

Even the keeper, honest fellow,
By the chain who holds and leads her,

Marks a something scarcely moral
In the manner of her dancing.

And he often reaches over
With his whip to reprimand her;
Then the swarthy Mumma bellows
Till the mountain echoes waken.

On his pointed cap he carries
Six Madonnas to protect him
From the bullets of his foemen,
Or from lice to shield and guard him.

On his shoulder, brightly coloured
Hangs an altar-cloth that serves him
As a mantle; while he leads them
With him—Atta Troll and Mumma,

Whom he forced to dance in public
On the open market-places:
In the square in fetters dances
Atta Troll at Cauterets!

The Escape of Atta Troll

But conceive the consternation
In the square at Cauterets
When a bear has burst his fetters!

Dumb the laughter, dumb the music;
How the people fly and scatter!

Yes, the fetters that enslaved him,
Atta Troll at last has riven.
Through the narrow streets he rushes;
Bounding, rushing in his frenzy—

(None so rude as to delay him)—
Up the rocky steep he clambers,
Glances downward, as if mocking,
And is lost among the mountains.

On the market-place forsaken
Stands alone the swarthy Mumma
With her leader.   In his fury
To the ground his cap he dashes,

And he tramples the Madonnas
Underfoot!   He tears the cover
From his hideous naked body;
The ingratitude he curses,

Black and cruel, of the ingrate
Atta Troll; for as a comrade
And a friend has he not used him,
And instructed him in dancing?

All he has, to him he owes it,
Even his life!   A hundred thalers
He was offered, offered vainly,
For the skin of Atta Troll!

On the black and wretched Mumma,
Who, a form of silent sorrow,
On her hinder paws imploring,
Stands before him in his passion,

Falls at length his rage and fury
Doubly heavy; and he beats her,
Even names her Queen Christina,
Madame Muños, and *putana*.—

In Roncesvalles

Roncesvalles, thou noble valley!
When I hear thy name, the fragrance
Of the blue, forgotten flower
In my heart awakes and quivers!

And the shining dream-world rises
From the dim and vanished ages;
And the great-eyed ghosts regard me
Till I shrink and am afraid!

And, with crash and roar of battle,
Frank and Saracen meet headlong;
As if wounded and despairing,
Rings and echoes Roland's horn.

In the Vale of Roncesvalles,
By the yawning gap of Roland—
Named in honour of the hero
Who, to hew himself a pathway,

With such fierce and deadly fury,
With his trusty sword Duranda,
Smote the rocky wall, that traces
Linger yet to wake our wonder—

There, the mountain gorge o'ershadowed
By the wayward growth of pine-trees,
Deeply hidden in the brushwood,
Is the hole of Atta Troll.

Atta Troll muses

In the hole among his dear ones,
Sick and ailing in his spirit,
On his back lies Atta Troll,
And he sucks his paws and muses:

'Mumma, Mumma, dark-hued pearl
That I fished from out the ocean
Of our life, within its waters
I have lost thee to my sorrow!

'Shall I never more behold thee,
Till, beyond the grave transfigured,
I shall see thy soul untrammelled
By the shaggy locks of earth?

'Ah! ere then might I but lick her,
Lick my Mumma on the muzzle!
Muzzle fair as if anointed
With the sweet of virgin honey!

'Once again to sniff the odour
Clinging only to my Mumma,
To my dear, my swarthy Mumma,
Like the scent of fragrant roses!

'But my Mumma 's left to languish
In the fetters of the race
That is known as Man, and prides it
On the lordship of the world.

'Death and hell! Those men so mighty,
Those aristocrats exalted,
Look contemptuously downward
On all animals created;

'Steal our wives from us and children,
Chain us, shamefully entreat us;
Even kill us, in our bodies
And our skins that they may traffic!

'And they deem themselves entitled
To inflict such deeds of evil
On the bears beyond all others,
And they call it Rights of Man!

'Rights of Man, forsooth! Who was it
That enfeoffed you with the rights, then?
Nature? No; for Nature never
Was unnatural to any.

'How, O men! are ye then better
Than we others? Upright, truly,
Ye can hold your heads, but abject
Are the thoughts that crawl within them.

'Are ye better, then, than others,
O ye men! because your skin is
Smooth and shining? That advantage
With the snakes ye have in common.

'Snakes bifurcated ye men are;
I can well conceive the uses
Of your trousers; serpent-naked,
Ye must borrow wool to clothe you.

'Flee and shun them, O my children!
Always shun those bald abortions!
Never trust the thing, my daughters,
That approaches you in breeches!'

Atta Troll's Republic

'Children!' grumbles Atta Troll,
As uneasily he tosses
On his bed without a blanket,
'Ours at least shall be the Future!

'Were each bear of my opinion—
Thought the other beasts as I do—
With our forces leagued together,
We should fight and throw the tyrants.

'What we need to-day is union—
Union! Union! Disunited,
They enslave us; but, united,
We shall overreach the despots.

'On the basis we shall found it,
That God's creatures all are equal,
Irrespective of their odour,
Or their hide, or their religion.

'Yea, the very Jews shall share in
Civic rights, and taste of freedom:
By the law shall be acknowledged
On a par with other mammals.

'Only dancing in the market
For the Jews shall be illegal;
I but mention this amendment
In the interests of art.

'For the race is sadly lacking
In a sense of style: in motion
The severe and plastic misses:
And might spoil the public taste.'

Atta Troll swears his Son, One-Ear, on the Altar

Now going forward on all fours,
Savage, fierce, a pair of figures
Force a pathway, pioneering
Through the forest-depths at midnight.

It is Atta Troll, the father,
With his youngest son, Sir One-Ear.
Where the moonlight glimmers faintly
By the stone of blood they halt.

'Once this stone,' growls Atta Troll,
'Was the altar where the Druids
In an age of superstition
Offered human sacrifices.

'Oh, the ghastly, gruesome horror!
Why, my hair, uprising, bristles
On my back to think that ever
God was glorified by murder!

'Grown toward a clearer vision,
It is true that men no longer
Slay each other, fiercely zealous
In the interests of Heaven.

''Tis no more a dream fantastic,
Foolish frenzy, fond delusion:
'Tis the love of self constrains them
Now to homicide and slaughter.

'After worldly wealth and treasure
Now they strive as for a wager,
Each purloining and amassing
In an endless brawl and scuffle.

'Yes, the earth we all inherit
Has been seized by private plunder,
And the thief discourses blandly
On the rights of private owners.

'Oh, my hate is deep and burning!
I bequeath to thee my hatred.
O my son, upon this altar
Swear eternal hate to man!

'Be the mortal foe, I charge thee,
Foe implacable and deadly,
Of the wicked, vile oppressors.
Swear it, swear it, O my son!'

So, like Hannibal, the stripling
Swore the oath.   The moon shone yellow
On the grisly stone of slaughter
And the misanthropic couple.

How the youthful bear unbroken
Kept his solemn oath we 'll tell you,
To his praise another epic
On our lyre anon entuning.

As for Atta Troll, him also
We will turn from now, that later
We may find him all the surer
With the death-bestowing bullet.

Lascaro the Bear-Hunter

At the dawn of day I started,
Started hunting with Lascaro
For the bear.   'Twas noon already
When we reached the Pont-d'Espagne:

When we reached the bridge that crosses
Into Spain, into the country
Of those savage West-barbarians
Who, in social modes and customs
Lag a thousand years behindhand.

On the bridge an aged Spaniard
Sat in squalor; want was peeping
Through the tatters of his mantle,
There was famine in his eye.

And he strummed with bony fingers
On a mandoline—an old one—

Till the discords shrilled and clamoured
Through the deep, re-echoing gorges.

And he leaned at times and nodded,
Laughing down to the abysses;
Then would strum the wilder, singing
To his music strangest song. . . .

As I passed I murmured, musing,
'Strange that madness should be singing
On the bridge that crosses over
To the land of Spain from France!' . . .

To the dusk the day was darkening
When we reached the mean *posada*.
There we found the Spanish hotch-potch
In the dirty vessel steaming.

And my supper was of chick-peas,
Heavy, big, like rifle bullets,
Taxing even the digestion
Of a German reared on dumplings.

Fitting sequel to the cooking
Was the bed with insects peppered—
Ah! the foes most dire and deadly
Of the human race are bugs.

The Witch Uraka

Like a black and rocky cauldron
Lie the lake's unfathomed waters;
Pale and melancholy stars
Gaze from heaven.   Night and silence.

Night and silence.   Splash of oars;
And the skiff, a murmuring secret,
Floats along; the swinging oars
Break the silence of the starlight.

And beside me sits Lascaro,
Pale as ever, still and speechless,
And the fancy shudders through me:
Can the man indeed be dead?

Am I dead myself, and sailing
To the darksome underworld,
With a ghost-companion steering
To the chilly realm of shadows?

Is this lake the gloomy water
Of the Styx? Has Proserpine,
Disappointed of her Charon,
Sent her maidens forth to fetch me?

Nay, I am not dead; within me
Unextinguished, unabated,
Leaps the vital flame exultant,
In my soul it burns and blazes. . . .

Like a lane deep runs the valley
Which they call the Pass of Spirits.
Dizzy precipices bound it,
Rising ruggedly and sheer.

From that awful slope the hovel
Of Uraka, like a watch-tower,
Views the valley. Thither wending,
In Lascaro's wake I followed.

By a code of secret signals
He consulted with his mother
As to methods for enticing
And for slaying Atta Troll.

For, his trail with zeal pursuing,
We had tracked him down so surely,
That no loop-hole now was left him.
Atta Troll, thy days are numbered!

Whether old Uraka really
Was a witch of wondrous powers,
And as potent as the people
Of the Pyrenees asserted,

I will never try to settle;
But I know that her exterior
Was suspicious; most suspicious
Were her bloodshot eyes and rheumy.

There she crouched, the old Uraka,
In the chimney-corner cowered,
Melting lead and casting bullets,
By her side her son Lascaro:

Casting fatal bullets destined
For the death of Atta Troll.
On the witch's face how swiftly
Dance the leaping flames, and quiver!

With her thin old lips she murmurs
Low and toneless, never pausing.
Is she crooning incantations
On the casting of the bullets?

To her son she nods and chuckles,
But, unmoved and unregarding,
He pursues his work as grimly
And as silently as death.

The Eve of St. John : Herodias

Now it is the time, at full moon,
On Saint John the Baptist's Eve,
That the spectral hunt goes coursing
Through the Spirit-Pass at midnight.

Crack of whips, hallooing, shouting!
Baying hounds and neighing horses!
Winding horns and merry laughter!
How triumphantly it echoed!

Bounding forward like a vanguard
Flew the strange fantastic quarry:
Stags and boars in herds careering,
The pursuing hounds behind them.

In the wild procession many
Seemed familiar—yonder horseman
In the golden harness gleaming,
Was not he the great King Arthur?

And Sir Ogier, he of Denmark,
Wore he not that iridescent
Coat of mail, in which he glimmered
Like a frog gigantic, greenly?

In the train was many a hero
For his thought and learning famous.
By his glance of genial brightness
I identified our Wolfgang—

For, since Hengstenberg has damned him,
In his grave he cannot slumber,
And with pagans now indulges
In the chase he loved while living. . . .

There were many damsels also
In that ghostly train fantastic:
Slender nymphs whose youthful bodies
Were a miracle of beauty,

Set astride upon their horses,
Mythologically naked,
But whom ringlets long and flowing,
Like a golden mantle, covered.

On their heads were twisted garlands,
And in gay, abandoned postures,
Backward leaning, bold and merry,
Leafy wands they swung and balanced.

Tightly habited beside them,
Medieval damosels
Sat obliquely on their saddles,
On the wrist a chainèd falcon.

On their skinny palfreys mounted,
As in parody, behind them
Came a cavalcade of women,
Like comedians, decked, bedizened.

Very lovely were their faces,
If, perchance, a trifle brazen;
And they cried and clamoured madly,
With their rouged and wanton cheeks.

How the echoes rang, rejoicing!
Winding horns and merry laughter!
Bay of hounds and horses neighing!
Crack of whips, hallooing, shouting!

Three were fair as beauty's trefoil,
Far excelling all the others:
Gracious forms of lovely women—
Ah, I never shall forget them!

Unmistakable the first was,
From the crescent on her forehead;
Pure and proudly, like a statue,
Rode and passed the mighty goddess.

High upgirdled was her tunic,
Veiling half the hips and bosom;
On her white voluptuous body
Played the torch-light and the moonlight.

White as marble was her face, too,
And as cold as marble; fearful
Were the fixity and pallor
Of the stern and noble features.

But within her eye of shadow
Leapt and flamed an awful fire,
Sweet, uncanny, and mysterious,
Spirit-blinding and consuming.

Ah! how altered is Diana:
She who changed the young Actaeon
To a stag, for dogs to mangle,
In her chastity unbending.

Does she expiate her error
'Mid this company licentious?
Like the frailest among mortals
Now, a ghost, by night she travels. . . .

By her side there rode a beauty
From whose features, less severely
On the classic model chiselled,
Shone the Celtic grace and charm.

'Twas the lovely fay Abunde,
And I knew her, knew her straightway,
By the sweetness of her smiling,
By her mad and merry laughter.

Ah, the blooming face and rosy,
Such as Greuze had haply painted!
Like a heart her mouth, and open,
With enchanting pearly teeth.

And her gown was blue; it fluttered,
For the wind was fain to lift it.
In the fairest of my visions
I have never seen such shoulders.

From the window, in my longing,
I had almost leapt to kiss her—
And my neck had surely broken
In the hazardous adventure. . . .

Was the third, the third and fairest
Of the women that so deeply
And so strangely stirred my bosom,
But a devil like the others?

Whether fiend she was, or angel,
For my life I could not tell you.
It is hard to say, with women,
Where the fiend in angel merges.

On her face aglow with fever,
Lay the Morning-land's enchantment,
And her costly robes reminded
Of the tales of Scheherazade.

And her lips were pomegranates,
And her nose a curving lily,
And her limbs were cool and slender
As the palm in the oasis.

On a palfrey white she rode,
Led by negroes twain who trotted
Swift afoot beside the princess,
By the golden bridle holding.

Oh, in truth, a royal lady
Was the queen of old Judaea:
Herod's lovely wife who lusted
For the head of John the Baptist!

For this deed of blood accursèd,
As a night-tormented spirit
She must join the rout and gallop
Till the final day of doom.

In her hand she holds the charger
With the head of John the Baptist,
Holds it evermore and kisses,
Yes, she kisses it with fervour. . . .

From the grave uprising nightly,
As I said, she rides a-hunting,
In her hand the bloody charger;
Yet, with woman's mad caprice,

Now and then with childish laughter
She will hurl the gruesome burden
Through the air, and catch it lightly
And adroitly like a plaything.

As she galloped past she saw me;
And her nod was so coquettish
And so languishing, that deeply
To its core my heart was shaken.

Thrice the cavalcade went surging,
As I watched, before my window,
And the lovely ghost in passing
Nodded thrice to me in greeting. . . .

And the livelong night I tumbled,
Tossing fevered limbs and weary
On the straw—Uraka's hovel
Was unblest with beds of down;—

And I mused upon the meaning
Of that strange, mysterious greeting.
Why so tenderly and softly
Didst thou gaze on me, Herodias? . . .

But at early dawn we started,
And descended to the valley.
While Lascaro followed nimbly
On the traces of his bear,

I made shift to speed the passage
Of the moments with my musing.
Thought, however, only wearied,
Also saddened me a little.

Weary, sad, at last I flung me
On a soft and mossy bed
By a great ash overshadowed,
Where a little brook was flowing.

The mysterious, gentle murmur
Fooled and charmed my soul so strangely,
That the thoughts I had been thinking
From my head entirely faded.

And a frantic yearning filled me
For a dream, for death, for madness,
For those fair and phantom riders
In the cavalcade of ghosts.

Oh, ye lovely midnight faces
That the fires of morning banished,
I would know where ye have fleeted,
Where by day ye have your dwelling. . . .

Where, in mirth and joy untroubled,
And in youth that blooms immortal,
Dwells our sweet and merry lady—
Dwells our gay and blonde Abunde. . . .

Tell me too, Herodias, tell me
Where thou tarriest.—I know it!
Thou art dead, and liest buried
By the town Jerusalem.

With the dead by day thou sleepest
In thy cold and marble coffin;
But at midnight thou awakest
To the crack of whips and shouting;

And the frantic host thou joinest,
With Diana and Abunde,
With thy merry fellow-hunters,
Who abhor both cross and anguish.

Ah, companionship how blissful!
Could I only follow after
Through the forests!   Thou, Herodias,
Art the one that I would ride by!

For 'tis thou I love the dearest!
More than stately Grecian goddess,
More than laughing northland fairy,
I adore thee, Jewess dead! . . .

Every midnight I will gallop
In the reckless rout beside thee;
We will talk and laugh together
At my wild and foolish speeches.

I will while away and shorten
Thus the night; but joy will vanish
With the dawn of day; then, weeping,
I will sit upon thy tomb.

I will sit me down and weep there
On the crumbled tomb of kings,
On the grave of my beloved,
By the town Jerusalem.

And the ancient Jews, in passing,
Will imagine that I mourn
The destruction of the Temple
And the town Jerusalem.

Death of Atta Troll

But hence ye ghosts and midnight faces!
Forms of air, and dreams of fever!
Let us sensibly devote us
To the death of Atta Troll.

In the hole beside the young ones
Lies the father lapped in slumber:
Snores the snore of honest virtue
And at last awakens yawning.

Perched beside him, Master One-Ear
At his furry head keeps scratching,
Like a rhyme-pursuing poet;
With his claws he marks the scansion.

Atta Troll's beloved daughters,
On their backs beside the father,
Lie in slumber, softly dreaming—
Lilies innocent, four-footed.

Ah, what fond and tender fancies
Fill the budding souls with yearning—
Souls of bears so white and virgin?
Tear-bedewed their gentle eyes are. . . .

In the cavern, by his children,
Pensive, mild, lies Atta Troll.
Yearning fills him—solemn omen—
For the land of the hereafter!

With a sigh he murmurs, 'Children'—
And the sudden tears well over—
'Now the pilgrimage is ended
On the earth, and we must part.

'For I dreamed this noon while sleeping,
Dreamed a dream of solemn import;
To my soul the blissful foretaste
Of approaching death was granted.

'While the world and fate I pondered,
Yawning wearily, I slept;
And I dreamed that I was lying
With a spreading tree above me.

'Yes, I dreamed that purest honey
From the branches green was dropping:
That it glided down my muzzle,
And I felt a wondrous bliss.

'Blinking upward in my rapture,
I could see that on the topmost
Of the boughs were seven bears,
Little bears that slid and gambolled.

'They were tender, dainty creatures,
And their coats were red as roses,
With a fluffy, silky something
Like a wing upon the shoulders.

'Yes, those little bears like roses
Were adorned with silken wings,
And they sang a song celestial
With their sweet and flute-like voices!

'While they sang, my skin grew icy,
But my soul from out my body
Like a flame to heaven mounted,
With a bright and burning glory.'

Thus with tremulous emotion
Softly grunted Atta Troll;
Sat a moment sad and silent;
Then he pricked excited ears,

And began to quiver strangely;
From his couch he sprang, and shaking
With his joy, for joy he bellowed,
'Did ye hear that sound, my children?

'Was not that the voice belovèd
Of your mother?   Oh, I know it,
Know the growling of my Mumma,
Of my own, my swarthy Mumma!'

Atta Troll, when he had spoken,
Darted headlong from the cavern
Like a madman, to his ruin!
Ah, he rushed upon his doom! . . .

In the Vale of Roncesvalles,
On the spot where once the nephew
Of King Charlemagne in battle
Fell and yielded up his spirit;

Fell and perished Atta Troll:
Fell by treason, as that other
Fell by Ganelon of Mainz
Who gave Chivalry its Judas.

What, alas! in bears is noblest—
Faithful conjugal affection—
Was the snare by which Uraka
Lured our hero to perdition.

With such mastery she mimicked
Swarthy Mumma's growl and bellow,
That poor Atta Troll was tempted
From the safety of his cavern.

Borne along on wings of yearning,
To a rock below he hurried;
Stood with puzzled tender snuffing;
Fancied Mumma was behind it—

'Twas, alas! Lascaro hidden
With the gun; who aimed and shot him
Through the heart that beat so gladly—
Forth the crimson blood came streaming.

Once or twice his head he waggled;
Then he sank with piteous groaning;
Gave a last convulsive quiver;
And his latest sigh was, 'Mumma!'

So the noble hero fell.
So he died.   But from his ashes
He will rise, and live for ever
In the bard's immortal numbers.

He will rise again in song,
And his fame will be colossal.
On four-footed trochees proudly
He will stride across the world.

And a monument King Louis
Will erect him in Valhalla,
And inscribe it with this legend
In his lapidary manner:

'Atta Troll, a bear of bias;
Good, religious; loving husband;
Sans-culotte of sylvan breeding:
With the age's folly tainted;

'Wretched dancer; stern convictions
In his shaggy bosom nursing;
Stinking badly on occasion;
Talents *nil*; a character!' . . .

Epilogue

(*To August Varnhagen von Ense*)

You, my good old friend Varnhagen,
As you read I hear you laughing!
But at times the furrows deepen,
As old memories awaken.

'Was it not the very music
Of the dreams I dreamed by moonlight
In my youth, beside Chamisso,
And Brentano, yes, and Fouqué?

'Was not that the holy chiming
Of the long-lost forest chapel,
With the cap and bells familiar
In the pauses slyly jingling?

'Through the nightingale's sweet chorus
Booms the double-bass of bears,
Which, in turn, resolves and changes
Into soft and ghostly sighing.

'Here would madness pose as wisdom!
Here is wisdom gone demented!
Dying groans that in a moment
Cease, and bubble into laughter!'

Yes, the sounds, my friend, come ringing
From that time of dreams forgotten,
Though some modern trills and quavers
To the olden tunes are added.

And for all the gay bravado,
You will find despair in plenty—
To your charity long-proven
Be this poem, then, commended!

'Tis perhaps the last unfettered
Woodland song of the Romantic!
In our daylight din of battle
It will sadly die and cease.

Other times and other birds!
Other birds and other songs!
What a cackling!   It reminds one
Of the geese who saved the city.

What a chirping!   'Tis of sparrows,
In their claws a farthing rushlight,
Aping Jove's celestial eagles
With the awful thunderbolt!

What a cooing!   'Tis of doves,
Turtle-doves no longer lovers:
Haters now who, false to Venus,
Draw the chariot of Bellona!

What a buzzing shakes the world!
'Tis the loud colossal may-bugs
Of the spring-time of the people,
With insensate fury smitten.

Other times and other birds!
Other birds and other songs!—
That belike would give me pleasure
Had I only other ears!

The Knave of Bergen

In Düsseldorf castle beside the Rhine
  There 's frolic and masquerading;
The candles glimmer, and revellers dance
  To the music's sweet persuading.

The beautiful Duchess trips with the rest,
  And often she laughs and loudly.
Her partner 's a slender and courteous youth,
  And gaily he moves and proudly.

He wears a velvet mask of black,
  His eye is merry and beaming,
And bright and keen as a naked dirk,
  Half-sheathed, from the scabbard gleaming.

And the carnival mummers gleefully shout
  As the pair go waltzing by them;
With growls and grunts Marizzebill
  And Drickes nod and eye them.

The trumpets crash, and the deafening roll
  Of the double-bass increases,
Till revel and dance at last are done,
  And the sound of the music ceases.

'Illustrious lady, allow me to go;
  I must leave you.' But, for answer,
The Duchess laughs and says, 'Nay, first
  I must see your face, Sir Dancer.'

'Illustrious lady, allow me to go;
  My face is feared, all flee it.'
But the Duchess laughs, 'No coward am I;
  Uncover, that I may see it.'

'Illustrious lady, allow me to go,
    To darkness and death I am wedded.'
But the Duchess laughs, 'Ere you leave my side,
    I must see this face so dreaded.'

With stern and sinister words he strove
    To deny the thing she asked him;
Till, bent on her will, by force at last
    The woman herself unmasked him.

'The headsman of Bergen!' The horrified crowd,
    As if fearing to come in his clutches,
Fall back in alarm. To her husband's side
    In terror flies the Duchess.

But the Duke is crafty and saves his wife
    From shame; while the whole room wonders
He approaches the man and unsheathes his sword,
    'Sirrah, down on your knees!' he thunders.

'With the stroke of this sword, be it known to all,
    I dub you noble and knightly;
As Sir Knave of Bergen arise,' he said;
    'You 're a knave, so we 've named you rightly.'

So the headsman became a noble, the first
    Of the Knaves of Bergen, who boldly
And proudly throve by the Rhine, but now
    In coffins of stone sleep coldly.

Valkyries

Down below, the battle loud;
Overhead, on steeds of cloud
Three Valkyries. With a clang,
As of hurtling shields, they sang:

'Princes quarrel, nations fight
For the mastery by might;
Power the highest boon they crave;
None has virtue but the brave.

'Ha! no helmet proud can sheathe
Heads that Fate has doomed to death.
And the hero's race is run,
And the weaker man has won.

'Laurel crowns, triumphal arches!
To the gates to-morrow marches
He who slew the better foe,
Land and lieges winning so.

'Senators and burgomaster
Haste—they cannot hasten faster—
With the keys, and favour win,
And the conqueror enters in.

'From the ramparts cannons roar,
Trumpets brazen music pour,
Bells take up the joyful tale,
And the populace shouts, "Hail!"

'Garlands fall on every side;
Lovely women watch him ride;
On the balconies they crowd;
And he greets them calm and proud.'

Marie Antoinette

How the window-panes of the Tuileries
  In the merry sunshine glow!
And yet, by broad daylight within,
  The old ghosts come and go.

Flora's Pavilion is haunted still
  By Marie Antoinette;
She holds her morning levee there
  With strictest etiquette.

Court ladies in point and gold brocade
  And satins and jewels shine;
They stand or sit on their tabourets,
  Bedizened and decked and fine.

How slim their waist!   The petticoat
    Is hooped and amply spreads;
The little high-heeled shoes peep out—
    If only they had their heads!

Not a single head can the company boast;
    Not even the queen has one—
Which forces her gracious Majesty
    To go with her hair undone.

Yes, the queen with her toupee like a tower,
    Who once so proudly smiled:
The descendant of German Emperors,
    And Maria Theresa's child:

Sits headless now, with never a curl,
    Amid her maids of honour,
Who, headless too, with no hair to frizz,
    Stand round and wait upon her.

The French Revolution of course is to blame
    For the sad and pitiful scene:
Rousseau and Voltaire and their doctrines vile
    That led to the guillotine.

But the strange thing is, I am almost sure
    That not one of those ladies flaunting
Has any idea how dead she is,
    Or knows that her head is wanting.

Affectedly still they fawn and bow,
    And mince and strut as they go.
How horrid to watch the headless trunks
    As they dip and curtsy low!

The first of the ladies brings a chemise
    Of linen without a flaw;
The second one hands the chemise to the queen,
    And, curtsying, both withdraw.

A third and a fourth advance in turn,
    When the first and the second are gone,
And, kneeling down at her Majesty's feet,
    They pull her stockings on.

Then a maid of honour curtsying comes,
    And hands her her morning sacque;
Another one brings her her petticoat,
    And, bowing low, falls back.

The Mistress of the Robes stands by;
    Her bosom she fans the while,
And, her head being gone, with her other end
    She does her best to smile.

The sun peeps in with a curious glance
    To see what the curtains hide,
But recoils in terror as soon as he spies
    The poor old ghost inside.

Voyage by Night

THE waves were rough, and the half-moon peeped
    From the clouds with a timid light.
We were three when we stepped aboard the boat:
    Three souls who sailed by night.

The oars in the water drearily plashed
    Like the sound of a listless sigh.
We were sprinkled wet by the white sea-foam
    As the waves went surging by.

So slender, still, and pale she stood,
    So wan and yet so sweet!
Like some marble statue of Italy:
    Diana's counterfeit.

The wind was whistling bleak and cold,
    The moon was hid away,
When overhead there rang a scream
    Of sudden, shrill dismay.

It was the cry of a sea-mew white,
    Like a ghost above in the gloom.
We three who heard it were afraid—
    It seemed a voice of doom.

Am I stricken with fever?   What fantasy wild
  Of midnight burns my brain?
Am I mocked of a dream?   What dream is this,
  Incredible, insane?

I dream I am the Lord himself,
  And that I carry, too,
The heavy cross that Jesus bore,
  Long-suffering and true.

The poor pale beauty is sore distressed,
  But I will end her pain:
From scorn and woe deliver her,
  And every earthly stain.

Ah, shudder not, thou lovely one,
  Though harsh the medicine be;
I 'll pour, albeit with breaking heart,
  The cup of death for thee.

O gruesome dream!   O folly wild!
  Delirium mad!   I rave!
The darkness yawns, the billows crash,
  Jehovah, hear and save!

O pitiful God, forsake me not!
  O merciful God Shaddai!
A something falls in the sea like lead.
  Shaddai!   Shaddai!   Adonai!—

The sun arose, and we steered for the land
  That glowed with the bloom of May.
We were two when we stepped ashore from the boat;
  We were three when we sailed away.

Countess Jutta

COUNTESS JUTTA crossed the Rhine
In a small boat 'neath the pale moonshine.
Her maiden rowed, and the Countess said:
'Seest not the bodies of seven dead
    That follow our boat
    In the stream afloat?'
Ah, wearily swim the dead!

'Young knights, apt for love, were they
Sweetly upon my heart they lay.—
To make all sure when they swore troth,
And lest perchance they should break their oath,
    I seized and bound them
    And forthwith drowned them.'
Ah, wearily swim the dead!

    The maiden rowed and Jutta laughed light.
Mocking the sound rang through the night!
Waist-deep from the waters the dead men rise,
Cursing, their skeleton hands to the skies
    In menace raising,
    Their dead eyes glazing.
Ah, wearily swim the dead!

LAMENTATIONS

From 'Lazarus'

Pious Exhortation

WHEN ended is thy sojourn here,
    Immortal soul, beware
    Lest evilly thou fare.
Through Death and Night the road lies drear.

In the city of light, at the golden gate,
    God's soldiers will stand and ask
    How thou hast done thy task,
Inquiring not thy name and state.

At the door the pilgrim takes from his feet
    The dusty shoes that pressed—
    Enter; within are rest
And easy slippers and music sweet.

Cooled

ONE lies so long when one is laid
Dead in the dust!   I am afraid,
Yes, much afraid the Day of Doom
May tarry long before it come.

From life and light ere I depart,
Oh once, before I break my heart—
Before I die, I fain would find
Some woman fair who would be kind.

But I will only have a blonde,
With eyes like moonlight, soft and fond.
Somehow at last I 've lost desire
For wild brunettes of sun and fire.

Young folk are strong and full of life;
They must have passion and its strife,

Frenzy and noisy vows—the whole
That makes for mutual pain of soul.

No longer young and far from strong,
As I am now, once more I long
To love as in the earlier years,
Dream and be happy—without tears.

Morphia

THE two young gracious forms are much alike,
Though of his mien more earnest and more grave—
More proud and noble, I had almost said—
The one is than that other, in whose arms
I lay so closely clasped.   Now soft and kind,
How exquisitely lovely was his smile,
How sweet and full of rapture was his gaze!
It may be that the poppy wreath he wore,
Touching my forehead with its drowsy petals,
With its mysterious fragrance chased away
All sorrow from my soul.—But brief, alas!
Is such assuagement.   I shall not be well
Until his torch the other shall have lowered:
The brother that so grave is and so pale—
For Sleep is good, but Death is better—best
Indeed were never to be born at all.

The Anniversary

THEY will sing for me no masses,
    Not a *kaddisch* will be said
In devout commemoration
    Of the day my spirit fled.

But I shall not be forgotten;
    If the weather is serene,
Frau Matilda may go walking
    On Montmartre with Pauline.

And some immortelles she 'll carry,
    On my grave the wreath she 'll set,
And she 'll sigh, 'Pauvre homme!' and sadly
    Drop a tear of soft regret.

And alas! too high in heaven
  I shall be to give my sweet
Even a chair to sit and rest on,
  Though she sways with weary feet.

Listen, plump and pretty darling;
  Home afoot you must not go.
You will see outside the gateway
  Hackney carriages arow.

Enfant Perdu

FOR thirty years, in Freedom's struggle glorious,
  I 've taken part in many a hope forlorn.
I knew that I could never be victorious,
  But wounded must return, and battle-worn.

I waked by day and night—there was no sleeping
  For me, as for the others in the tent—
(Their snores, good lads, did something toward
      keeping
  Slumber away, maybe, when I was spent).

I have known terror in those watches weary—
  (For only fools have never been afraid)—
Then I would whistle mocking tunes and cheery,
  Until the fear that haunted me was laid.

Yes, I have stood on guard, alert and steady,
  And, if a doubtful character was seen,
Have aimed, and the hot bullet that was ready
  Has found in his vile paunch a billet mean.

Yet all the same, one cannot but confess it,
  Such scurvy fellows often understood
The art of shooting—vain 'twere to suppress it—
  My wounds are gaping—ebbing is my blood.

Wide gape the wounds—the vacant post 's bespoken!
  One falls, another fills his place and part.
But I have fallen unvanquished—sword unbroken—
  The only thing that 's broken is my heart.

HEBREW MELODIES

Jehuda ben Halevy
(*A Fragment*)

I

'IF, Jerusalem, I ever
Should forget thee, to the roof
Of my mouth then cleave my tongue,
May my right hand lose its cunning—'

In my head the words and music
Round and round keep humming, ringing,
And I seem to hear men's voices,
Men's deep voices singing psalms—

And of long and shadowy beards
I can also catch some glimpses—
Say, which phantom dream-begotten
Is Jehuda ben Halevy?

But they swiftly rustle past me,
For the ghosts avoid, with terror,
Rude and clumsy human converse;
Yet, in spite of all, I knew him.

Yes, I knew him by his forehead
Pale and proud with noble thought,
By the eyes of steadfast sweetness:
Keen and sad they gazed in mine.

But more specially I knew him
By the enigmatic smiling
Of the lovely lips and rhythmic
That belong to poets only.

Years they come, and years they vanish;
Seven hundred years and fifty
It is now since dawned the birthday
Of Jehuda ben Halevy.

At Toledo in Castile
First he saw the light of heaven,
And the golden Tagus lulled him
In his cradle with its music.

The unfolding of his powers
Intellectual was fostered
By his father strict, who taught him
First the book of God, the Torah.

With his son he read the volume
In the ancient text, whose fair,
Picturesque and hieroglyphic,
Old-Chaldean, square-writ letters

From the childhood of our world
Have been handed down, and therefore
Seem familiarly to smile on
All with naïve, childlike natures.

And this ancient, uncorrupted
Text the boy recited also
In the Tropp—the sing-song measure,
From primeval times descended.

And the gutturals so oily
And so fat he gurgled sweetly,
While he shook and trilled and quavered
The Schalscheleth like a bird.

And the boy was learned early
In the Targum Onkelos,
Which is written in low-Hebrew
In the Aramaean idiom,

Bearing somewhat the resemblance
To the language of the prophets
That the Swabian does to German—
In this curious bastard Hebrew,

As we said, the boy was versed,
And ere long he found such knowledge
Of most valuable service
In the study of the Talmud.

Yes, his father led him early
To the Talmud, and threw open
For his benefit that famous
School of fighting, the Halacha,

Where the athletes dialectic,
Best in Babylon, and also
Those renowned in Pumpeditha
Did their intellectual tilting.

He had here the chance of learning
Every art and ruse polemic;
How he mastered them was proven
In the book Cosari, later.

But the lights are twain, and differ,
That are shed on earth by heaven;
There 's the harsh and glaring sunlight,
And the mild and gentle moonlight.

With a double radiance also
Shines the Talmud; the Halacha
Is the one, and the Hagada
Is the other light. The former

I have called the school of fighting;
But the latter, the Hagada
I will call a curious garden,
Most fantastic, and resembling

Much another one that blossomed
Too in Babylon—the garden
Of Semiramis; 'mongst wonders
Of the world it was the eighth.

Queen Semiramis, whose childhood
With the birds was spent, who reared her,
Many birdlike ways and habits
In her later life retained;

And, unwilling to go walking
On the flat and common earth,
Like us other common mortals,
Made a garden in the air—

High on pillars proud, colossal,
Shone the cypresses and palms,
Marble statues, beds of flowers,
Golden oranges and fountains;

All most cunningly and surely
Bound by countless hanging bridges,
That might well have passed as creepers,
And on which the birds kept swinging—

Birds of many colours, solemn,
Big, contemplative and songless,
While the tiny, happy finches,
Gaily warbling, fluttered round them—

All were breathing, blest and happy,
Breathing pure and balmy fragrance,
Unpolluted by the squalid,
Evil odours of the earth.

The Hagada is a garden,
Is just such another whimsy
Of a child of air; and often
Would the youthful Talmud scholar,

When his heart was dazed and dusty
With the strifes of the Halacha,
With disputes about the fatal
Egg the hen laid on a feast day,

Or concerning other problems
Of the same profound importance—
He would turn to seek refreshment
In the blossoming Hagada,

Where the beautiful old sagas,
Legends dim, and angel-fables,
Pious stories of the martyrs,
Festal hymns and proverbs wise,

And hyperboles the drollest,
But withal so strong and burning
With belief—where all, resplendent,
Welled and sprouted with luxuriance!

And the generous heart and noble
Of the boy was taken captive
By the wild romantic sweetness,
By the wondrous aching rapture,

By the weird and fabled terrors
Of that blissful secret world,
Of that mighty revelation
For which poetry our name is.

And the art that goes to make it,
Gracious power, happy knowledge,
Which we call the art poetic,
To his understanding opened.

And Jehuda ben Halevy
Was not only scribe and scholar,
But of poetry a master,
Was himself a famous poet;

Yes, a great and famous poet,
Star and torch to guide his time,
Light and beacon of his nation;
Was a wonderful and mighty

Fiery pillar of sweet song,
Moving on in front of Israel's
Caravans of woe and mourning
In the wilderness of exile.

True and pure, and without blemish
Was his singing, like his soul—
The Creator having made it,
With His handiwork contented,

Kissed the lovely soul, and echoes
Of that kiss for ever after
Thrilled through all the poet's numbers,
By that gracious deed inspired.

As in life, in song the highest
Good of all is simply grace,
And who hath it cannot sin in
Either poetry or prose.

And that man we call a genius,
By the grace of God a poet,
Monarch absolute, unquestioned,
In the realm of human thought.

None but God can call the poet
To account, the people never—
As in art, in life the people
Can but kill, they cannot judge us.

II

'By the Babylonish waters
We sat down and wept for Zion,
Hung our harps upon the willows—'
Dost remember the old song?

Dost remember the old tune
That begins so elegiac,
Groaning, humming like a kettle,
Humming, singing on the hearth?

Long—a thousand years already—
It has boiled in me—dark sorrow!
And Time licks my wounds in passing
As the dog the boils of Job.

Dog, I thank thee for thy spittle—
But it merely cools and soothes me—
Only death can ever heal me,
And, alas! I am immortal!

Years, revolving, come and vanish;
To and fro the spool is humming
In the loom, and never resting;
What it weaves no weaver knows.

Years they come and years they vanish,
And the tears of men keep trickling,
Running earthward, and the earth
Sucks them in in greedy silence.

Seething wild! The lid is off now!—
Hail to him with ruthless hand
Who shall seize thy helpless children
And shall dash them 'gainst a rock.

God be praised! The steam's escaping,
And the kettle sinks to silence.
Gone the anger of the Orient,
Seething gloomy in the west—

And my wingèd steed, grown merry,
Whinnies glad again, appearing
To shake off the horrid nightmare.
His sagacious eyes seem asking:

'Shall we turn, and back to Spain now,
To the little Talmud scholar
Who became a famous poet,
To Jehuda ben Halevy?'

Yes, he grew to be a poet!
In the realms of dream a ruler:
King of thought, whom none might question,
Crowned, a poet by God's favour,

Who devoutly in sirventes,
In sweet madrigals, ghaselas,
Canzonets and terza rima
Poured out freely all the ardours

Of his God-kissed poet's soul!
Yes, this troubadour was equal
To the best who played aforetime
On the lute in old Provence,

In Poitou and in Guienne,
Roussillon, and all the other
Lands where golden grows the orange,
Gallant lands of Christendom.

Lands of gallant Christendom,
Of the orange, sweet and golden,
How they shine and ring, still fragrant
In the twilight of remembrance.

World of nightingales, how fair!
Where instead of worship rendered
To the true God, Love, the false god,
And the muses were adored.

Clergy, crowned with wreaths of roses
On their tonsures, sung the psalms
In the happy Languedoc,
And the laity, good knights,

Proudly ambled on their chargers,
Conning rhymes and amorous verses
To the glory of the lady
Whom their heart was happy serving.

For with love there must be ladies,
And the lady was as needful
To the tuneful minnesinger
As, to bread and butter, butter.

And the hero whom we sing of,
Our Jehuda ben Halevy,
Had his heart's belovèd lady,
But a strange one he had chosen.

For the lady was no Laura,
She whose eyes, sweet mortal stars,
In the minster on Good Friday
Lit the fire for ever famous—

Was no chatelaine who, radiant
In the bloom of youthful beauty,
O'er the tourneying presided,
And bestowed the wreath of laurel—

Was no casuist who lectured
On the law concerning kisses,
In the college of a court of
Love, a learned doctrinaire.

She, belovèd of the Rabbi,
Was most sorrowful and wretched,
Piteous spectacle of ruin,
And was called Jerusalem.

In the early days of childhood
All his love was hers already,
And his soul would thrill and quiver
At the name Jerusalem.

With a cheek of flaming scarlet,
Stood the boy, and hearkened, eager,
When a pilgrim to Toledo
From the distant Orient journeyed,

And described the desolation
And pollution of the city,
Where a trail of light still lingered
From the prophets' holy feet;

Where the air with God's eternal
Breath is balmy still and fragrant—
'Oh, the spectacle how piteous!'
Cried a pilgrim with a beard

Flowing down as white as silver,
But which turned, towards the tip,
Sable-hued again, thus seeming
To renew its vanished youth.

A most strange and curious pilgrim
Must the man have been; his eyes
Peered from centuries of sorrow,
And he groaned, 'Jerusalem!

'She, the thronged and holy city,
Is become a barren desert,
Where baboons and jackals, werwolves
Go their wicked way unhindered.

'Serpents, birds of night are nesting
In the walls decayed and crumbling,
Through the windows' airy arches
Gaze the foxes unmolested.

'And at times some ragged bondsman
Of the desert will appear,
And will feed his hump-backed camel
On the high untrodden grasses.

'On the noble heights of Zion,
Where the golden fortress towered,
Bearing witness, in its splendour,
To a mighty monarch's glory,

'There is nothing left but ruins,
Grey and overgrown with weeds,
And they gaze on one so sadly
That one fancies they are weeping.

'And the story goes that truly
Once a year they weep, and namely
On the ninth day of the month of
Ab—myself, with streaming eyes,

'I have seen the heavy tear-drops
From the mighty stones that trickled,
Heard the broken temple pillars
Utter cries and lamentations.' . . .

Such reports of pious pilgrims
Wakened longings in the bosom
Of Jehuda ben Halevy:
Towards Jerusalem he yearned.

Poets' yearning!   Bodeful, dreamy,
And as fatal as the longing
That once filled the noble Vidam
To his hurt in Castle Blay—

Messer Geöffroy Rudello,
When the knight, returning homeward
From the East, amid the ringing
Of the festal goblets swore

That the type of every virtue,
Pearl and flower of all women,
Was the lovely Melisanda,
Margravine of Tripoli.

How the troubadour adoring
Sang and raved about the lady,
All have heard; at length too narrow
Seemed his home at Castle Blay.

By resistless longing driven,
He took ship at Cette to seek her,
But grew sick on board, and, dying,
Reached the town of Tripoli.

Here his eyes beheld the lady,
Gazed indeed on Melisanda,
But the self-same hour they darkened
With the dreary shades of death.

Here, his final love-song singing,
At her feet he breathed his last,
At the feet of Melisanda,
Margravine of Tripoli.

Strange the wonderful resemblance
In the fate of both the poets;
Only, one was old already
When on pilgrimage he started.

At the feet of his beloved
Died Jehuda ben Halevy;
And his dying head he rested
On Jerusalem's fair knees.

III

After great King Alexander
Won the fight at Arabella
All the wealth of King Darius,
Land and people, court and harem,

Women, elephants, and horses,
Sceptre, crown, and coins, he stuck them—
Golden plunder—in his roomy,
Baggy Macedonian trousers.

In the tent of great Darius,
Who had fled lest he should also
Be impounded thus, the youthful
Hero found a precious casket,

Found a little gilded casket
Decked with cameos, and gorgeous
With encrusted stones and precious,
And with dainty miniatures.

Now, this box, itself a gem
Of inestimable value,
Was the case in which Darius
Kept his priceless body-jewels.

These were given by Alexander
To the bravest of his soldiers,
With a smile to think that men could
Care for coloured stones like children.

One, a gem most fair and costly,
He presented to his mother:
'Twas the signet ring of Cyrus,
And was made into a brooch.

And his champion debater,
Aristotle, got an onyx,
To be placed in his museum
Of the curious things of nature.

In the casket there was also
A most wondrous string of pearls,
Which the false and self-styled Smerdis
Once had given to Atossa.

But the pearls were rare and real,
And the merry victor gave them
To the pretty dancer Thais,
Her whose birthplace was at Corinth.

In her hair this Thais wore them—
Hair that streamed like a Bacchante's—
On the night of conflagration
At Persepolis, when, dancing,

With an impious hand she flung her
Torch and struck the royal fortress,
Which flamed upward, crackling loudly
Like the fireworks at a fête.

On the death of lovely Thais,
Who in Babylon fell victim
To a Babylonish sickness,
Straight disposed of were the pearls.

They were sold by public auction.
'Twas a priest of Memphis bought them,
And he carried them to Egypt,
Where they graced the toilet-table

Of Queen Cleopatra later,
Who the fairest of the pearls
Crushed and swallowed in her wine,
Quizzing Antony, her lover.

With the latest of the Ommiads
Came the string of pearls to Spain,
And at Cordova was twisted
Round the turban of the Caliph.

Abderam the Third then wore it
As a breast-knot at the tourney,
Where through thirty golden rings
And Zuleima's heart he pierced.

When the Moors were overthrown,
Into Christian hands the pearls
Passed with other things, and figured
As crown jewels of Castile.

And their majesties, the papish
Spanish queens thereafter wore them
At their courtly routs and revels,
At the bull-fights and processions;

On the high occasions, also,
When the heretics were burning,
And the smell of old Jews roasting,
On their balconies refreshed them.

Later still that son of Satan,
Mendizabel, pawned the pearls
To procure a sum to cover
Gaps and deficits financial.

And at last the string of pearls
In the Tuileries appeared,
Madame Salomon adorning:
On the Baroness's bosom.

Such the story of the pearls.
Less adventurous the fortunes
Of the casket.　Alexander
For his royal use retained it,

And he locked therein the songs
Of divine, ambrosial Homer—
Bard he loved beyond all others—
By his couch at night it stood.

Slept the king, the shining figures
Of the heroes, from the casket
Slipping forth, in fond illusion
Lived and wandered in his dreams.

Other times, and other birds—
I, of yore I loved them also,
Loved the songs and deeds heroic
Of Pelides, of Odysseus.

Then I felt that all was golden
As the sun, and flaming purple,
And my brow was crowned with vine leaves,
And I heard the fanfares blowing.

But enough!—O'erthrown and broken
Lies my proud, victorious chariot,
And the panthers that once drew it
Now are dead, and dead the women,

Who with drum and clash of cymbals
Danced around me.　I, myself,
On the floor am turning, tossing,
Weak and crippled here—no more!

Hush!　No more!—Our present subject
Is the casket of Darius,
And I thought if I should ever
Gain possession of that casket,

And was not compelled directly
By financial straits to sell it,
I should like to lock within it
All the poems of our Rabbi,

Of Jehuda ben Halevy;—
Festal songs and lamentations,
The ghaselas, and description
Of the pilgrimage he went on.

Written plainly it should be
By a skilful scribe, on parchment
Of the purest, and bestowed
In the little golden casket.

It should stand upon a table
By my bed, and when my friends
Came and marvelled at the splendour
Of the little chest beside me,

At the curious bas-reliefs
So diminutive, yet perfect
In their finish, at the inlay
Of the big and costly jewels,

I would smile and I would tell them:
That is nothing but the shell
Which contains the nobler treasure
In this little casket lying.

There are diamonds that mirror,
With their light, the light of heaven;
There are rubies red as heart's blood,
There are turquoises unblemished,

Also emeralds of promise,
Yes, and pearls of purer beauty
Than those given to Atossa
By the rank impostor Smerdis;

And which ornamented later
All the great, distinguished figures
Of this moon-encircled planet—
Thais first, then Cleopatra,

Priests of Isis, Moorish princes,
And the queens of old Hispania,
And the worthy baron's lady,
Madame Salomon, at last.

For those pearls of world-wide glory
Are but pale, secreted mucus
Of a sick and wretched oyster
At the bottom of the sea;

While the pearls within this casket
Are the precious overflow
Of a lovely spirit, deeper
Than the deepest depths of ocean.

For these pearls, they are the tear-drops
Of Jehuda ben Halevy,
That he wept for the destruction
Of the town Jerusalem.—

Pearly tears that, strung together
On the golden thread of rhyme,
From the poet's golden forge
Issued perfect, as a song.

And this string of pearly tears
Is the famous lamentation
Sung in all the tents of Jacob
Lying scattered through the world,

On the ninth day of the month
Known as Ab, which was the date
Of Jerusalem's destruction
By the Emperor Vespasian,

Yes, Jehuda ben Halevy
Sang that famous hymn of Zion
As he lay amid the ruins
Of Jerusalem, and died.

There, in penitential raiment
He sat barefoot on a fragment
Of a crumbled, fallen pillar;
To his breast his hair fell matted,

Like a white and snowy forest,
From whose strange, fantastic shadow
Gleamed the pallid face of sorrow
With its wan and ghostly eyes.

So Jehuda ben Halevy
Sat, and singing, seemed a prophet
Of the olden days: seemed ancient
Jeremiah grave-arisen.

And the wild lament of sorrow
Tamed the birds amid the ruins,
And the very vultures hearkened,
Neared and hearkened, as in pity.

But a Saracen came riding
Bold and haughty down the pathway,
In his lofty saddle swaying,
Swung his impious, naked lance.

Pierced the poor old singer's bosom
With the fatal spear of death,
Swiftly galloped off and left him,
Like a wingèd form of shadow.

And the Rabbi's blood flowed softly,
And he calmly finished singing,
Sang his song out, and his death-sigh
Was the name Jerusalem!—

But an ancient legend has it
'Twas no insolent and evil
Wretched Saracen that slew him,
But an angel in disguise,

Who was sent express from heaven
To deliver God's belovèd
From the earth, and speed him painless
To the kingdom of the blessed;

And it tells us that, up yonder,
A reception was awaiting
Full of flattery to a poet:
A most heavenly surprise;

For a festal choir of angels
Came with music forth to meet him,
And the hymn they sang in welcome
Was composed of his own verses:

Sabbath's hymeneal numbers
Sung in synagogues at bridals,
With the melodies familiar—
Ah, what notes of jubilation!

Little angels blew the hautbois,
Little angels played the fiddle,
Others swept the strings of viols
To the clash of drum and cymbal.

And it rang and sang so sweetly,
Sweetly sounded and re-echoed
In the vasty halls of heaven:
'Lecho dodi likrath kallah.'

LAST POEMS

Body and Soul

THE poor Soul speaketh to its Clay:
'I cannot leave thee thus; I 'll stay
With thee, with thee in death I 'll sink,
And black Annihilation drink!
Thou still hast been my second *I*,
Embracing me so lovingly,
A satin feast-robe round my form,
Doubled with ermine, soft and warm.
Woe 's me! I dare not face the fact—
Quite disembodied, quite abstract,
To loiter as a blessed naught
Above there, in the realms of thought,
Through heavenly halls, immense and frigid,
Where the Immortals dumb and rigid
Yawn to me as they clatter by
With leaden clogs so wearily.
Oh, it is horrible! Oh, stay,
Stay with me, thou beloved Clay!'
The Body to the poor Soul said:
'Oh, murmur not, be comforted!
We all should quietly endure
The wounds of Fate, which none can cure.
I was the lamp's wick, and to dust
Consume; but thou, the Spirit, must
Be saved with care, and lifted far
To shine in heaven, a little star
Of purest light. I am but cinder,
Mere matter, rubbish, rotten tinder,
Losing the shape we took at birth,
Mouldering again to earth in earth.
Now, fare thee well, and grieve no more!
Perchance life is not such a bore
In Heaven, as you expect up there.
If you should meet the old Great Bear
(Not Meyer-Bear) i' the starry climes,
Greet him from me a thousand times!'

Babylonian Sorrows

DEATH calls me—sweet, 'twere almost kind
To leave thee in some wood behind,
Some drear and lonely pinewood filled
With howling wolves, where vultures build,
And the wild sow with horrid snore
Grunts to her mate, the tawny boar.

Death calls me—O my wife, my child,
Better upon the ocean wild
To leave thee, where the great floods roll,
And maddened north winds from the Pole
Lash the loud waves, while, from the deep,
The monstrous things that hidden sleep—
The sharks and crocodiles—with grim
And gaping jaws come forth and swim!
Trust me, Matilda, child and wife,
The daunting wood is not so rife
With dangers, nor the angry foam
Of churning seas, as this our home.
Dread though the wolf and vulture be,
And sharks and monsters of the sea,
Far deadlier beasts are housed than they
In lovely Paris, brilliant, gay,
Where song and mirth and dancing dwell,
The heaven of fiends, the angels' hell.
To leave thee here!   It is a thought
With fever and with madness fraught!

Black flies are whirling round me now;
They tease and buzz—on nose and brow
I feel them light—detested race!
They have an almost human face,
With elephants' trunks between their eyes,
Like India's god, Ganesa wise.—
There 's someone packing up a box
Inside my head—how loud he knocks!
My reason will be gone, alas!
Ere I myself, so soon to pass.

Lass die heil'gen Parabolen

HOLY parables discarding,
　Hypothetical and pious,
Our accursèd questions answer,
　And with truth direct supply us.

Tell us plainly why the good man
　'Neath a heavy cross should bleed,
While the wicked man rides proudly
　Like a conqueror on his steed.

Whose the fault? Is God in heaven
　Not almighty after all?
Is the wrong of His contriving?
　That were surely base and small.

So we ask and ask unceasing,
　Till a handful of cold clay
Stops our mouths and we are silenced.
　But is that an answer, pray?

Wie langsam kriechet sie dahin

OLD Time is lame and halt,
　The snail can barely crawl:
But how should I find fault,
　Who cannot move at all?

No gleam of cheerful sun!
　No hope my life to save!
I have two rooms, the one
　I die in and the grave.

Maybe I 've long been dead,
　Maybe a giddy train
Of phantoms fills my head,
　And haunts what was my brain.

These dear old gods or devils,
　Who see me stiff and dull,
May like to dance their revels
　In a dead poet's skull.

Their rage of weird delight
Is luscious pain to me:
And my bony fingers write
What daylight must not see.

Du warst ein blondes Jungfräulein, so artig

THOU wast a blonde-haired maid without a stain,
So neat, so prim, so cool!   I stayed in vain
To see thy bosom's guarded gates unroll,
And Inspiration breathe upon thy soul.

A zeal and ardour for those lofty themes,
By chilly Reason scorned for airy dreams,
But wringing from the noble and the good
The toil of hand and heart, and brain and blood.

On hills with vineyards' clambering leafage gay,
Glassed in the Rhine, we roamed one summer day;
Bright was the sun, and from the shining cup
Of every flower a giddy scent flew up.

A kiss of fire, a deep voluptuous blush,
Burned on each pink and every rosy bush,
Ideal flames in dandelions glowed,
And lit each sorriest weed that edged our road.

But thou went'st on with even-stepping feet,
Clad in white satin, elegant and neat;
No child of Netcher's brush more trim and nice,
And 'neath thy stays a little heart of ice.

Dich fesselt mein Gedankenbann

My spirit binds you with a spell,
And all my thoughts are yours as well;
Your fancies have their source in me,
And from my soul you cannot flee.

My breath impassioned fans your face;
From you I have my dwelling-place,
And even asleep you cannot lie
Safe from my kiss and whisper sly.

My body 's rotting in the ground,
My spirit lives, and it has found
A house, belovèd, in your heart:
It plays the household kobold's part.

Grudge not the strange, uncanny thing
His cosy nest, for there he 'd cling,
The little thief, although you ran
Hot-foot to China and Japan.

Where'er you fled, from Pole to Pole,
Within your heart would sit my soul—
My spirit binds you with a spell,
And all my thoughts are yours as well.

Ich war, O Lamm, als Hirt bestellt

O LITTLE lamb, I was assigned
To be thy shepherd true and kind;
And 'mid this barren world and rude
To shelter thee as best I could.
I gave thee of my bread thy fill,
I brought thee water from the rill;
And through the raging winter storm
Safe in my bosom kept thee warm.
I held thee close in that embrace;
And when the cold rain fell apace,
When through the gorge the torrents poured,
And wolves and floods in concert roared,
Thou didst not tremble then, nor fear,
E'en when the lightning's mighty spear
Cleft the tall pine—upon my breast
Still thou didst sleep and calmly rest.

My arm grows weak, and faint my heart,
Pale Death creeps near.   The shepherd's part
Is now played out, the game is o'er.
O God, then in Thy hands once more
I lay the crook, and do Thou keep
My little lamb, when I to sleep
Am laid.   Oh, guard her day by day
From every harm: and shield, I pray,
Her fleece from storms that may bring pain,

And from the miry swamps that stain.
Beneath her feet, in field and wood,
Let greenest pastures spring for food;
And let her calmly sleep and rest,
As once she slept upon my breast.

Stunden, Tage, Ewigkeiten

DAYS and hours unending, slow,
Crawl along and never go;
With their horns protruding, trail—
Each a grey, gigantic snail.

Often in the misty sea,
In the void eternity,
Shines a beacon fair and bright,
Like my darling's eyes of light.

But the bliss—can it have shone?—
Gleams a moment and is gone.
And the only thing I know
Is my leaden weight of woe.

Ewigkeit, wie bist du lang

ETERNITY, how long art thou!
   Years, a thousand, sooner pass.
For a thousand years I 've roasted,
   And am not yet cooked, alas!

Thou art long, Eternity!
   Years a thousand sooner stop.
In the end will come the Devil,
   And devour me neck and crop.

Worte! Worte! keine Thaten!

WORDS, words always and deeds never,
   Never meat, beloved poppet!
Wit for roast meat still, nor ever
   Dumplings in the soup for soppet!

Yet less good for thee, perhaps,
   Were the wild loin-strength, that gaily
To the steed of passion claps
   Spurs and makes him gallop daily.

Yes, I fear me, tender child,
   Thou at last wouldst find it wearing,
Love's unceasing gallop wild,
   Cupid's steeple-chase unsparing.

Healthier far, indeed, for thee
   Is, meseems, an ailing man
To a lover, who, like me,
   Scarcely move a finger can.

To our heart's bond, then thy sport of
   Love, dear, sacrifice: it were
Healthier far for thee, a sort of
   Sanitary love-affair.

Mittelälterliche Roheit

TAMED is medieval rudeness
By the advent of the fine arts:
Chief 'mongst instruments of culture
In our time is the piano.

And on family life the railway
Has a wholesome influence also,
Minimizing much the pain of
Separation from one's kindred.

I regret that the consumption
Of my spinal cord prevents me
From continuing my sojourn
In a world so full of progress.

Es kommt der Tod—jetzt will ich sagen

Now death draws near, and what unknown,
   Pride counselled, should for ever be,
   I will declare: for thee, for thee,
My heart has beat for thee alone.

My coffin 's made, and to my bed
  They lower me, that I may sleep.
  But thou, Maria, thou wilt weep,
And think on me when I am dead.

Thy pretty hands thou 'lt even wring.
  Oh, grieve not—'tis the human lot:
  At last defiled in death must rot
Each good and great and lovely thing.

The Affinities

You weep, and gaze at me, believing
'Tis for my sorrow you are grieving.
Be not deceived, O woman! know
'Tis for yourself your tears o'erflow.

Did no foreboding ever steal
Across your spirit, and reveal
That the eternal will of Fate
Had formed us, each for each, as mate?
Happy together and as one,
But, parted, ruined and undone.

In the great Book 'twas writ that we,
While life endured, should lovers be.
My bosom was the place for you;
There you had waked to knowledge new.
From the plant kingdom, with a kiss,
I would have drawn you up to bliss,
To higher life: to me, your goal;
I would have given you a soul.

Now that the riddle 's solved at last,
The dwindling sands are fleeting fast.
It was ordained. Why weep and moan?
I go, and you must fade alone,
Before you bloom your blossom 's shed,
The fire, before it burned, is dead.
Death holds you, and you cannot fly;
You, who have never lived, must die.

'Tis you I love. My God! I know
The truth at last. What bitter woe
When, at the moment heart finds heart,
The hour has struck for them to part!
When welcome is farewell! To-day
We go asunder, and for aye.
Nor will there any meeting be
In heaven above for you and me.
Beauty beneath the ground shall rot;
You 'll moulder in the clay forgot.
But with the poets 'tis not thus;
Death cannot wreak his will on us.
Safe from annihilation's wrong,
Still in the faëry land of song,
In Avalon our spirits dwell—
Sweet corpse, for evermore farewell!

A Recollection of Krähwinkel's Days of Terror

By us, the Mayor and Senate framed,
The following mandate is proclaimed,
In love paternal to all classes
Who represent the civic masses:

'"Tis mostly foreigners, we own,
By whom rebellion's seed is sown;
Such sinners seldom, praised be God,
Are children of our German sod.

'And atheists also share the crime;
He who denies his Lord, in time
A faithless renegade will prove him
To those on earth who rank above him.

'Obey your rulers: this be ever
The Jew's, the Christian's first endeavour,
And Christians, Jews, shall, every one,
Shut up their shops at set of sun.

'Should three of you together meet,
Disperse at once; and in the street
Let none of you be seen at night,
Abroad on foot, without a light.

'Straight to the guildhall of the town
Repair and lay your weapons down;
And subject to the same condition
Is every sort of ammunition.

'Whoever in a public spot
Attempts to argue shall be shot;
To reason by gesticulation
Will bring the self-same castigation.

'Your mayor ye must trust in blindly;
He guards the town and watches kindly,
With anxious care, o'er old and young.
Your business is to hold your tongue.'

La Mouche

It was a summer night of which I dreamed,
  And mouldering remains of ancient glory,
Stonework of a Renaissance fabric, gleamed
  Around me in the moonlight, wan and hoary.

And here and there, from out the ruinous sward,
  A pillar with grave, Doric capital
Arose and gazed defiant heavenward,
  As challenging the thunderbolts to fall;

Everywhere crumbling fragments, strewn, confounded,
  Sculptures and portals, many a curious gable,
Centaur and sphinx, of man and beast compounded,
  Satyrs, chimeras—figures of old fable.

Among the débris was a marble tomb,
  Wide open, still intact and undefiled,
And in the coffin, brave in manhood's bloom,
  A dead man lying; sad his face and mild.

With necks upreaching, Caryatides
  Seemed to support him with much toil and strain;
And carven on both sides I could, with ease,
  Figures in bas-relief decipher plain.

Here was portrayed Olympus in its glory,
  The Pagan gods, still unashamed and glad;
Adam and Eve from out the Bible story,
  Each in the fig-leaf apron chastely clad.

And here was burning Troy—in classic poses,
  Paris and Helen, and bold Hector too;
Haman and Esther, Aaron and great Moses;
  Judith, and Holofernes whom she slew.

And yonder, lo! the God of Love divine;
  Phoebus Apollo, Vulcan and Dame Venus,
Mercury, Pluto and his Proserpine,
  God Bacchus, and Priapus and Silenus.

Beside them stood the ass of Balaam wise—
  For speech an ass was surely chosen well;
And Abraham, prepared for sacrifice,
  And Lot, who with his daughters drank and fell.

I saw Herodias dancing, and the head
  Of John the Baptist, which the charger bore;
And hell with all the fiends, and Satan dread,
  And Peter with the keys of heaven's door.

Again the subject changed; on stone was drawn
  Lascivious Jove's outrageous crimes of old,
When he pursued poor Leda as a swan,
  And Danae as a shower of ducats gold.

I also saw Diana's headlong chase,
  With dogs, and following nymphs up-girdled high;
And Hercules in woman's garb and place—
  Distaff 'neath arm, he made the spindle fly:

And, close to Hercules, Mount Sinai rising,
  And Israel with his oxen on the height;
And, in the Temple, Christ, the child, surprising
  The Pharisees, and arguing aright.

So, in a contrast glaring and grotesque,
  Judea's Godward yearning was combined
With the Greek sense of joy! Its arabesque
  The clinging ivy about both had twined

But strange! While of those sculptures thus I dreamed,
  A curious fancy stole into my head,
And on a sudden to myself I seemed
  The man within the marble lying dead.

And at the far end of the bier there grew
  A flower of a rare, mysterious form,
The petals sulphur-gold and violet-blue;
  The flower breathed of love's resistless charm.

The name we give it is the passion-flower;
  On Golgotha it blossomed from the sod,
When flowed the blood of world-redeeming power,
  What time they crucified the Son of God.

And it bears witness to the blood they shed;
  All instruments of torture which the malice
Of the vile murderers employed, 'tis said,
  Are counterfeited plainly on its chalice.

Yes, all the Passion-requisites, 'tis urged,
  The torture-chamber quite complete is here:
The crown of thorns, the ropes that bound and scourged,
  Nails, hammer, cup and cross, depicted clear.

Such was the flower by my grave that grew,
  And, o'er my lifeless body bending low
As mourning women in their sorrow do,
  Eyes, brow, and hand it kissed in silent woe.

But magic of a dream, how strange and fleet!
  The sulphur-yellow passion-flower moved,
And grew into a woman's likeness sweet,
  And it is she herself, the best beloved!

Yes, dearest child; thyself, thou art the flower;
  I recognize thee by thy kisses yearning.
No flower-lips could have such tender power,
  No flower-tears could ever be so burning.

Mine eyes were closed and dead, and yet how plain
  My soul could see, and feast upon thy face;
And thou didst look on me enraptured, fain,
  Touched by the moonlight with a ghostly grace.

My heart, although we spoke not, could behold
   The thoughts unuttered in thy spirit move.
The spoken word is shameless, overbold;
   Oh, silence is the modest flower of love!

A soundless dialogue! One scarce would deem
   How, by the dumb and tender talk, time fled.
Swift was the summer night of lovely dream,
   Woven of dear delight and shuddering dread.

But what we talked of bid me not betray.
   What does the glowworm glimmer to the grass?
What does the brooklet murmur on its way?
   What sigh the west winds, grieving as they pass?

Ask the carbuncle why it shines; discover
   What rose and rocket by their scent betoken;
Ask not the passion-flower and her dead lover
   What 'neath the moon was said, although unspoken.

I know not for how long, all sorrow banished,
   Within my cool and slumbrous marble chest
I dreamed of joy. But ah, too quickly vanished
   The rapture of my calm, untroubled rest!

Thou only givest bliss without annoy,
   O death, within the silent grave; this life,
Foolish and vulgar, gives unquiet joy,
   And passion always warring and at strife.

Ah, woe is me! A tumult rose without,
   And chased the calm and happiness away.
I heard them arguing with stamp and shout,
   My gentle flower was seized with sore dismay.

Yes, from without, alas! we were surprised
   By sounds of hate—assertion and dissent;
And, from their voices, soon I recognized
   The bas-reliefs about my monument.

Does the old superstition haunt my bier,
   And are the marble phantoms still debating?
Is sylvan Pan, with his loud cry of fear,
   The anathemas of Moses emulating?

Oh, well I know they never will agree;
    Beauty and truth will always be at variance.
The army of mankind will always be
    Split in two camps: the Hellenes and Barbarians.

Denunciations, insults, and alas!
    No sign at all of burying the hatchet;
While loud above the din brayed Balaam's ass—
    The voice of neither god nor saint could match it.

Hee-haw! it went, both in and out of season—
    That hideous sound, half hiccough and half choke.
I think that I should soon have lost my reason,
    But in despair I cried aloud—and woke.

Epilogue

THAT our grave is warmed by glory—.
Stuff and nonsense! 'Tis a story!
Better warmth than that's imparted
By a milkmaid loving-hearted,
Kissing full-lipped and afire,
Though she reeks of dung and byre.
Why, a better, truer heat
Comes of drinking brandy neat:
Comes of drinking punch and swallowing
All the grog you can, and wallowing
In the dens of vilest stamp,
Filled with every sort of scamp
That has dodged the gallows-tree,
But who's living, breathing free,
And who tastes of more that sweet is
Than the famous son of Thetis.—
Yes, Pelides spoke the truth:
'It is better, in good sooth,
On the earth to live a slave
Than to rule on Styx's wave,
'Mid the shadows first in glory,
Even though Homer sing your story.'

The Dying Man

WITHIN my breast desire is done
For vain delight beneath the sun.
I hate no longer what is bad:
Hate too is dead.   I am not sad
For others' sorrow or my own—
'Tis death that lives in me alone.
The curtain falls upon the play
And, yawning on its homeward way,
My worthy German public hies.
The honest folk are very wise,
They 're dining now in ease and pleasure,
They sing and laugh and drink their measure.

'Twas truth the noble hero told
Who spoke in Homer's book of old:
The Philistine of least renown
Alive to-day in Stukkert town
Beside the Neckar—ah, he still is
More blest than I, the great Achilles,
Dead hero who, the king of ghosts,
In Hades rule my shadowy hosts.

PART II

THE PROSE

A TOUR IN THE HARZ

THE town of Göttingen, so celebrated for its sausages and university, belongs to the King of Hanover, and contains 999 inhabited houses, various churches, a lying-in hospital, an observatory, a university prison, a library, and a town hall tavern, where the beer is excellent. The stream that flows past the town is the Leine, and serves in summer for bathing. The water is very cold, and in some places it is so broad that Ponto had to take a really good run to clear it. The town itself is pretty, and presents the most agreeable aspect—when we have turned our backs upon it. Of its antiquity there can be no doubt, for I remember when I matriculated there five years ago (just before I was requested to take my name off the books), it had the same grey knowing look about it that it has now, and was as fully provided as now with Charleys,[1] beadles, dissertations, *thés dansants*, washerwomen, cram-books, pigeon-pies, Guelfic orders, graduates' visiting coaches, pipe-bowls, court-councillors, law-councillors, rustication councillors, bull-dogs, and other sad dogs. Some authorities actually maintain that the town dates from the days of the barbaric invasions, and according to them each German tribe dropped on its way a rough copy of itself, which accounts for all the Vandals, Frisians, Swabians, Teutons, Saxons, Thuringians, etc., who may be found in Göttingen even to the present day. Our young barbarians still go in hordes, and you may distinguish them by the colours of their caps and pipe-tassels. They lounge along the Weenderstrasse on their way to the sanguinary battlefields of Rasenmühle, Ritchenkrug, and Bovden, where they are always pitching into one another. Their manners and customs are survivals from the age of the barbaric invasions, and they are governed partly by their *Duces* (prize cocks they style them), partly by their primitive code styled the *Comment*. It well deserves a place among the *leges barbarorum*.

The inhabitants of Göttingen may be roughly classified under the heads of student, professor, philistine, and brute; but between these four estates there is no clearly marked distinction. The most important class are the brutes. To commemorate by name all the students and all the regular and irregular professors,

[1] Night-watchmen.

would exceed my limits, and at the present moment I cannot call to mind the names of all the students, while of the professors many have, as yet, no name. The Göttingen philistines must be numerous as the sand, or rather as the flakes of scum on the seashore; indeed, when I see them in the morning, planted before the gates of the academic court with their white bills and dirty faces, I can hardly conceive how God can ever have created such a pack of rascals.

Further details about the town may be conveniently studied in Marx's *Topography of Göttingen*. Although I am devotedly attached to the author, who was my doctor, and dosed me with nothing but kindness, yet I am unable to praise his work without reservation; and it is my painful duty to take him to task for not expressly and emphatically contradicting the current scandal about the big feet of Göttingen women. Indeed, I have been occupied for some time past with a serious refutation of this heresy, and with this express object have joined a class of comparative anatomy, made extracts from the rarest volumes in the library, stood in the Weenderstrasse for hours at a spell studying the feet of the ladies as they walked by, and in the exhaustive treatise which embodies the result of these studies, I treat of (1) feet in general, (2) feet in the old world, (3) elephants' feet, (4) the feet of Göttingen women, (5) I collate the various remarks on their feet that have been overheard in Ulrich's tea-gardens, (6) I consider these feet in their further relations, and take the opportunity of enlarging on calves, knees, etc., (7) and lastly, if I can obtain paper of sufficient size, I will add some copperplate facsimiles of the Göttingen female foot.

I left Göttingen at an early hour, and the learned Eichhorn was doubtless still in bed and dreaming, as usual, that he was walking in a beautiful garden, the flower-beds planted with nothing but slips of white paper inscribed with quotations. These paper flowers were radiant with sunlight, and in his dream he went about plucking one and another, and carefully transplanted them to a new bed, while the nightingales enraptured his old heart with their sweetest melodies.

Near the Weender gate I was met by two small schoolboys, both genuine natives. One of them was saying to the other: 'I really must cut that Theodore; he's a cad; why yesterday he actually did not know the genitive of *mensa*.' Trivial as these words may sound, I feel bound to report them, and I should even like to inscribe them straightway on the gate, as the town motto; for according to the proverb the young birds peep as the old birds pipe, and these words are a sign and summary of the dry, narrow pedantry of the learned University of Göttingen.

Past Nordheim the country begins to rise, and here and there some fine hills come in view. On the road I met mostly hucksters bound for the Brunswick fair, and also a crowd of women, each of them carrying on her back a huge cage almost as high as a house, covered with white linen. These contained all sorts of singing-birds, which kept up a constant piping and twittering; while their bearers hopped along and chattered also. It was comic to see one bird carrying other birds to market.

It was pitch dark when I reached Osterode. I had no appetite for supper and went straight to bed.

I awoke with music still in my ears. It was the bells of the cows being driven to pasture. The golden sun smiled in at my window and lit up the paintings on the walls—scenes from the War of Liberation, which faithfully portrayed what heroes we all were; execution scenes from the French Revolution, Louis XVI at the guillotine, and similar beheadings, a sight of which makes a man thank God that he is lying safe in bed, drinking excellent coffee, with his head still on his shoulders. After my cup of coffee I dressed, read all the inscriptions on the window-panes, settled my score, and then left Osterode. Osterode has x houses, y inhabitants, including z souls. For particulars, *vide* Gottschalk's *Guide to the Harz Country*. Before striking the high road I ascended the ruins of the ancient Osterode fortress. All that is left of it is one half of a large, thick-walled, honey-combed tower. The way to Klausthal is still uphill, and from one of the first heights I looked back once again at Osterode with its red roofs peeping from the green fir-forests like a moss rose. The sun poured on it the innocent brightness of a newborn day. Seen from the rear the half-fallen tower has an imposing look.

The next morning I had to lighten my knapsack again. I threw overboard the pair of boots it contained, and journeyed on my way to Goslar. I got there somehow, but I can't say how. All I remember is sauntering along uphill and downhill, looking down on many a pretty dell; the rippling of silver rivulets, the sweet twittering of wood birds, and tinkling of cow-bells; while the varied greens of the woodland were all tinged with gold by the bright sun, and, above, the blue silken canopy of the heavens was so transparent that one could gaze straight into the very holy of holies, and see the angels sitting at God's feet, and studying in His features their thorough-bass. I, however, was still absorbed by a dream of the night before that I could not get out of my head. It was the old tale of a knight descending into a deep well-spring, beneath which the loveliest of princesses lies as dead under the spell of a magic sleep. I was the knight, and the well the dark Klausthal mine; and suddenly there appeared a multitude of lights, and out of every cranny leapt the guardians of the mine—dwarfs who made angry faces cut at me with their short swords, blew a shrill blast on their horns, which brought more and more to the rescue, their big heads wagging horribly. As I struck out at them, and blood began to flow, it flashed upon me that these were the red-bearded thistles growing by the roadside whose heads I had struck off with my stick the day before. So the dwarfs were all scattered and fled, and I entered a brightly-lighted state chamber. In the middle, veiled in white, cold and motionless as a statue, stood the lady of my heart; and I kissed her mouth, and, by the living God, I felt the blessed breath of her soul and the sweet trembling of her lips. It was as though I heard God saying: 'Let there be light!' I was dazzled by a sudden ray of the eternal light, but instantly it was night again, and all was chaos, mingled and merged in one wild waste of waters. A wild waste of waters! over the yeasty ocean scudded the ghosts of the dead, their white shrouds fluttered in the wind; behind them, hounding them on with cracking whip, ran a motley harlequin, and the harlequin was I—— And suddenly from the dark waves the monsters of the deep raised their misshapen heads and rushed at me with their claws, and with terror I awoke.

How often we spoil the prettiest fairy tales. Properly the knight, on finding the sleeping princess, should cut a piece out of her veil, and when by his daring her magic sleep has been broken and she is sitting again in her palace on her golden throne, the knight should approach her, and say: 'My fairest princess, dost thou know me?' And she should answer: 'My bravest knight, I know thee not.' And then he shows her the bit he cut from her veil, which exactly fits the gap in it, and they fall into each other's arms, and the trumpets blow, and the marriage is celebrated.

It is, I suppose, a part of my bad luck that my love-dreams rarely have such a happy ending.

The name of Goslar has such a pleasant sound, and is associated with so many imperial memories of old days, that I expected to see an imposing, stately city. But, as is usual with a near view of greatness, I found a mere rookery, mostly a maze of narrow streets, through the middle of which a foul, sluggish stream flows, apparently the Gose, while the pavement is as rough and jolting as Berlin hexameters. What piquancy it has must be sought in the antiquities of the outskirts, remains of walls, towers, and battlements. The walls of one of the towers, called the Donjon, are so thick that full-sized chambers are cut in them. The open place outside the town, where the famous shooting matches are held, is a fine large meadow surrounded by hills. The market-place is small; in the middle is a fountain, which falls into a large metal basin. When there is a fire in the town, the alarm is sometimes given by striking on the basin; the ringing sound can be heard at a great distance. Of the origin of this basin nothing is known. Some say the Devil put it one night in the market-place. In those days people were stupid, and the Devil was stupid too, and it was a case of give and take.

The town hall at Goslar is a whitewashed guard-room. The adjoining guildhall is a more decent-looking building. About half-way between the ground and the roof are ranged statues of the German emperors, black with smoke, and with patches of gilding, the sceptre in one hand and the orb in the other, looking like roasted university beadles. One of these emperors has a sword instead of the sceptre. I could not discover the meaning of this distinction, though it undoubtedly has some meaning of its own, for it is a remarkable peculiarity of the Germans to have some deep meaning in all that they do.

Gottschalk's guide has a great deal to say about the defunct cathedral and the famous emperor's chair at Goslar; but on asking for them I was told that the cathedral had been pulled down, and the chair removed to Berlin. We live in an age of revolutions; immemorial cathedrals are demolished and imperial thrones stowed away in the lumber-room.

A few curiosities from the old cathedral are now exhibited in the church of St. Stephen—some very fine painted glass, some daubs, one of which is said to be a Lucas Cranach, a wooden crucifix, and a pagan sacrificial altar made of some unknown metal. The altar has the shape of a long box, and is supported by four caryatides with bent backs and upturned hands, a horrible grimace on their faces. Still more horrible is the great wooden crucifix which is near the altar. The head of the Christ, with natural hair and thorns and blood-besmeared face, is a masterly representation of the death-struggle of a mortal, but not of a God-born Saviour. The carving of the face portrays only material suffering, not the poetry of pain. The figure is better fitted for an anatomical museum than a sacred edifice. The pew-opener who took me round was a bit of a connoisseur, and showed me further as a special rarity a well-polished polygon of black wood with white figures on it, hanging like a candelabrum in the middle of the church. What a splendid instance of the inventive powers of the Protestant Church! Who would have thought it? The figures on this polygon are the numbers of the hymns which are generally written in chalk on a blackboard, and so produce a depressing effect on our aesthetic feelings; whereas by this invention they actually serve as an ornament to the church, and fully compensate for the missing Raphaels. Such improvements afford me infinite satisfaction. As I am a Protestant, and a Lutheran to boot, it would annoy and pain me if a Catholic antagonist could twit me with the bare God-forsaken appearance of Protestant churches.

The night that I passed at Goslar a strange thing happened to me. At this very day I cannot look back on it without terror. I am not nervous by nature, and God knows that I never experienced any special sinking at the heart, when, for instance, a naked rapier was trying to make acquaintance with my nose, or when I had lost my way at night in an ill-reputed forest, or when at a concert a gaping lieutenant threatened to swallow me; but of spirits I am nearly as much afraid as the *Austrian Observer*. What is fear? Is it a process of reason or a matter of temperament? This question was a standing subject of dispute between Dr. Saul Ascher and myself whenever we chanced to meet in Berlin at the Café Royal, where for some time I regularly dined. The doctor always asserted that we fear anything because we know it to be fearful by a process of reasoning. Reason alone is a motive force, not temperament. All the while that I was making a good dinner, he went on demonstrating the pre-eminence of reason. As his demonstration was drawing to a close, he used to look at his watch, and invariably ended off with 'Reason is the highest principle.' Reason! Even now when-ever I hear the word, I see before me Dr. Saul Ascher with his abstractions of legs, his close-fitting coat of transcendental grey, and his angular frozen face which might have served for a diagram in a treatise on geometry. He was well over fifty, and so thin that he looked like an incarnate and personified straight line. In his endeavour after positive fact, the poor man had philosophized away all the brightness of life, all sunbeams, all beliefs and all flowers, and nothing was left him but the cold fact of the grave. Against the Apollo Belvedere and Christianity he had a special grudge. He actually wrote a pamphlet against Christianity, proving its irrationality and untenability. There are numerous other works of his, in all of which the admirable nature of reason is extolled. In so far as these expressed the poor doctor's most serious convictions (of which there can be no doubt), he deserved all respect. But the best joke of it all was to see his solemn puzzled look when he failed to understand what every child understands just because it is a child. Sometimes, too, I visited the doctor of reason at his own house, where I used to find him with pretty girls, for reason does not forbid sensibility. One day, when I was going to pay him a visit, his servant, who opened the door, told me: 'The doctor has just died.' I felt no more concern than if he had told me: 'The doctor is out.'

But to return to Goslar. 'The highest principle is reason,' I repeated to myself to calm my nerves, as I got into bed. It was, however, no good. I had just been reading in Varnhagen von Ense's *German Tales*, which I had taken with me from Klausthal, the terrible story of the son on the point of being murdered by his own father, who is warned in the night by the ghost of his mother. The story is told so graphically that a cold shiver ran through me as I read it; and generally ghost stories affect one's nerves more when read on a journey, especially if at night in a town, in a house, in a room where one has never been before. You cannot help thinking of the horrors that may have been perpetrated on the very spot where you are now lying. Moreover, the moon at this moment cast so ambiguous a light into my bedroom; all sorts of shadows began moving on the wall without visible cause; and, as I sat up in bed to look, I beheld——

There's nothing more uncanny than casually to see your own face in the glass by moonlight. At the same instant a ponderous sleepy clock struck, so solemnly and slowly that by the time the twelfth stroke was finished I made sure that twelve full hours must have passed, and it was bound to begin striking twelve over again. Between the last stroke and the last but one, another clock struck, fast and almost shrewishly shrill, as if angry with the slowness of its gossip. When both iron tongues had stopped, and the whole house was still as death, I suddenly seemed to hear a shuffling and hobbling in the passage outside my room, like the uncertain steps of an old man. At last my door opened and there entered slowly the late Dr. Saul Ascher. My blood ran cold, I shivered like an aspen leaf, and hardly dared look at the ghost. He had the same appearance as of old, the same coat of transcendental grey, the same abstract legs, the same mathematical face—only it was a shade yellower —and the mouth that used to make two angles of 22½ degrees was pinched, and his eye-balls had a larger radius. Tottering, and supporting himself, as his wont was, on his malacca cane, he approached me, and addressing me in his familiar drawling tones: 'Fear not,' he said, 'do not imagine that I am a ghost. It is an illusion of your imagination if you take me for a ghost. What is a ghost? I will trouble you to define a ghost, and deduce by logical reasoning the possibility of a ghost. What reasonable connection can there be between such an appearance and reason. Reason, I say,'—and hereupon the ghost proceeded to an analysis of reason, quoted Kant's *Critique of Pure Reason*, Part II, Sect. 1, Book II, para. 3: 'On the distinction of Phenomena and Noumena,' constructed next a hypothetical ghost creed, piled syllogism on syllogism, and ended by drawing the logical conclusion that there is no such thing as a ghost. All the time cold sweat ran down my back, my teeth chattered like castanets, in my agony I nodded unqualified assent to each proposition by which the ghostly doctor proved the absurdity of all fear of ghosts, growing so eagerly excited in his demonstration, that once in his excitement, instead of his gold watch, he pulled out of his fob a handful of worms, and noticing his mistake nervously thrust them back with comic haste. 'Reason is the highest——' the clock struck one, and the ghost vanished.

. . . .

We took a cordial farewell, and I merrily clomb the mountain. Very soon I entered a forest of fir-trees, heaven-kissing, and in every way worthy my regard. For such trees the process of growing is no easy matter, and they have had a rough time of it in their youth. The mountain in this part is strewn with huge granite blocks, and nearly all these trees must have either writhed round the rocks with their roots or split them, in order to work their way to the soil from which they draw their nourishment. Now and again the rocks lie one on another, forming a sort of gateway, and the trees that grow above it let down their bare roots over the stone gate, not reaching earth till they get to the bottom of it, so that they seem to grow in air. And yet, having stormed this mountain height, they have grown one, as it were, with the rocks they cling to, and are more firmly rooted than their staid brethren in the tame plantation of the lowlands—a type of those great men who have gained their strength and firmness by overcoming the straits and stumbling-blocks that barred their path at starting. Squirrels were clambering among the branches, and, beneath, the yellow deer were straying. I never understand what pleasure men of education can find in hunting such a lovable and noble animal, an animal more tender-hearted than man himself, who once suckled Schmerzenreich, the starving infant of St. Genovefa.

Very beautiful was the effect of the golden sunlight piercing the thick green of the fir-trees. The roots formed a natural flight of stairs. Everywhere were swelling beds of moss, for the rocks are covered foot-deep with all sorts of lovely mosses like cushions of light green satin. Delicious coolness and dreamy murmur of unseen springs. Here and there you can see a thread of silvery water trickling beneath the stones, and splashing the roots and fibres. Bend down and listen, and you surprise, as it were, the secret of plant life, and perceive the calm pulsation of the mountain's heart. In many places the water spurts up in larger volume from the stems and roots and forms small cascades. This is the spot for a rest. The murmuring and splashing of waters, the notes of birds like snatches of love songs, the whispering of leaves like myriad maiden voices, the myriad eyes of strange mountain flowers gazing at us like wistful maidens, the fan-like, curiously jagged leaves they stretch out at us, the merry sunbeams playing at hide and seek, the tales of greenery that plant whispers to plant,—all is fairy-land; the witchery grows stronger, a vision of the dim past takes form and substance, the beloved appears—alas! that she so quickly disappears again.

The higher one ascends, the more dwarfed become the fir-trees. They seem to shrink and shrivel up till nothing is left but bilberries, raspberries, and mountain vegetation. The air, too, is perceptibly colder. Here you first get a proper view of the wonderful groups of granite blocks. Some of them are of astounding size, and one can easily fancy them the balls that the evil spirits play at catch with on Walpurgis night, when the witches troop in, riding on broomsticks and pitchforks, and join in the wild devilry of which the old nurses tell such marvellous tales, and which is so admirably portrayed in Master Retzsch's illustrations to *Faust*. By the same token, a young poet who was riding past the Brocken after sunset on the 1st of May, on his way from Berlin to Göttingen, observed a company of literary ladies having an aesthetic tea-party in a quiet nook of the mountain, comfortably reading aloud their *Evening Times*, extolling the poetic bleatings of their pet billy-goats, who hopped round the table, as the utterances of inspired genius, and sitting in judgment on every production of German literature. But when the turn of *Ratcliff* and *Almansor* came, and the author was pronounced outside the pale of morality and Christianity, the young man's hair stood on end, panic seized him—I set spurs to my horse and rode for my life.

In ascending the upper half of the Brocken it is in fact impossible to avoid thinking of the enchanting story of the Blocksberg, and particularly of the great mystic national tragedy of 'Doctor Faust.' I had a constant sense of the horse's foot scrambling up at my side, and seemed to hear the ironic panting of the fiend. And I do believe Mephisto himself must find it hard to keep his breath when he climbs his favourite mountain. It is a most exhausting ascent, and I was heartily glad to catch sight at last of the welcome Brockenhaus.

The house, as is well known from pictures and engravings, consists of a single story, and stands on the summit of the mountain. It was erected in 1800 by Count Stolberg-Wernigerode, and is managed for his profit as an inn. The walls are wonderfully thick, to stand the wind and frost in winter. The roof is low; from the middle of it rises a sort of watch-tower; and there are two adjoining outbuildings, one of which used to serve as shelter for visitors to the Brocken before the house was built.

My entrance into the Brockenhaus produced on me a strange eerie sensation. After a long solitary scramble among rocks and firs one finds oneself suddenly transplanted to a house in the clouds; after leaving towns, mountains, and forests below, one meets above a mixed company of strangers, by whom, as is natural in such places, one is received almost like an expected acquaintance, with a mixture of curiosity and indifference. I found the house full, and, like a prudent traveller I thought at once about night quarters and the discomfort of a shakedown in the straw. In a die-away voice I at once asked for tea, and the landlord had the sense to see that one so ill as I must have a proper bed. This he procured me in a room the size of a closet, where a young merchant, who looked like an emetic powder in a long brown wrapper, had already established himself.

In the coffee-room I found nothing but life and movement. Students of various universities, some just arrived and refreshing themselves; others just off again, strapping on their knapsacks, writing their names in the visitors' book, receiving Brocken nosegays from the chambermaids, chucking them under the chin, singing, jumping, yodelling, questioning, answering questions, 'fine weather, short cut, your health, adieu.' Some of the departing students were more or less fuddled, and these, as drunken men see double, must have doubly enjoyed the view.

After recruiting myself a little, I ascended the observatory, where I found a short gentleman with two ladies, one young, the other oldish. The young lady was very beautiful. A magnificent form, curling hair confined by a black satin helmet-shaped hat, with a white feather, which waved in the wind; a close-fitting black silk jacket which revealed the fine lines of her slim figure; great open eyes looking calmly out on the great open world.

When I was a boy I thought of nothing but fairy tales and stories of magic, and every pretty woman I saw with ostrich feathers in her bonnet was for me an elfin queen: and if I did chance to notice that her skirts were wet, I thought her a water-witch. Now that I have studied natural history, and know that those symbolic feathers are plucked from the stupidest of birds, and that the skirts of a lady's dress may get wet by a very natural process, I have lost my early faith. But if I could have seen with my boyish eyes the fair lady as and where I have described her on the Brocken, I should certainly have thought: This is the fairy of the mountain, and 'tis she that spoke the spell that cast such a wondrous glamour on the whole scene beneath. Yes, very wonderful is our first view from the Brocken; each side of our nature receives new impressions, and these separate impressions, mostly distinct, nay contradictory, produce on us a powerful effect, though we cannot as yet analyse or understand it. If we succeed in grasping the conception which underlies this state of feeling, we recognize the character of the mountain. Its character is wholly German in its weakness no less than in its strength. The Brocken is a German. With German thoroughness he shows us clearly and plainly as in a giant panorama the hundreds of cities, towns, and villages (mostly to the north), and all around, the hills, forests, rivers, and plains stretching away to the distant horizon. But this very distinctness gives everything the sharp definition and clear colouring of a local chart; there is nowhere a really beautiful landscape for the eye to rest on. This is just our way. Thanks to the conscientious exactitude with which we are bent on giving every single fact, we German compilers never think about the form that will best represent any particular fact. The mountain, too, has something of German calmness, intelligence, and tolerance, just because it can command such a wide, clear view of things. And when such a mountain opens its giant eyes, it may well happen that it sees more than we dwarfs do, clambering with purblind eyes upon its sides. Many, indeed, declare that the Brocken is bourgeois, and Claudius has sung of 'The Blocksberg, that tall Philistine.' But that is a mistake. It is true that owing to his bald pate, over which he sometimes draws his white cap of mist, he gives himself an air of philistinism, but, as with many other great Germans, this is pure irony. Nay, it is notorious that the Brocken has his wild freshman days, e.g. the 1st of May. Then he tosses his cloud cap in the air and goes romantic mad, like a genuine German.

I tried at once to engage the pretty lady in a conversation, for one never properly enjoys the beauties of nature unless one can talk them over on the spot. She was not clever, but bright and intelligent. Really distinguished manners, not the common stiff and starched distinction, a negative quality which knows what *not* to do, but that rare positive quality, the ease of manner which tells us exactly how far we may go, and by setting us at our ease give us a perfect sense of social self-possession. I displayed an amount of geographical knowledge that astonished myself, satisfied the curiosity of my fair inquirer by telling her the names of all the towns that lay at our feet, looked them out and showed them to her on my pocket map, which I unrolled on the stone table in the middle of the observatory with the air of a regular professor. Several towns I failed to find, perhaps because I sought them with my finger rather than with my eyes, which were engaged in taking the bearings of the fair face and finding there more attractive regions than Schierke and Elend. The face was one of those that always please, though we are rarely enchanted, and never fall in love with them. I like such faces because they smile to rest my susceptible heart. The lady was not married, although she had reached the full flower of beauty which gives its possessor a claim to matrimony. But it's a matter of everyday experience that the prettiest girls find it hardest to get a husband. Even in ancient times this was the case, and we all know that the three Graces were all old maids.

In what relationship the short gentleman stood to the ladies he was escorting I could not make out. He was a spare, odd-looking figure. A small head, with a sprinkling of grey hairs straggling over his low forehead as far as his green dragon-fly eyes; a broad prominent nose; mouth and chin, on the other hand, receding almost to the ears. The face seemed made of that soft, yellowish clay that sculptors use for their first models; and when he pursed up his thin lips, some thousands of faint semicircular wrinkles spread over the cheeks. The little man never said a word; only now and then, when the elder lady made some pleasant remark to him in a whisper, he smiled like a lap-dog with a cold in its head.

The elder lady was the mother of the younger, and had, like her, a most distinguished manner. Her eyes betrayed a sort of sickly mysticism, and the lips wore an expression of austere piety; yet I detected traces of past beauty, and it seemed to me as though they had laughed much, felt many a kiss, and given many a kiss in return. Her face was like a palimpsest, where beneath the black modern monkish manuscript of one of the fathers you can trace the half-obliterated characters of an old Greek love-song. Both ladies had this year been to Italy with their companion, and were full of the beauties of Rome, Florence, and Venice. The mother talked about the Raphaels in St. Peter's, the daughter of the opera in the Fenice theatre. Both were enchanted with the improvisatori. Their native town was Nuremberg, but they could tell me little of its ancient glories. The divine art of the Meistersingers has grown dumb, and in Wagenseil's verse we hear its dying echoes. Now the dames of Nuremberg are edified by the silly extemporizations of Italians and the songs of castrati. Saint Sebaldus! thou art truly but an indifferent patron to-day.

Whilst we were conversing twilight approached: the air grew cooler, the sun was sinking, and the platform of the watch-tower began to fill—students, mechanics, and a few respectable citizens with their wives and daughters, all intent on seeing the sunset. It is a solemnizing spectacle, which frames the beholder's mind to prayer. For full a quarter of an hour we all stood in solemn silence, and gazed at the fiery orb sinking slowly into the west. The ruddy glow lit up our faces, and our hands instinctively were clasped as in prayer. We seemed a silent congregation, standing in the nave of a giant cathedral, at the moment when the priest is elevating the Host, and the organ rolls forth Palestrina's immortal chorale.

While I was standing thus absorbed in devotion, I heard a voice near me exclaiming: 'As a general rule, how very beautiful nature is!' These words proceeded from the sentimental breast of the young merchant who shared my bedroom. They restored me to my work-a-day frame of mind, and I was ready to address to the ladies any number of appropriate remarks about the sunset, and conduct them back to their rooms with perfect nonchalance, as if nothing had happened. They allowed me, moreover, to stay with them for an hour more. Our conversation, like the earth revolved round the sun. The mother thought that the sun, as it sank in mist, looked like a glowing rose thrown down by her lover the heavens into the outspread white veil of his bride the earth. The daughter smiled and observed that a too frequent sight of such natural phenomena would weaken their impressiveness. The mother corrected her daughter's heresy by quoting a passage from Goethe's *Reisebriefe*, and asked me whether I had read his *Werther*. I believe we talked besides of Angora cats, Etruscan vases, Turkish shawls, macaroni, and Lord Byron, from whose poems the elder lady recited some sunset descriptions with a pretty lisp and sigh. The younger lady, who did not understand English, wanted to know something of the poems, so I recommended her the translation of my fair and accomplished countrywoman Baroness Elise von Hohenhausen, and I did not miss the opportunity of holding forth, as I make a point of doing to all young ladies I meet, on Byron's godlessness, lovelessness, hopelessness, and heaven knows what besides.

All descriptions must fail to render the impression of unmixed joyousness and artless grace that is left by a sight of the Ilse as it plunges over the fantastic fragments of rock that hem its path. Here its water spurts up wildly or overflows in a foaming cascade, there it jets in delicate curves from every cleft and cranny of the rocks, and again trips below over the pebbles like a merry maiden. Yes, the myth is true: the Ilse is a princess who leaps down the mountain-side with the light laughter of youth. See her white foam-robe shimmering in the sunshine, her silver streamers fluttering in the wind, her diamonds sparkling and flashing! The tall beech-trees beside her are like solemn fathers regarding with secret satisfaction the waywardness of a favourite daughter; the white birches nod their heads like aunts, proud, but alarmed at the girl's mad leaps; the stately oak looks down like a surly uncle, who knows he must pay the piper; the birds of the air trill out their approval; the flowers on the bank murmur tenderly: 'Oh, take us with thee, take us with thee, sister dear!' But the merry maiden will not stay; on she bounds, and suddenly lays hold of the dreaming poet, and there streams upon him a flowery rain of rippling sunbeams and sunny ripples, and my senses fail with too much loveliness, and nothing but an echo of a flute-like voice remains on my ear.

How infinitely blissful is the feeling when the outer world of phenomena blends and harmonizes with the inner world of feeling, when green trees, thought, birds' songs, sweet melancholy, the azure of heaven, memory, and the perfume of flowers run together, and form the loveliest of arabesques. Women know this feeling best; this is why an amiable smile of incredulity plays about their lips when we men, with our pedantic conceit, expatiate on our logical achievements, our neat universal categories of objective and subjective, our provision of drawers and pigeon-holes for thought, which makes our brain resemble an apothecary's shop—in one drawer reason, in a second understanding, in the third wit, in the fourth false wit, and in the fifth nothing at all—that is to say, the Idea.

REISEBILDER

CHAPTER I

She was lovable, and he loved her. But he was not lovable,
and she did not love him.—*Old Play*.

MADAME, do you know the old play? It is quite an extraordinary play, only a little too melancholy. I once played the
leading part in it myself, so that all the ladies wept; only one
did not weep, not even a single tear, and that was the point of
the whole play, the whole catastrophe.

Oh, that single tear! it still torments my thoughts. When
Satan wishes to ruin my soul, he hums in my ear a ballad of
that unwept tear, a deadly song with a more deadly tune.
Ah! such a tune is only heard in hell!

You can readily form an idea, madame, of what life is like in
heaven, the more readily as you are married. There people
amuse themselves altogether superbly, every sort of entertain-
ment is provided, and one lives in mere desire and delight.
One eats from morning to night, and the cookery is as good as
Jagor's; roast geese fly round with gravy-boats in their bills,
and feel flattered if any one eats them; tarts gleaming with
butter grow wild like sunflowers; everywhere there are brooks
of *bouillon* and champagne, everywhere trees on which napkins
flutter, and you eat and wipe your lips and eat again without
injury to your stomach; you sing psalms, or flirt and joke with
the dear, delicate little angels, or take a walk on the green
Hallelujah-Meadow, and your white flowing garments fit very
comfortably, and nothing disturbs the feeling of blessedness,
no pain, no vexation—even when one accidentally treads on
another's corns and exclaims, '*Excusez!*' he smiles as if enraptured, and assures, 'Thy foot, brother, did not hurt in the
least; quite *au contraire*, a deeper thrill of heavenly rapture
shoots through my heart!'

But of hell, madame, you have no idea. Of all the devils
you know, perhaps, only the little Amor, the pretty *croupier* of
hell, Beelzebub, and you know him only from *Don Juan*, and
doubtless think that for such a betrayer of innocence hell can
never be made hot enough, though our praiseworthy theatre

directors spend upon him as much flame, fiery rain, powder, and colophony as any Christian could desire in hell.

But things in hell look much worse than our theatre directors know, or they would not bring out so many bad plays. For in hell it is infernally hot, and when I was there, in the dog-days, it was past endurance. Madame, you can have no idea of hell! We have very few official returns from that place. Still, it is rank calumny to say that down there all the poor souls are compelled to read, the whole day long, all the dull sermons that are printed on earth. Bad as hell is, it has not come to that; Satan will never invent such refinements of torture. On the other hand, Dante's description is too mild on the whole, too poetic. Hell appeared to me like a great kitchen, with an endlessly long stove, on which stood three rows of iron pots, and in these sat the damned, and were cooked. In one row were placed Christian sinners, and, incredible as it may seem, their number was anything but small, and the devils poked the fire up under them with especial good-will. In the next row were Jews, who continually screamed and cried, and were occasionally mocked by the fiends, which sometimes seemed very amusing, as, for instance, when a fat, wheezy old pawnbroker complained of the heat, and a little devil poured several buckets of cold water on his head, that he might realize what a refreshing benefit baptism was. In the third row sat the heathen, who, like the Jews, could take no part in salvation, and must burn for ever. I heard one of these, as a burly devil put fresh coals under his kettle, cry out from his pot: 'Spare me! I was Socrates, the wisest of mortals. I taught Truth and Justice, and sacrificed my life for Virtue.' But the stupid, burly devil went on with his work, and grumbled: 'Oh, shut up, there! All heathens must burn, and we can't make an exception for the sake of a single man.' I assure you, madame, the heat was terrible, with such a screaming, sighing, groaning, quacking, grunting, squealing—and through all these terrible sounds rang distinctly the deadly tune of the song of the unwept tear.

CHAPTER II

MADAME! that old play is a tragedy, though the hero in it is neither killed nor commits suicide. The eyes of the heroine are beautiful — very beautiful — madame, do you smell the perfume of violets?—very beautiful, and yet so piercing that they struck like poniards of glass through my heart and probably came out through my back—and yet I was not killed by those treacherous, murderous eyes. The voice of the heroine was also sweet—madame, did you hear a nightingale just then?—a soft, silken voice, a sweet web of the sunniest tones, and my soul was entangled in it, and choked and tormented itself. I myself—it is the Count of the Ganges who now speaks, and the story goes on in Venice—I myself soon had enough of these tortures, and had thoughts of putting an end to the play in the first act, and of shooting myself through the head, fool's-cap and all. I went to a fancy shop in the Via Burstah, where I saw a pair of beautiful pistols in a case—I remember them perfectly well—near them stood many pleasant playthings of mother-of-pearl and gold, steel hearts on gilt chains, porcelain cups with delicate devices, and snuff-boxes with pretty pictures, such as the divine history of Susannah, the Swan Song of Leda, the Rape of the Sabines, Lucretia, a fat, virtuous creature, with naked bosom, in which she was lazily sticking a dagger; the late Bethmann, *la belle Ferronière* —all enrapturing faces—but I bought the pistols without much ado, and then I bought balls, then powder, and then I went to the restaurant of Signor Somebody, and ordered oysters and a glass of hock.

I could eat nothing, and still less could I drink. The warm tears fell in the glass, and in that glass I saw my dear home, the holy, blue Ganges, the ever-gleaming Himalaya, the giant banyan woods, amid whose broad arcades calmly wandered wise elephants and white-robed pilgrims; strange dream-like flowers gazed on me with meaning glance, wondrous golden birds sang wildly, flashing sun-rays and the sweet, silly chatter of monkeys pleasantly mocked me, from far pagodas sounded the pious prayers of priests, and amid all rang the melting, wailing voice of the Sultana of Delhi—she ran impetuously around in her carpeted chamber, she tore her silver veil, with her peacock fan she struck the black slave to the ground, she wept, she raged, she cried. I could not, however, hear what she said; the restaurant of Signor Somebody is three thousand miles distant from the Harem of Delhi, besides the fair sultana had been dead three thousand years—and I quickly drank up the wine, the clear, joy-giving wine, and yet my soul grew darker and sadder—I was condemned to death.

As I left the restaurant I heard the 'bell of poor sinners' ring, a crowd of people swept by me; but I placed myself at the corner of the Strada San Giovanni, and recited the following monologue:

In ancient tales they tell of golden castles,
Where harps are sounding, lovely ladies dance,
And gay attendants gleam, and jessamine,
Myrtle, and roses spread their soft perfume—
And yet a single word of sad enchantment
Sweeps all the glory of the scene to naught,
And there remain but ruins old and grey,
And screaming birds of night and foul morass.
Even so have I, with but a single word,
Enchanted Nature's blooming loveliness.
There lies she now, lifeless and cold and pale,
Just like a monarch's corse laid out in state,
The royal deathly cheeks fresh stained with rouge,
And in his hand the kingly sceptre laid,
Yet still his lips are yellow and most changed,
For they forgot to dye them, as they should,
And mice are jumping o'er the monarch's nose,
And mock the golden sceptre in his grasp.

It is everywhere agreed, madame, that one should deliver a soliloquy before shooting himself. Most men, on such occasions, use Hamlet's 'To be, or not to be.' It is an excellent passage, and I would gladly have quoted it—but charity begins at home, and when a man has written tragedies himself, in which such farewell-to-life speeches occur, as, for instance, in my immortal *Almansor*, it is very natural that one should prefer his own words even to Shakespeare's. At any rate, the delivery of such speeches is a very useful custom; one gains at least a little time. And so it came to pass that I remained a rather long time standing at the corner of the Strada San Giovanni—and as I stood there like a condemned criminal awaiting death, I raised my eyes, and suddenly beheld *her*.

She wore her blue silk dress and rose-red hat, and her eyes looked at me so mildly, so death-conqueringly, so life-givingly—madame, you well know, out of Roman history, that when the vestals in ancient Rome met on their way a malefactor led to death, they had the right to pardon him, and the poor rogue lived. With a single glance she saved me from death, and I stood before her revived, and dazzled by the sunbeams of her beauty, and she passed on—and left me alive.

CHAPTER III

And she left me alive, and I live, which is the main point.

Others may, if they choose, enjoy the good fortune of having their lady love adorn their graves with garlands and water them

with the tears of fidelity. O women! hate me, laugh at me,
jilt me—but let me live! Life is all too laughably sweet, and
the world too delightfully bewildered; it is the dream of an
intoxicated god, who has taken French leave of the carousing
multitude of immortals, and has laid himself down to sleep in
a solitary star, and knows not himself that he creates all that
he dreams—and the dream images form themselves in such a
mad variegated fashion, and often so harmoniously reasonable
—the Iliad, Plato, the battle of Marathon, Moses, Medicean
Venus, Strasburg Cathedral, the French Revolution, Hegel,
the steamboat, etc., are single good thoughts in this divine
dream—but it will not last long, and the god awakes and rubs
his sleepy eyes, and smiles—and our world has run to nothing
—yes, has never been.

No matter! I live. If I am but a shadowy image in a dream,
still this is better than the cold, black, void annihilation of
death. Life is the greatest good and death the worst evil.
Berlin lieutenants of the guard may sneer and call it cowardice,
because the Prince of Homburg shudders when he beholds his
open grave. Henry Kleist had, however, as much courage as
his high-breasted, tightly-laced colleagues, and has, alas! proved
it. But all strong men love life. Goethe's Egmont does not
part willingly from 'the cheerful wont of being and working.'
Immerman's Edwin clings to life 'like a little child to its mother's
breast,' and though he finds it hard to live by stranger mercy,
he still begs for mercy: 'For life and breath is still the highest.'

.   .   .   .   .   .

CHAPTER IV

BUT a day will come when the fire in my veins will be quenched,
when winter will dwell in my heart, when his snowflakes will
whiten my locks, and his mists will dim my eyes. Then my
friends will lie in their lonely graves, and I alone shall remain
like a solitary stalk forgotten by the reaper. A new race will
have sprung up with new desires and new ideas; full of wonder
I shall hear new names and listen to new songs, for the old names
will be forgotten, and I myself forgotten, perhaps still honoured
by a few, scorned by many and loved by none! And then the
rosy-cheeked boys will spring around me and place the old harp
in my trembling hand, and say, laughing: 'You have been long
silent, you greybeard; sing us again songs of your youthful
dreams!'

Then I will grasp the harp, and my old joys and sorrows will awake, tears will again spring from my dead eyes; there will be spring again in my breast, sweet tones of sorrow will tremble on the harpstrings, I shall see again the blue stream and the marble palaces and the lovely faces of women and girls—and I will sing a song of the flowers of Brenta.

It will be my last song; the stars will gaze on me as in the nights of my youth, the loving moonlight will once more kiss my cheeks, the spirit chorus of nightingales long dead will sound from afar, my sleep-drunken eyes will close, my soul will echo with the notes of my harp; I shall smell the flowers of Brenta.

A tree will shadow my grave. I would gladly have it a palm, but that tree will not grow in the north. It will be a linden, and on summer evenings lovers will sit there and caress; the greenfinch, who rocks himself on the branches, will be listening silently, and my linden will rustle tenderly over the heads of the happy ones, who will be so happy that they will have no time to read what is written on the white tombstone. But when later the lover has lost his love, then he will come again to the well-known linden, and sigh, and weep, and gaze long and oft upon the stone, and read the inscription: 'He loved the flowers of Brenta.'

CHAPTER V

MADAME! I have deceived you. I am not the Count of the Ganges. Never in my life have I seen the holy stream, nor the lotus flowers which are mirrored in its sacred waves. Never did I lie dreaming under Indian palms, nor in prayer before the Diamond Deity Juggernaut, who with his diamonds might have easily aided me out of my difficulties. I have no more been in Calcutta than the turkey, of which I ate yesterday at dinner, had ever been in the realms of the Grand Turk. Yet my ancestors came from Hindustan, and therefore I feel so much at my ease in the great forest of song of Valmiki. The heroic sorrows of the divine Ramo move my heart like familiar griefs; from the flower lays of Kalidasa the sweetest memories bloom; and when a few years ago a gentle lady in Berlin showed me the beautiful pictures which her father, who had been governor in India, had brought from thence, the delicately painted, holy, calm faces seemed as familiar to me as though I were gazing at my own family gallery.

Franz Bopp—madame, you have, of course, read his *Nalus*

and his *System of Sanscrit Conjugations*—gave me much information relative to my ancestry, and I now know with certainty
that I am descended from Brahma's head, and not from his
corns. I have also good reason to believe that the entire
Mahabharata, with its two hundred thousand verses, is merely
an allegorical love letter which my first forefather wrote to my
first foremother. Oh! they loved dearly, their souls kissed, they
kissed with their eyes, they were both but one single kiss.

An enchanted nightingale sits on a red coral bough in the
silent sea, and sings a song of the love of my ancestors; the
pearls gaze eagerly from their shells, the wonderful water-
flowers tremble with sorrow, the cunning sea-snails, bearing on
their backs many-coloured porcelain towers, come creeping
onwards, the ocean-roses blush with shame, the yellow, sharp-
pointed starfish and the thousand-hued glassy jelly-fish quiver
and stretch, and all swarm and listen.

Unfortunately, madame, this nightingale song is far too long
to be set down here; it is as long as the world itself, even its
dedication to Anangas, the God of Love, is as long as all Scott's
novels, and there is a passage referring to it in Aristophanes,
which in German reads thus:

> Tiotio, tiotio, tiotinx,
> Totototo totototo tototinx.
> —Voss's Translation.

No, I was not born in India. I first beheld the light of the
world on the shores of that beautiful stream, in whose green
hills folly grows and is plucked in autumn, laid away in cellars,
poured into barrels, and exported to foreign lands. In fact,
only yesterday I heard someone speaking a piece of folly which
in the year 1811, was imprisoned in a bunch of grapes, which
I myself then saw growing on the Johannisburg. But much
folly is also consumed at home, and men are the same there as
everywhere: they are born, eat, drink, sleep, laugh, cry, slander
each other, are greatly troubled about the propagation of their
race, try to seem what they are not and to do what they cannot, never shave until they have a beard, and often have beards
before they get discretion, and when they at last have discretion,
they drink it away in white and red folly.

Mon dieu ! if I had faith, so that I could remove mountains—
the Johannisburg would be just the mountain which I would
carry with me everywhere. But as my faith is not strong
enough, imagination must aid me, and she quickly sets me by
the beautiful Rhine.

Oh, that is a fair land, full of loveliness and sunshine. In the blue stream are mirrored the mountain shores, with their ruined towers, and woods, and ancient towns. There, before the house door, sit the good townspeople, of a summer evening, and drink out of great cans, and gossip confidentially about how the wine—the Lord be praised!—thrives, and how justice should be free from all secrecy, and how Marie Antoinette's being guillotined is none of our business, and how dear the tobacco tax makes tobacco, and how all mankind are equal, and what a glorious fellow Goerres is.

I have never troubled myself about such conversation, and sat rather with the maidens in the arched window, and laughed at their laughter, and let them throw flowers in my face, and pretended to be ill-natured until they told me their secrets, or some other important stories. Fair Gertrude was half wild with delight when I sat by her. She was a girl like a flaming rose, and once, as she fell on my neck, I thought that she would burn away into perfume in my arms. Fair Katharine flamed into sweet music when she talked with me, and her eyes were of a pure, internal blue, which I have never seen in men or animals, and very seldom in flowers—one gazed so gladly into them, and could then think such sweet things. But the beautiful Hedwig loved me, for when I came to her she bowed her head till her black curls fell down over her blushing face, and her bright eyes shone like stars from the dark heaven. Her bashful lips spoke not a word, and I too could say nothing to her. I coughed and she trembled. She often begged me, through her sisters, not to climb the rocks so rashly, or to bathe in the Rhine when I was hot with running or drinking wine. Once I overheard her pious prayer before the Virgin Mary, which she had adorned with gold leaf and illuminated with a lamp, and which stood in a corner at the entrance. I plainly heard her pray to the Mother of God to keep him from climbing, drinking, and bathing. I should certainly have been desperately in love with her if she had been indifferent to me, and I was indifferent to her because I knew that she loved me. —Madame, to win my love, I must be treated *en canaille*.

Johanna was the cousin of the three sisters, and I was glad to be with her. She knew the most beautiful old legends, and when she pointed with her white hand through the window out to the mountains where all had happened which she narrated, I became enchanted; the old knights rose visibly from the ruined castles and hewed away at each other's iron clothes, the Lorelei sat again on the mountain summit, singing a-down her sweet, seductive song, and the Rhine rippled so reasonably soothing—and yet so mockingly horrible—and the fair Johanna looked at me so strangely, with such enigmatic tenderness, that she seemed herself one with the legend that she told. She was a slender, pale girl, sickly and musing, her eyes were clear as truth itself, her lips piously arched, in her face lay a great story—was it a love legend? I know not, and I never had the courage to ask. When I looked at her long, I grew calm and cheerful—it seemed to me as though it were Sunday in my heart and the angels held service there.

In such happy hours I told her tales of my childhood, and she listened earnestly, and, strangely, when I could not think of the names she remembered them. When I then asked her with wonder how she knew the names, she would answer with a smile that she had learned it of the birds that had built a nest on the sill of her window—and she tried to make me believe that these were the same birds which I once bought with my pocket-money from a hard-hearted peasant boy, and then let fly away. But I believed that she knew everything because she was so pale, and really soon died. She knew, too, when she would die, and wished that I would leave Andernach the day before. When I bade her farewell she gave me both her hands—they were white, sweet hands, and pure as the Host—and she said: 'You are very good, and when you are not, think of the little dead Veronica.

Did the chattering birds also tell her this name? Often in hours of remembrance I had wearied my brain in trying to think of that dear name, but could not.

And now that I have it again, my earliest infancy shall bloom into memory again—and I am again a child, and play with other children in the castle court at Düsseldorf on the Rhine.

CHAPTER VI

YES, madame, there was I born, and I am particular in calling attention to the fact, lest after my death seven cities—those of Schilda, Krähwinkel, Polkwitz, Bockum, Dülken, Göttingen, and Schöppenstadt—should contend for the honour of being my birthplace. Düsseldorf is a town on the Rhine; sixteen thousand people live there, and many hundred thousands besides are buried there. And among them are many of whom my mother says it were better if they were still alive—for example, my grandfather and my uncle, the old Herr von Geldern, and the young Herr von Geldern, who were both such celebrated doctors, and saved the lives of so many men, and yet must both die themselves. And pious Ursula, who carried me as a child in her arms, also lies buried there, and a rose-bush grows over her grave—she loved rose-perfume so much in her life, and her heart was all rose-perfume and goodness. And the shrewd old Canonicus also lies there buried. Lord, how miserable he looked when I last saw him! He consisted of nothing but soul and plasters, and yet he studied night and day as though he feared lest the worms might find a few ideas missing in his head. Little William also lies there—and that is my fault. We were schoolmates in the Franciscan cloister, and were one day playing on that side of the building where the Düssel flows between stone walls, and I said: 'William, do get the kitten out which has just fallen in!' and he cheerfully climbed out on the board which stretched over the brook, and pulled the cat out of the water, but fell in himself, and when they took him out he was cold and dead. The kitten lived to a good old age.

The town of Düsseldorf is very beautiful, and if you think of it when in foreign lands, and happen at the same time to have been born there, strange feelings come over the soul. I was born there, and feel as if I must go directly home. And when I say *home*, I mean the Volkerstrasse and the house where I was born. This house will be some day very remarkable, and I have sent word to the old lady who owns it, that she must not for her life sell it. For the whole house she would now hardly get as much as the present which the green-veiled distinguished English ladies will give the servant when she shows them the room where I was born, and the hen-house wherein my father generally imprisoned me for stealing grapes, and also the brown door on which my mother taught me to write with chalk. Ah me! should I ever become a famous author, it has cost my poor mother trouble enough.

But my fame still slumbers in the marble quarries of Carrara; the waste-paper laurel with which they have bedecked my brow has not yet spread its perfume through the wide world, and when the green-veiled distinguished English ladies visit Düsseldorf, they leave the celebrated house unvisited, and go direct to the market place, and there gaze on the colossal black equestrian statue which stands in its midst. This represents the Prince Elector, Jan Wilhelm. He wears black armour and a long, hanging wig. When a boy, I was told that the artist who made this statue observed with terror while it was being cast that he had not metal enough, and then all the citizens of the town came running with all their silver spoons, and threw them in to fill the mould; and I often stood for hours before the statue puzzling my head as to how many spoons were sticking in it, and how many apple-tarts all that silver would buy. Apple-tarts were then my passion—now it is love, truth, freedom, and crab-soup—and not far from the statue of the Prince Elector, at the theatre corner, generally stood a curiously constructed sabre-legged rascal with a white apron, and a basket girt around him full of smoking apple-tarts, which he knew how to praise with an irresistible treble voice. 'Apple tarts! quite fresh! so delicious!' Truly, whenever in my later years the Evil One sought to win me, he always cried in just such an enticing treble, and I should certainly have never remained twelve hours with the Signora Giulietta, if she had not thrilled me with her sweet, fragrant, apple-tart-tones. And, in fact, the apple-tarts would never have so enticed me, if the crooked Hermann had not covered them up so mysteriously with his white apron—and it is aprons, you know, which—but I wander from the subject. I was speaking of the equestrian statue which has so many silver spoons in its body and no soup, and which represents the Prince Elector, Jan Wilhelm.

He must have been a brave gentleman, very fond of art, and skilful himself. He founded the picture gallery in Düsseldorf, and in the observatory there they show a very artistic piece of woodwork, which he, himself, had carved in his leisure hours, of which latter he had every day four-and-twenty.

In those days princes were not the persecuted wretches that they now are; their crowns grew firmly on their heads, and at night they drew their night-caps over them and slept peacefully, and their people slumbered peacefully at their feet, and when they awoke in the morning, they said: 'Good morning, father!' and they replied: 'Good morning, dear children!'

But there came a sudden change over all this. One morning when we awoke in Düsseldorf and would say, 'Good morning, father!' the father had travelled away, and in the whole town there was nothing but dumb sorrow. Everywhere there was a funeral-like expression, and people slipped silently to the market and read the long paper on the door of the town hall. It was bad weather, yet the lean tailor, Kilian, stood in his nankeen jacket, which he generally wore only at home, and his blue woollen stockings hung down so that his little bare legs peeped out in a troubled way, and his thin lips quivered as he murmured the placard. An old invalid soldier from the Palatine read it rather louder, and at some words a clear tear ran down his white honourable old moustache. I stood near him, crying too, and asked why we were crying. And he replied: 'The Prince Elector has abdicated.' And then he read further, and at the words, 'for the long manifested fidelity of my subjects,' 'and hereby release you from allegiance,' he wept still more. It is a strange sight to see, when an old man, in faded uniform, and scarred veteran's face, suddenly bursts into tears. While we read, the Princely Electoral coat of arms was being taken down from the town hall, and everything began to appear as anxiously dreary as though we were waiting for an eclipse of the sun. The town councillors went about at an abdicating, wearisome gait; even the omnipotent beadle looked as though he had no more commands to give, and stood calmly indifferent, although the crazy Aloysius stood upon one leg and chattered the names of French generals with foolish grimaces, while the tipsy, crooked Gumpertz rolled around in the gutter, singing *ça ira! ça ira!*

But I went home crying and lamenting: 'The Prince Elector has abdicated.' My mother might do what she would, I knew what I knew, and went crying to bed, and in the night dreamed that the world had come to an end—the fair flower gardens and green meadows of the world were taken up and rolled away like carpets from the floor, the beadle climbed up on a high ladder and took down the sun, and the tailor Kilian stood by and said to himself: 'I must go home and dress myself neatly, for I am dead and am to be buried this afternoon.' And it grew darker and darker—a few stars glimmered on high, and even these fell down like yellow leaves in autumn, men gradually vanished, and I, poor child, wandered in anguish around, until before the willow fence of a deserted farmhouse I saw a man digging up the earth with a spade, and near him an ugly, spiteful-looking woman, who held something in her apron like a human head, but it was the moon, and she laid it carefully in the open grave —and behind me stood the Palatine soldier sobbing, and spelling: 'The Prince Elector has abdicated.'

When I awoke the sun shone as usual through the window, there was a sound of drums in the street, and as I entered our sitting-room and wished my father—who sat in his white dressing-gown—good morning, I heard the little light-footed barber, as he made up his hair, narrate very minutely that homage

would that morning be offered at the town hall to the Archduke
Joachim. I heard, too, that the new ruler was of excellent
family, that he had married the sister of the Emperor Napoleon,
and was really a very respectable man, that he wore his beautiful
black hair in curls, that he would shortly enter the town, and
would certainly please all the ladies. Meanwhile, the drumming
in the streets continued, and I stood before the house-door and
looked at the French troops marching, those joyous and famous
people who swept over the world, singing and playing, the merry,
serious faces of the grenadiers, the bearskin shakos, the tri-
coloured cockades, the glittering bayonets, the *voltigeurs* full
of vivacity and *point d'honneur*, and the giant-like silver-laced
tambour-major, who cast his baton with the gilded head as
high as the first story, and his eyes to the second, where pretty
girls gazed from the windows. I was so glad that soldiers
were to be quartered in our house—my mother was not glad—
and I hastened to the market-place. There everything looked
changed; it was as though the world had been new white-washed.
A new coat of arms was placed on the town hall, its iron
balconies were hung with embroidered velvet drapery, French
grenadiers stood as sentinels, the old town councillors had put
on new faces and Sunday coats, and looked at each other French
fashion, and said, '*Bon jour!*' ladies peeped from every window,
inquisitive citizens and soldiers filled the square, and I, with
other boys, climbed on the shining Prince Elector's great
bronze horse, and looked down on the motley crowd.

Neighbour Peter and Long Conrad nearly broke their necks
on this occasion, and that would have been well, for the one
afterwards ran away from his parents, enlisted as a soldier,
deserted, and was finally shot in Mayence; while the other,
having made geographical researches in strange pockets, became
a working member of a public treadmill institute. But having
broken the iron bands which bound him to his fatherland, he
passed safely beyond sea, and eventually died in London, in
consequence of wearing a much too long cravat, one end of
which happened to be firmly attached to something, just as a
royal official removed a plank from beneath his feet.

Long Conrad told us there was no school to-day on account
of the homage. We had to wait a long time till this was over.
At last the balcony of the council house was filled with gay
gentlemen, flags and trumpets, and our burgomaster, in his
celebrated red coat, delivered an oration, which stretched out
like india-rubber, or like a night-cap into which one has thrown

a stone—only that it was not the stone of wisdom—and I could distinctly understand many of his phrases, for instance, that 'we are now to be made happy'—and at the last words the trumpets and drums sounded, and the flags waved, and the people cried 'Hurrah!'—and as I myself cried 'Hurrah!' I held fast to the old Prince Elector. And that was necessary, for I began to grow giddy; it seemed to me that the people were standing on their heads while the world whizzed around, and the Prince Elector, with his long wig, nodded and whispered, 'Hold fast to me!'—and not till the cannon re-echoed along the wall did I become sobered, and climbed slowly down from the great bronze horse.

As I went home I saw crazy Aloysius again dancing on one leg, while he chattered the names of French generals, and crooked Gumpertz was rolling in the gutter, drunk, and growling *ça ira, ça ira*—and I said to my mother that we were all to be made happy, and so there was no school to-day.

CHAPTER VII

THE next day the world was again all in order, and we had school as before, and things were got by heart as before—the Roman kings, chronology—the *nomina* in *im*, the *verba irregularia*—Greek, Hebrew, geography, German, mental arithmetic —Lord! my head is still giddy with it!—all must be learnt by heart. And much of it was eventually to my advantage. For had I not learnt the Roman kings by heart, it would subsequently have been a matter of perfect indifference to me whether Niebuhr had or had not proved that they never really existed. And had I not learnt chronology, how could I ever, in later years, have found out any one in Berlin, where one house is as like another as drops of water, or as grenadiers, and where it is impossible to find a friend unless you have the number of his house in your head. Therefore I associated with every friend some historical event which had happened in a year corresponding to the number of his house, so that the one recalled the other, and some curious point in history always occurred to me whenever I met an acquaintance. For instance, when I met my tailor I at once thought of the Battle of Marathon; if I saw the well-dressed banker, Christian Gumpel, I remembered the destruction of Jerusalem; if a Portuguese friend, deeply in debt, the flight of Mahomet; if the university judge, a man whose probity is well known, the death of

Haman; and if Wadzeck, I was at once reminded of Cleopatra. *Ach, lieber Himmel!* the poor creature is dead now, our tears are dry, and we may say of her, with Hamlet: 'Take her for all in all, she was a hag—we oft shall look upon her like again!' As I said, chronology is necessary. I know men who have nothing in their heads but a few years, yet who know exactly where to look for the right houses, and are, moreover, regular professors. But oh, the trouble I had at school with dates!—and it went even worse with arithmetic. I understood *subtraction* best, and for this I had a very practical rule—'four from three won't go, I must borrow one'—but I advise every one, in such a case, to borrow a few extra shillings, for one never knows.

But as for the Latin, madame, you can really have no idea how muddled it is. The Romans would never have found time to conquer the world if they had been obliged first to learn Latin. Those happy people knew in their cradles the nouns with an accusative in *im*. I, on the contrary, had to learn them by heart, in the sweat of my brow, but still it is well that I knew them. For if, for example, when I publicly disputed in Latin in the college hall of Göttingen, on the 20th of July 1825—madame, it was well worth while to hear it—if, I say, I had said *sinapem* instead of *sinapim*, the blunder would have been evident to the freshmen, and an endless shame for me.

. . . . . .

I will say nothing of Greek; I should irritate myself too much. The monks of the Middle Ages were not so very much in the wrong when they asserted that Greek was an invention of the Devil. Lord knows what I suffered through it. It went better with Hebrew, for I always had a great predilection for the Jews, although they to this very hour have crucified my good name; but I never could get so far in Hebrew as my watch, which had an intimate intercourse with pawnbrokers, and in consequence acquired many Jewish habits—for instance, it would not go on Saturday—and learned the holy language, and was subsequently occupied with its grammar, for often when sleepless in the night I have to my amazement heard it industriously repeating: *katal, katalta, katalki—kittel, kittalta, kittalti—pokat, pokadeti—pikat—pik—pik.*

Meanwhile I learned much more German, and that is not such child's play. For we poor Germans, who have already been sufficiently plagued with soldiers quartered on us, military duties, poll-taxes, and a thousand other exactions, must needs, over and above all this, torment each other with accusatives and datives. I learned much German from the old Rector Schallmeyer, a brave, clerical gentleman, whose protégé I was from childhood. Something of the matter I also learned from Professor Schramm, a man who had written a book on eternal peace, and in whose class my schoolfellows fought with especial vigour.

.   .   .   .   .   .

But I succeeded best of all in the French class of the Abbé d'Aulnoi, a French *émigré* who had written a number of grammars, and wore a red wig, and jumped about very nervously when he recited his *Art poétique*, and his *Histoire allemande*. He was the only one in the whole gymnasium who taught German history. Still, French has its difficulties, and to learn it there must be much quartering of troops, much drumming in, much *apprendre par cœur*, and, above all, no one should be a *bête allemande*. Thus many bitter words came in. I remember still, as though it happened yesterday, the scrapes I got into through *la religion*. Six times came the question: 'Henry, what is the French for "faith"?' And six times, ever more tearfully, I replied: 'It is called *le crédit*.' And at the seventh question, with a deep cherry-red face, my furious examiner cried: 'It is called *la religion*'—and there was a rain of blows, and all my schoolfellows laughed. Madame!—since that day I can never hear the word *religion* but my back turns pale with terror, and my cheeks red with shame. And to speak truly, *le crédit* has during my life stood me in better stead than *la religion*. It occurs to me at this moment that I still owe the landlord of the 'Lion,' in Bologna, five thalers. And I pledge you my word of honour that I would owe him five thalers more if I could only be certain that I should never again hear that unlucky word, *la religion*.

Parbleu, madame! I have succeeded well in French! I understand not only *patois*, but even aristocratic nurse-maid French. Not long ago, when in noble society, I understood full one-half of the conversation of two German countesses, each of whom could count at least sixty-four years, and as many ancestors. Yes, in the Café Royal in Berlin, I once heard Monsieur Hans Michel Martens talking French, and understood every word, though there was no understanding in it. We must know the spirit of a language, and this is best learned by drumming. *Parbleu !* how much do I not owe to the French drummer who was so long quartered in our house, who looked like a devil, and yet had the heart of an angel, and who drummed so excellently.

He was a little, nervous figure, with a terrible black moustache, beneath which the red lips turned suddenly outwards, while his fiery eyes glanced around.

I, a youngster, stuck to him like a burr, and helped him to rub his military buttons like mirrors, and to pipe-clay his vest —for Monsieur Le Grand liked to look well—and I followed him to the watch, to the roll-call, to the parade—in those times there was nothing but the gleam of weapons and merriment— *les jours de fête sont passés !* Monsieur Le Grand knew only a little broken German, only the chief expressions: 'Bread,' 'kiss,' 'honour,' but he could make himself very intelligible with his drum. For instance, if I did not know what the word *liberté* meant, he drummed the *Marseillaise*—and I understood him. If I did not understand the word *égalité*, he drummed the march, *Ça ira, . . . les aristocrats à la lanterne!'* and I understood him. If I did not know what *bêtise* meant, he drummed the *Dessauer March,* which we Germans, as Goethe also declares, have drummed in Champagne—and I understood him. He once wanted to explain to me the word *l'Allemagne,* and he drummed the all too simple primeval melody, which on market-days is played to dancing dogs—namely *dum—dum—dum.* I was vexed, but I understood him.

In the same way he taught me modern history. I did not understand the words, it is true, but as he constantly drummed while speaking, I knew what he meant. At bottom this is the best method. The history of the storming of the Bastille, of the Tuileries, and the like, we understand first when we know how the drumming was done. In our school compendiums of history we merely read: 'Their excellencies, the baron and count, with the most noble spouses of the aforesaid, were beheaded. Their highnesses the dukes, and princes, with the most noble spouses of the aforesaid, were beheaded. His majesty the king, with his most sublime spouse, the queen, was beheaded.' But when you hear the red guillotine march drummed, you understand it correctly, for the first time, and you know the how and why. Madame, that is indeed a wonderful march! It thrilled through marrow and bone when I first heard it, and I was glad that I forgot it. One forgets so much as one grows older, and a young man has nowadays so much other knowledge to keep in his head—whist, boston, genealogical tables, parliamentary data, dramaturgy, the liturgy, carving — and yet, notwithstanding all jogging up of my brain, I could not for a long time recall that tremendous tune! But, only think, madame! not long ago I sat at table with a whole menagerie of counts, princes, princesses, chamberlains, court-marshallesses, seneschals, upper court mistresses, court-keepers-of-the-royal-plate, court-hunters' wives, and whatever else these aristocratic domestics are termed, and their under-domestics ran about behind their chairs and shoved full plates before their mouths —but I, who was passed by and neglected, sat without the least occupation for my jaws, and I kneaded little bread-balls, and drummed for ennui with my fingers—and, to my astonishment, I suddenly drummed the red, long-forgotten guillotine march!

'And what happened?' Madame, the good people were not disturbed in their eating, nor did they know that other people, when they have nothing to eat, suddenly begin to drum, and that, too, very queer marches, which people thought long forgotten.

But to return to our muttons, I listened to international law in the lecture-room of the Herr Privy Councillor Schmaltz, and it was a sleepy summer afternoon, and I sat on the bench and heard less and less—my head had gone to sleep —when all at once I was wakened by the noise of my own feet, which had stayed awake, and had probably observed that the exact opposite of international law and constitutional tendencies was being preached, and my feet which, with the little eyes of their corns, had seen more of how things go in the world than the privy councillor with his Juno-eyes—these poor dumb feet, incapable of expressing their immeasurable meaning by words, strove to make themselves intelligible by drumming, and they drummed so loudly that I thereby nearly came to grief.

Cursed, unreflecting feet! They once played me a similar trick, when I on a time in Göttingen sponged without subscribing on the lectures of Professor Saalfeld, and as, with his angular activity, he jumped about here and there in his pulpit, and heated himself in order to curse the Emperor Napoleon in regular set style—no, my poor feet, I cannot blame you for drumming then; indeed, I would not have blamed you if in your dumb naïveté you had expressed yourselves by still more energetic movements. How could I, the scholar of Le Grand, hear the Emperor cursed? The Emperor! the Emperor! the great Emperor!

When I think of the great Emperor, my thoughts again grow summer-green and golden; a long avenue of lindens rises blooming around, on the leafy twigs sit singin gnightingales, the waterfall rustles, flowers are growing from full round beds, dreamily nodding their fair heads—I was once wondrously intimate with them; the rouged tulips, proud as beggars, condescendingly greeted me, the nervous sick lilies nodded with melancholy tenderness, the drunken red roses laughed at me from afar, the night-violets sighed — with the myrtles and laurels I was not then acquainted, for they did not entice with a shining bloom, but the mignonette, with whom I now stand so badly, was very intimate. I am speaking of the court garden of Düsseldorf, where I often lay upon the bank, and piously listened while Monsieur Le Grand told of the warlike feats of the great Emperor, beating meanwhile the marches which were drummed during the deeds, so that I saw and heard all to the life. I saw the passage over the Simplon—the Emperor in advance and his brave grenadiers climbing on behind him, while the scream of frightened birds of prey sounded around, and avalanches thundered in the distance—I saw the Emperor with flag in hand on the bridge of Lodi—I saw the Emperor in his grey cloak at Marengo—I saw the Emperor mounted in the battle of the Pyramids—naught around save powder-smoke and mamelukes—I saw the Emperor in the battle of Austerlitz —ha! how the bullets whistled over the smooth, icy road!— I saw, I heard the battle of Jena—*dum, dum, dum*—I saw, I heard the battles of Eylau, of Wagram——ah, I could hardly bear it! Monsieur Le Grand drummed so that the drums of my ears nearly burst.

CHAPTER VIII

But what were my feelings when I saw with my own highly-graced eyes himself? Hosanna! the Emperor!

It was in that very avenue of the court garden at Düsseldorf. As I pressed through the gaping crowd, thinking of the doughty deeds and battles which Monsieur Le Grand had drummed to me, my heart beat the 'general march'—yet at the same time I thought of the police regulation, that no one should dare ride through the avenue under penalty of a fine of five thalers. And the Emperor with his retinue rode directly down the avenue. The trembling trees bowed towards him as he advanced, the sunbeams quivered, frightened, yet curious, through the green leaves, and in the blue heaven above there swam visibly a golden star. The Emperor wore his invisible-green uniform and the little world-renowned hat. He rode a white steed, which stepped with such calm pride, so confidently, so nobly—had I then been Crown Prince of Prussia I would have envied that steed. Carelessly, almost lazily, sat the Emperor, holding his reins with one hand, and with the other good-naturedly patting the horse's neck. It was a sunny, marble hand, a mighty hand —one of those two hands which bound fast the many-headed monster of anarchy, and ordered the war of races—and it good-naturedly patted the horse's neck. Even the face had that hue which we find in the marble of Greek and Roman busts; the traits were as nobly cut as in the antique, and on that face was written: 'Thou shalt have no gods before me.' A smile, which warmed and soothed every heart, flitted over the lips— and yet all knew that those lips needed but to whistle—*et la Prusse n'existait plus*—those lips needed but to whistle—and the entire clergy would have stopped their ringing and singing— those lips needed but to whistle—and the entire Holy Roman Empire would have danced. And those lips smiled and the eye smiled too. It was an eye clear as heaven; it could read the hearts of men, it saw at a glance all the things of this world, while we others see them only one by one and by their coloured shadows. The brow was not so clear, the phantoms of future battles were nestling there; there was a quiver which swept over that brow, and those were the creative thoughts, the great seven-mile-boot thoughts, wherewith the spirit of the Emperor strode invisibly over the world—and I believe that every one of those thoughts would have given to a German author full material wherewith to write, all the days of his life.

The Emperor rode quietly straight through the avenue. No policeman opposed him; proudly, on snorting horses and laden with gold and jewels, rode his retinue; the drums were beating, the trumpets were sounding; close to me the wild Aloysius was muttering his general's name; not far away the drunken Gumpertz was grumbling, and the people shouted with a thousand voices: 'Long live the Emperor!'

CHAPTER IX

THE Emperor is dead. On a waste island in the Atlantic ocean is his lonely grave, and he for whom the world was too narrow lies quietly under a little hillock, where five weeping willows hang their green heads, and a little brook, murmuring sorrowfully, ripples by. There is no inscription on his tomb; but Clio, with a just pen, has written thereon invisible words, which will resound, like spirit-tones, through thousands of years.

Britannia! the sea is thine. But the sea has not water enough to wash away the shame with which the death of that Mighty One has covered thee. Not thy windy Sir Hudson—no, thou thyself wert the Sicilian bravo with whom perjured kings bargained, that they might revenge on the man of the people that which the people had once inflicted on one of themselves. —And he was thy guest, and had seated himself by thy hearth.

Until far ages the boys of France will sing and tell of the terrible hospitality of the *Bellerophon*, and when those songs of mockery and tears resound across the Channel, the cheeks of every honourable Briton will blush. Some day, however, this song will ring thither, and Britannia will be no more; the people of pride will be humbled to the earth, Westminster's monuments will be broken, and the royal dust which they enclosed forgotten. —And St. Helena is the Holy Grave, whither the races of the East and of the West will make their pilgrimage in ships with flags of many a colour, and their hearts will grow strong with great memories of the deeds of the worldly Saviour, who suffered and died under Hudson Lowe, as it is written in the evangelists, Las Cases, O'Meara, and Autommarchi.

Strange! A terrible destiny has already overtaken the three greatest enemies of the Emperor. Londonderry has cut his throat, Louis XVIII has rotted away on his throne, and Professor Saalfeld is still professor in Göttingen.

CHAPTER X

On a clear, frosty autumn morning, a young man of student-like appearance slowly loitered through the avenue of the Düsseldorf Court Garden, often, with childlike pleasure, kicking aside the leaves which covered the ground, and often sorrowfully gazing towards the bare trees, on which a few golden-hued leaves still hung. As he thus gazed up, he thought on the words of Glaucus:

Like the leaves in the forests, so are the races of mortals;
Leaves are blown down to the earth by the wind, while others are
    shooting
Again in the green budding wood, when fresh up-liveth the spring-
    tide;
So are the races of man—this grows and the other departeth.

In earlier days the youth had gazed with far different eyes on the same trees. He was then a boy, and sought birds' nests or summer insects, which delighted him as they merrily hummed around, and were glad in the beautiful world, and contented with a sap-green leaf and a drop of water, with a warm sunbeam and the sweet perfumes of the grass. In those times the boy's heart was as gay as the fluttering insects. But now his heart had grown older, its little sunbeams were quenched, all its flowers had faded, even its beautiful dream of love had grown dim; in that poor heart was nothing but pride and care, and, saddest of all, it was my heart.

I had returned that day to my old father-town, but I would not remain there overnight, and I longed for Godesberg, that I might sit at the feet of my girl-friend and tell of the little Veronica. I had visited the dear graves. Of all my living friends I had found but an uncle and an aunt. Even when I met once known forms in the street they knew me no more, and the town itself gazed on me with strange glances. Many houses were coloured anew, strange faces gazed on me through the window-panes, worn-out old sparrows hopped on the old chimneys, everything looked dead and yet fresh, like a salad growing in a graveyard; where French was once spoken I now heard Prussian; even a little Prussian court had taken up its retired dwelling there, and the people bore court titles. My mother's old hairdresser had now become the court-hairdresser, and there were court-tailors, court-shoemakers, court-bedbug-destroyers, court-grogshops—the whole town seemed to be a court-asylum for court-lunatics. Only the old Prince Elector knew me; he still stood in the same old place, but he seemed to have grown thinner. For just because he stood in the market-place, he had had a full view of all the miseries of the time, and people seldom grow fat on such sights. I was in a dream, and thought of the legend of the enchanted city, and hastened out of the gate lest I should awake too soon. I missed many a tree in the court garden, and many had grown crooked with age, and the four great poplars, which once seemed to me like green giants, had become smaller. Pretty girls were walking here and there, dressed as gaily as wandering tulips. And I had known these tulips when they were but little buds; for ah! they were the neighbours' children with whom I had once played 'Princes in the Tower.' But the fair maidens, whom I had once known as blooming roses, were now faded roses, and in many a high brow whose pride had once thrilled my heart, Saturn had cut deep wrinkles with his scythe. And now for the first time, and alas! too late, I understood what those glances meant, which they had once cast on the adolescent boy; for I had meanwhile in other lands fathomed the meaning of similar glances in other lovely eyes. I was deeply moved by the humble bow of a man whom I had once known as wealthy and respectable, and who had since become a beggar. Everywhere in the world we see that men, when they once begin to fall, do so according to Newton's law, ever faster and faster as they descend to misery. One, however, who did not seem to be in the least changed was the little baron, who tripped merrily as of old through the court garden, holding with one hand his left coat-skirt on high, and with the other swinging hither and thither his light cane;—he still had the same genial face as of old, its rosy bloom now somewhat concentrated towards the nose, but he had the same comical hat and the same old queue behind, only that the hairs which peeped from it were now white instead of black. But merry as the old baron seemed, it was still evident that he had suffered much sorrow—his face would fain conceal it, but the white hairs of his queue betrayed him behind his back. Yet the queue itself seemed striving to lie, so merrily did it shake.

I was not weary, but a fancy seized me to sit once more on the wooden bench, on which I had once carved the name of my love. I could hardly discover it there, so many new names were cut around. Ah! once I slept upon this bench, and dreamed of happiness and love. 'Dreams are foam.' And the old games of childhood came again to my memory, and with them old and beautiful stories; but a new treacherous game and a new terrible tale ever resounded through them, and it was the story of two poor souls who were untrue to each other, and went so far in their untruth, that they were at last untrue to the dear God Himself. It is a sad story, and when one has nothing better to do, one can weep over it. Oh, Lord! once the world was so beautiful, and the birds sang Thy eternal praise, and little Veronica looked at me with silent eyes, and we sat by the marble statue before the castle court; on one side lies an old ruined castle, wherein ghosts wander, and at night a headless lady in long, trailing black-silken garments sweeps around, and on the other side is a high, white dwelling, in whose upper rooms gay pictures gleamed beautifully in their golden frames, while below stood thousands of mighty books, which Veronica and I beheld with longing when the good Ursula lifted us up to the window. In later years, when I had become a great boy,

I climbed every day to the very top of the library ladder, and brought down the topmost books, and read in them so long, that finally I feared nothing—least of all ladies without heads —and became so wise that I forgot all the old games and stories and pictures and little Veronica, even her name.

But while I sat upon the old bench in the court garden, and dreamed my way back into the past, there was a sound behind me of the confused voices of men lamenting the ill-fortune of the poor French soldiers, who, having been taken in the Russian war and sent to Siberia, had there been kept prisoners, for many a long year, though peace had been re-established, and who now were returning home. As I looked up, I beheld in reality these orphan children of Fame. Through their tattered uniforms peeped naked misery, deep sorrowing eyes were couched in their desolate faces, and though mangled, weary, and mostly lame, something of the military manner was still visible in their mien. Singularly enough, they were pre-ceded by a drummer who tottered along with a drum, and I shuddered as I recalled the old legend of soldiers, who had fallen in battle, and who by night rising again from their graves on the battle-field, and with the drummer at their head, marched back to their native city. And of them the old ballad sings thus:

> He beat on the drum with might and main,
> To their old night-quarters they go again;
>   Through the lighted street they come;
>   Trallerie—trallerei—trallera,
> They march before Sweetheart's home.
>
> And their bones lie there at break of day,
> As white as tombstones in cold array,
>   And the drummer he goes before;
>   Trallerie—trallerei—trallera,
> And we see them come no more.

Truly the poor French drummer seemed to have risen but half repaired from the grave. He was but a little shadow in a dirty patched grey capote, a dead yellow countenance, with a great moustache which hung down sorrowfully over his faded lips, his eyes were like burnt-out tinder, in which but a few sparks still gleamed, and yet by one of those sparks I recognized Monsieur Le Grand.

He too recognized me and drew me to the turf, and we sat down together as of old, when he taught me French and Modern History on the drum. He had still the well-known old drum, and I could not sufficiently wonder how he had preserved it from Russian plunderers. And he drummed again as of old, but without speaking a word. But though his lips were firmly pressed together, his eyes spoke all the more, flashing fiercely and victoriously as he drummed the old marches. The poplars near us trembled, as again he thundered forth the red guillotine march. And he drummed as before the old war of freedom, the old battles, the deeds of the Emperor, and it seemed as though the drum itself were a living creature which rejoiced to speak out its inner soul. I heard once more the thunder of cannon, the whistling of balls, the riot of battle; I saw once more the death rage of the Guards—the waving flags, again, the Emperor on his steed—but little by little there fell a sad tone in amid the most stirring confusion; sounds rang from the drum, in which the wildest hurrahs and the most fearful grief were mysteriously mingled; it seemed a march of victory and a march of death. Le Grand's eyes opened spiritlike and wide, and I saw in them nothing but a broad white field of ice covered with corpses—it was the battle of Moscow.

I had never thought that the hard old drum could give forth such wailing sounds as Monsieur Le Grand had drawn from it. They were tears which he drummed, and they sounded ever softer and softer, and, like a troubled echo, deep sighs broke from Le Grand's breast. And he became ever more languid and ghostlike; his dry hands trembled, as if from frost; he sat as in a dream, and stirred with his drumstick nothing but the air, and seemed listening to voices far away, and at last he gazed on me with a deep, entreating glance—I understood him—and then his head sank down on the drum.

In this life Monsieur Le Grand never drummed more. And his drum never gave forth another sound; it was not destined to serve the enemies of liberty for their servile roll-calls. I had well understood Le Grand's last entreating glance, and at once drew the sword from my cane, and pierced the drum.

CHAPTER XI

Du sublime au ridicule il n'y a qu'un pas, madame !

But life is in reality so terribly serious, that it would be insupportable without such union of the pathetic and the comic; as our poets well know. The most harrowing forms of human madness Aristophanes exhibits only in the laughing mirror of wit; Goethe only presumes to set forth the fearful pain of thought comprehending its own nothingness in the doggerel of a puppet show; and Shakespeare puts the most deadly lamentation over the misery of the world into the mouth of a fool, who rattles his cap and bells in agony.

They have all learned from the great First Poet, who in his world tragedy in thousands of acts, knows how to carry humour to the highest point, as we see every day. After the departure of the heroes, the clowns and *graciosos* enter with their baubles and wooden swords, and after the bloody scenes of the Revolution there came waddling on the stage the fat Bourbons, with their stale jokes and tender 'legitimate' *bons mots*, and the old noblesse with their starved laughter hopped merrily before them, while behind all swept the pious Capuchins with candles, cross and banners of the Church. Yes, even in the highest pathos of the world tragedy, bits of fun slip in. The desperate republican who, like Brutus, plunged a knife into his heart, perhaps smelt it first to see whether someone had not split a herring with it—and on this great stage of the world all passes exactly the same as on our beggarly boards. On it, too, there are tipsy heroes, kings who forget their part, scenes which obstinately stay up in the air, prompters' voices sounding above everything, danseuses who create astonishing effects with the poetry of their legs, and costumes which are the main thing. And high in heaven, in the first row of the boxes, sit the dear little angels, and keep their *lorgnettes* on us comedians here down below, and the blessed Lord Himself sits seriously in His great box, and, perhaps, finds it dull, or calculates that this theatre cannot be kept up much longer because this one gets too high a salary, and that one too little, and that they all play much too badly.

Du sublime au ridicule il n'y a qu'un pas, madame! As I ended the last chapter, narrating to you how Monsieur Le Grand died, and how I conscientiously executed the *testamentum militare* which lay in his last glance, someone knocked at my door, and there entered a poor old lady, who asked if I were not a doctor. And as I assented, she kindly asked me to go home with her and cut her husband's corns.

LAST WORDS

Written 29th November 1830

It was a depressed, an arrested time in Germany when I wrote the second volume of the *Reisebilder*, and had it printed as I wrote. But before it appeared something was whispered about it; it was said that my book would awaken and encourage the cowed spirit of freedom, and that measures were being taken to suppress it. When such rumours were afloat, it was advisable to advance the book as quickly as possible, and drive it through the press. As it was necessary, too, that it should contain a certain number of leaves, to escape the requisitions of the estimable censorship, I followed the example of Benvenuto Cellini, who, in founding his Perseus, was short of bronze, and to fill up the mould threw into the molten metal all the tin plates he could lay his hands on. It was certainly easy to distinguish between the tin—especially the tin termination of the book— and the better bronze; any one, however, who understands the craft will not betray the workman.

But as everything in this world is liable to turn up again, so it came to pass that, in this very volume, I found myself again in the same scrape, and I have been obliged again to throw some tin into the mould—let me hope that this renewed melting of baser metal will simply be attributed to the pressure of the times.

Alas! the whole book sprang from the pressure of the times, as well as the earlier writings of similar tendency. The more intimate friends of the writer, who are acquainted with his private circumstances, know well how little his own vanity forced him to the tribune, and how great were the sacrifices which he was obliged to make for every independent word which he has spoken since then and—if God will!—which he still means to speak. Nowadays, a word is a deed whose consequences cannot be measured, and no one knows whether he may not in the end appear as witness to his words in blood.

For many years I have waited in vain for the words of those bold orators, who once in the meetings of the German Bur-schenschaft so often claimed a hearing, who so often over-whelmed me with their rhetorical talent, and spoke a language spoken so oft before; they were then so forward in noise—they are now so backward in silence. How they then reviled the French and the foreign Babel, and the un-German frivolous betrayers of the Fatherland, who praised Frenchdom. That praise verified itself in the great week!

Ah, the great week of Paris! The spirit of freedom, which was wafted thence over Germany, has certainly upset the night-lamps here and there, so that the red curtains of several thrones took fire, and golden crowns grew hot under blazing night-caps; but the old catchpoles, in whom the royal police trusted, are already bringing out the fire-buckets, and now scent around all the more suspiciously, and forge all the more firmly their secret chains, and I mark well that a still thicker prison-vault is being invisibly arched over the German people.

Poor imprisoned people! be not cast down in your need. Oh, that I could speak catapults! Oh, that I could shoot *falaricae* from my heart!

The distinguished ice-rind of reserve melts from my heart, a strange sorrow steals over me—is it love, and love for the German people? Or is it sickness?—my soul quivers and my eyes burn, and that is an unfortunate occurrence for a writer, who should command his material, and remain charmingly objective, as the art school requires, and as Goethe has done—he has grown to be eighty years old in so doing, and a minister, and portly—poor German people! that is thy greatest man!

I still have a few octavo pages to fill, and I will therefore tell a story—it has been floating in my head since yesterday—a story from the life of Charles the Fifth. But it is now a long time since I heard it; and I no longer remember its details exactly. Such things are easily forgotten, if one does not receive a regular salary for reading them every half-year from his lecture-books. But what does it matter if places and dates are forgotten, so long as one holds their significance, their moral meaning, in his memory? It is this which stirs my soul and moves me even to tears. I fear I am getting ill.

The poor Emperor was taken prisoner by his enemies, and lay in stern imprisonment. I believe it was in Tyrol. There he sat in solitary sorrow, forsaken by all his knights and courtiers, and no one came to his help. I know not if he had even in those days that cheese-yellow complexion with which Holbein painted him. But the misanthropic under-lip certainly protruded, even more then than in his portraits. He must have despised the people who fawned around him in the sunshine of prosperity, and who left him alone in his bitter need. Suddenly the prison door opened, and there entered a man wrapped in a cloak, and as he cast it aside, the Emperor recognized his trusty Kunz von der Rosen, the court fool. One brought him consolation and counsel—and it was the court fool.

O German Fatherland! dear German people! I am thy Kunz von der Rosen. The man whose real office was pastime, and who should only make thee merry in happy days, forces his way into thy prison, in time of need; here, beneath my mantle,

I bring thee thy strong sceptre and the beautiful crown—dost thou not remember me, my Emperor? If I cannot free thee, I will at least console thee, and thou shalt have someone by thee who will talk with thee about thy most pressing oppressions, and will speak courage to thee, and who loves thee, and whose best jokes and best blood are ever at thy service. For thou, my people, art the true Emperor, the true lord of the land—thy will is sovereign and more legitimate than that purple *Tel est notre plaisir*, which grounds itself upon divine right, without any better guarantee than the quackery of shaven jugglers—thy will, my people, is the only righteous source of all power. Even though thou liest down there in fetters, thy good right will arise in the end, the day of freedom draws near, a new time begins—my Emperor, the night is over, and the dawn shines outside.

'Kunz von der Rosen, my fool, thou errest. Thou hast perhaps mistaken a bright axe for the sun, and the dawn is nothing but blood.'

'No, my Emperor, it is the sun, though it rises in the west—for six thousand years men have always seen it rise in the east—it is high time that it for once made a change in its course.'

'Kunz von der Rosen, my fool, thou hast lost the bells from thy red cap, and it now has such a strange look, that red cap!'

'Ah, my Emperor, I have shaken my head in such mad earnest over your distress that the fool's bells fell from my cap; but it is none the worse for that!'

'Kunz von der Rosen, my fool, what is that breaking and cracking outside there?'

'Hush! it is the saw and the carpenter's axe; the doors of your prison will soon be broken in, and you will be free, my Emperor!'

'Am I then really Emperor? Alas! it is only the fool who tells me so!'

'Oh, do not sigh, my dear lord, it is the air of the dungeon which so dispirits you; when you have once regained your power, you will feel the bold imperial blood in your veins, and you will be proud as an Emperor, and arrogant, and gracious, and unjust, and smiling, and ungrateful as princes are.'

'Kunz von der Rosen, my fool, when I am free again, what wilt thou be doing?'

'I will sew new bells on my cap.'

'And how shall I reward thy fidelity?'

'Ah! dear master—do not let me be put to death!'

ENGLISH FRAGMENTS

LONDON

I HAVE seen the greatest wonder which the world can show to the astonished spirit; I have seen it, and am more astonished than ever—and still there remains fixed in my memory that stone forest of houses, and amid them the rushing stream of faces, of living human faces, with all their motley passions, all their terrible impulses of love, of hunger, and of hate—I am speaking of London.

Send a philosopher to London, but no poet! Send a philosopher there, and stand him at a corner of Cheapside, he will learn more there than from all the books of the last Leipzig fair; and as the human waves roar around him, so will a sea of new thoughts rise before him, and the Eternal Spirit which moves upon the face of the waters will breathe upon him; the most hidden secrets of social harmony will be suddenly revealed to him, he will hear the pulse of the world beat audibly, and see it visibly—for, if London is the right hand of the world—its active, mighty right hand—then we may regard that street which leads from the Exchange to Downing Street as the world's radial artery.

But send no poet to London! This downright earnestness of all things, this colossal uniformity, this machine-like movement, this moroseness even in pleasure, this exaggerated London, smothers the imagination and rends the heart. And should you ever send a German poet thither—a dreamer, who stands staring at every single phenomenon, even a ragged beggar-woman, or a shining jeweller's shop—why, then he will find things going badly with him, and he will be hustled about on every side, or even be knocked over with a mild 'God damn!' God damn!—the damned pushing! I soon saw that these people have much to do. They live on a large scale, and though food and clothes are dearer with them than with us, they must still be better fed and clothed than we are—as gentility requires. Moreover, they have enormous debts, yet occasionally in a vainglorious mood they make ducks and drakes of their guineas, pay other nations to fight for their pleasure, give their respective kings a handsome *douceur* into the bargain—and, therefore, John Bull must work day and night to get the money for such expenses; by day and by night he must tax his brain to discover new machines, and he sits and reckons in the sweat of his brow, and runs and rushes without looking about much from the docks to the Exchange, and from the Exchange to the Strand, and, therefore, it is quite pardonable if, when a poor German poet, gazing into a print-shop window, stands in his way at the corner of Cheapside, he should knock him aside with a rather rough 'God damn!'

But the picture at which I was gazing as I stood at the corner of Cheapside, was that of the passage of the French across the Beresina.

And when, jolted out of my gazing, I looked again on the raging street, where a parti-coloured coil of men, women, and children, horses, stage-coaches, and with them a funeral, whirled groaning and creaking along, it seemed to me as though all London were such a Beresina Bridge, where every one presses on in mad haste to save his scrap of life, where the daring rider stamps down the poor pedestrian, where every one who falls is lost for ever; where the best friends rush, without feeling, over each other's corpses, and where thousands, weak and bleeding, grasp in vain at the planks of the bridge, and slide down into the ice-pit of death.

How much more pleasant and homelike it is in our dear Germany! How dreamily comfortable, how Sabbatically quiet all things glide along here! Calmly the sentinels are changed, uniforms and houses shine in the quiet sunshine, swallows flit over the flag-stones, fat court-councilloresses smile from the windows, while along the echoing streets there is room enough for the dogs to sniff at each other, and for men to stand at ease and chat about the theatre, and bow low—oh, how low!—when some small aristocratic scamp or vice-scamp, with coloured ribbons on his shabby coat, or some powdered and gilded court-marshal struts by, graciously returning salutations!

I had made up my mind not to be astonished at that immensity of London of which I had heard so much. But it happened to me as to the poor schoolboy, who had made up his mind not to feel the whipping he was to receive. The facts of the case were, that he expected to get the usual blows with the usual stick in the usual way on the back, whereas he received a most unusually severe thrashing on an unusual place with a slender switch. I anticipated great palaces, and saw nothing but mere small houses. But their very uniformity and their limitless extent are wonderfully impressive.

These houses of brick, owing to the damp atmosphere and coal smoke, become uniform in colour, that is to say, of a brown olive green; they are all of the same style of building, generally two or three windows wide, three stories high, and adorned above with small red tiles, which remind one of newly-extracted bleeding teeth; so that the broad and accurately-squared streets seem to be bordered by endlessly long barracks. This has its reason in the fact that every English family, though it consist of only two persons, must still have a house to itself for its own castle, and rich speculators, to meet the demand, build whole-sale entire streets of these dwellings, which they retail singly. In the principal streets of the city, where the business of London is most at home, where old-fashioned buildings are mingled with the new, and where the fronts of the houses are covered with names and signs, yards in length, generally gilt, and in relief, this characteristic uniformity is less striking—the less so, indeed, because the eye of the stranger is incessantly caught by the new and brilliant articles exposed for sale in the windows. And these articles do not merely produce an effect because the Englishman completes so perfectly everything which he manu-factures, and because every article of luxury, every astral lamp and every boot, every tea-kettle and every woman's dress, shines out so invitingly and so 'finished'; there is a peculiar charm in the art of arrangement, in the contrast of colours, and in the variety of the English shops; even the most common-place necessaries of life appear in a startling magic light through this artistic power of setting forth everything to advantage. Ordinary articles of food attract us by the new light in which they are placed, even uncooked fish lie so delightfully dressed that the rainbow gleam of their scales attracts us; raw meat lies, as if painted, on neat and many-coloured porcelain plates, garlanded about with parsley—yes, everything seems painted, reminding us of the brilliant, yet modest, pictures of Franz Mieris. Only the people are not so cheerful as in the Dutch paintings; they sell the most delightful playthings with the most serious faces, and the cut and colour of their clothes is as uniform as that of their houses.

At the opposite side of the town, which they call the West End, where the more aristocratic and less-occupied world lives, this uniformity is still more dominant; yet here there are very long and broad streets, where all the houses are large as palaces, though outwardly anything but distinguished, unless we except the fact that in these, as in all the better class of houses in

London, the windows of the first story are adorned with iron-barred balconies, and also on the ground floor there is a black railing protecting the entrance to certain cellar apartments buried in the earth. In this part of the city there are also great squares, where rows of houses, like those already described, form a quadrangle, in whose centre there is a garden enclosed by a black iron railing, and containing some statue or other. In all of these squares and streets the eye is never shocked by the dilapidated huts of misery. Everywhere we are stared down on by wealth and respectability, while crammed away in retired lanes and dark, damp alleys poverty dwells with her rags and her tears.

The stranger who wanders through the great streets of London and does not chance right into the regular quarters of the people, sees little or nothing of the misery there. Only here and there, at the mouth of some dark alley, stands a ragged woman with a suckling babe at her wasted breast, and begs with her eyes. Perhaps if those eyes are still beautiful, one glances into them and shrinks back at the world of wretchedness within them. The common beggars are old people, generally blacks, who stand at the corners of the streets cleaning pathways—a very necessary thing in muddy London—and ask for 'coppers' in reward. It is in the dusky twilight that Poverty with her mates, Vice and Crime, glide forth from their lairs. They shun daylight the more anxiously, the more cruelly their wretchedness contrasts with the pride of wealth which glitters everywhere; only hunger sometimes drives them at noonday from their dens, and then they stand with silent, speaking eyes, staring beseechingly at the rich merchant who hurries along, busy and jingling gold, or at the lazy lord who, like a surfeited god, rides by on his high horse, casting now and then an aristocratically indifferent glance at the mob below, as though they were swarming ants, or, at all events, a mass of baser beings, whose joys and sorrows have nothing in common with his feelings. Yes, over the vulgar multitude which sticks fast to the soil, soar, like beings of a higher nature, England's nobility, who regard their little island as only a temporary resting-place, Italy as their summer garden, Paris as their social saloon, and the whole world as their inheritance. They sweep along, knowing nothing of sorrow or suffering, and their gold is a talisman which conjures into fulfilment their wildest wish.

Poor Poverty! how agonizing must thy hunger be where others swell in scornful superfluity! And when someone casts with indifferent hand a crust into thy lap, how bitter must the tears be wherewith thou moistenest it! Thou poisonest thyself with thine own tears. Well art thou in the right when thou alliest thyself to Vice and Crime. Outlawed criminals often bear more humanity in their hearts than those cold, blameless citizens of virtue, in whose white hearts the power of evil is quenched; but also the power of good. I have seen women on whose cheeks red vice was painted, and in whose hearts dwelt heavenly purity. I have seen women—I would I saw them again!——

WELLINGTON

THIS man has the bad fortune to meet with good fortune wherever the greatest men in the world were unfortunate, and that angers us, and makes him hateful. We see in him only the victory of stupidity over genius—Arthur Wellington triumphant where Napoleon Bonaparte was overwhelmed! Never was a man more ironically gifted by Fortune, and it seems as though she would exhibit his empty littleness by raising him high on the shield of victory. Fortune is a woman, and perhaps, in womanly wise, she cherishes a secret grudge against the man who overthrew her former darling, though the very overthrow came from her own will. Now she lets him conquer again on the Catholic Emancipation question—yes, in the very fight in which George Canning was overwhelmed. It is possible that he might have been loved had the wretched Londonderry been his predecessor in the ministry; but he is the successor of the noble Canning, of the much-wept, adored, great Canning—and he conquers where Canning was overwhelmed. Without so unlucky a luck, Wellington would perhaps pass for a great man; people would not hate him, would not measure him too accurately, at least not with the heroic measure with which a Napoleon and a Canning is measured, and consequently it would never have been discovered how small a man he is.

He is a small man, and less than small. The French could say nothing more sarcastic of Polignac than that he was a Wellington without celebrity. In fact, what remains when we strip from a Wellington the field-marshal's uniform of celebrity?

I have here given the best apology for Lord Wellington—in the English sense of the word. My readers will be astonished, however, when I honourably confess that I once clapped on all sail in praise of this hero. It is a good story, and I will tell it here.

My barber in London was a radical named Mr. White, a poor little man in a shabby black dress, worn until it almost shone white; he was so lean that even his full face looked like a profile, and the sighs in his bosom were visible before they rose. These sighs were caused by the misfortunes of Old England, and by the impossibility of paying the National Debt.

'Ah!' I often heard him sigh, 'why need the English people trouble themselves as to who reigns in France, and what the French are doing at home? But the nobility, sir, and the Church were afraid of the principles of liberty of the French Revolution, and, to keep down these principles, John Bull must give his gold and his blood, and make debts into the bargain. We 've got all we wanted out of the war—the revolution has been put down, the French eagles of liberty have had their wings cut, and the Church may be quite sure that none of them will come flying over the Channel; and now the nobility and the Church ought to pay for the debts which were made for their own good, and not for any good of the poor people. Ah!—the poor people!'

Whenever Mr. White came to the 'poor people,' he always sighed more deeply than ever, and the refrain then was, that bread and beer were so dear that the poor people must starve to feed fat lords, staghounds, and priests, and that there was only one remedy. At these words he was wont to whet his razor, and as he drew it murderously up and down the strop, he muttered grimly to himself: 'Lords, priests, hounds.'

But his radical rage boiled most fiercely against the Duke of Wellington; he spat gall and poison whenever he alluded to him, and as he lathered me, he himself foamed with rage. Once I was fairly frightened, when he, while barbering just at my neck, burst out against Wellington, murmuring all the while: 'If I only had him so under my razor, I 'd save him the trouble of cutting his own throat, as his brother in office and fellow-countryman, Londonderry, did, who killed himself that way at North Cray, in Kent—God damn him!'

I felt already that the man's hand trembled, and fearing lest he might imagine in his excitement that I really was the Duke of Wellington, I endeavoured to allay his violence, and in an underhanded manner, to soothe him, I called up his national pride, I represented to him that the Duke of Wellington had advanced the glory of the English, that he had always been an innocent tool in the hands of others, that he was fond of beefsteak, and that he—but the Lord only knows what fine things I said of Wellington as that razor tickled my throat.

What vexes me most is the reflection that Arthur Wellington will be as immortal as Napoleon Bonaparte. It is true that in like manner the name of Pontius Pilate is as little likely to be forgotten as that of Christ. Wellington and Napoleon! It is a wonderful phenomenon that the human mind can at the same time think of both these names. There can be no greater contrast than these two, even in their external appearance. Wellington, the dull ghost, with an ashy grey soul in a buckram body, a wooden smile on his freezing face—and by the side one thinks of the figure of Napoleon, every inch a god!

That figure never disappears from my memory. I still see him, high on his horse, with eternal eyes in his marble, imperial face, gazing down calm as destiny on the Guards defiling past— he was then sending them to Russia, and the old grenadiers glanced up at him, so terribly devoted, so consciously serious, so proud in death:

Te, Caesar, morituri salutant!

There often steals over me a secret doubt whether I ever really saw him, if we were really his contemporaries, and then it seems to me as if his portrait, torn from the little frame of the present, vanished away more proudly and imperiously in the twilight of the past. His name even now sounds to us like a word of the early world, as antique and heroic as those of Alexander and Caesar. It has become a rallying word among races, and when the East and the West meet, they fraternize through that single name.

How significant and magical that name can sound I once felt in the deepest manner in the port of London, at the India Docks, as I stood on board an East Indiaman just arrived from Bengal. It was a gigantic ship, fully manned with Hindus. The grotesque forms and groups, the singularly variegated dresses, the enigmatical expressions, the strange gestures, the wild and foreign ring of their language, their shouts of joy and their laughter, and the seriousness ever rising and falling on certain soft, yellow faces, their eyes like black flowers which looked at me as with melancholy woe—all this awoke in me a feeling like that of enchantment; I was suddenly as if transported into Scheherazade's story, and I thought that broad-leaved palms, and long-necked camels, and gold-covered elephants, and other fablelike trees and animals, must forthwith appear. The supercargo who was on the vessel, and who understood as little of the language as I myself, could not, in his genuine English narrowness, narrate to me enough of what a ridiculous race they were, nearly all Mahommedans collected from every land of Asia, from the limits of China to the Arabian Sea, even jet-black, woolly-haired Africans.

To one whose whole soul was weary of the spiritless West, and who was as sick of Europe as I then was, this fragment of the East which moved cheerfully and changingly before my eyes was a refreshing solace; my heart enjoyed at least a few drops of that draught which I had so often longed for in gloomy Hanoverian or Prussian winter nights, and it is very possible that the foreigners saw how agreeable the sight of them was to me, and how gladly I would have spoken a kind word to them. It was also plain from the depths of their eyes that I pleased them well, and they would also have willingly said something pleasant to me, and it was a vexation that neither understood the other's language. At length a means occurred to me of expressing to them with a single word my friendly feelings, and stretching forth my hands reverently, as if in loving greeting, I cried the name, 'Mahommed!' Joy suddenly flashed over the dark faces of the foreigners; they folded their arms reverently in turn, and greeted me back with the exclamation, 'Bonaparte!'

THE MEMOIRS OF HERR VON SCHNABELEWOPSKI

FOR readers who do not know Hamburg—there are such, I suppose, in China or Upper Bavaria—I must remark that the most beautiful promenade of the sons and daughters of Hammonia bears the appropriate name of Jungfernstieg, and that it consists of an avenue of lime trees, which is bounded on one side by a row of houses, and on the other by the Alster Basin, and that before the latter, and built out into the water, are two tent-like pleasant cafés, called pavilions. It is nice to sit, especially before one called the Swiss Pavilion, of a summer day, when the afternoon sun is not too hot, but only smiles gaily and pours its rays as in a fairy dream over the lindens, the houses, the people, the Alster, and the swans, who cradle themselves in it. Yes, it is nice to sit there; and even so I sat on many a summer afternoon and thought, as a young man generally does, that is to say, about nothing at all, and looked at what a young man generally looks at, that is, the girls—yes, there they fluttered along, the charming things, with their winged caps, and covered baskets, containing nothing; there they tripped, the gay Vierlander maids, who provide all Hamburg with strawberries and new milk, and whose petticoats are still much too long; there swept proudly along the beautiful merchants' daughters, with whose love one gets just so much ready money; there skipped a nurse bearing on her arm a rosy boy, whom she constantly kissed while thinking of her lover; there wandered too the priestesses of Venus Aphrodite, Hanseatic vestals, Dianas on the hunt, Naiads, Dryads, Hamadryads, and similar clergymen's daughters; and ah! there with them Minka and Héloïse! How oft I sat in that pavilion fair and saw her wandering past in rose-striped gown—it cost four shillings and threepence a yard, and Herr Seligmann gave me his word that even though washed, and that full many times, the colour would not fade. 'What glorious girls!' exclaimed the virtuous youths who sat by me. I remember how a great insurance agent, who was always bedecked like a carnival ox, said: 'I'd like to have one of them for breakfast, and the other for supper, just at will, and I don't think I should want any dinner that day.' 'She is an angel!' cried a sea-captain, so loudly that both the damsels at a glance looked jealously at one another. I myself said nothing, and thought my sweetest nothings, and looked at the girls and the pleasant gentle sky, and the tall Petri tower with its slender waist, and the calm blue Alster, on which the swans swam so proud, and beautiful, and secure. The swans! I could look at them for hours—the lovely creatures, with their soft, long necks, as they so voluptuously cradled themselves on the soft flood, diving ever and anon, and proudly splashing, till the heaven grew dark and the golden stars came forth yearning, hope-giving, wondrously and beautifully tender and transformed. The stars! Are they golden flowers on the bridal bosom of heaven? Are they the eyes of enamoured angels, who with yearning mirror themselves in the blue streams of earth below and rival the swans?

Ah! that is all long, long ago. Then I was young and foolish. Now I am old and foolish. Many a flower has withered since that time, and many too been trodden into earth; even the rose-striped stuff of Seligmann has lost the colour warranted to wash. He has faded himself; the firm is now the widow Seligmann. And Héloïse, the gentle creature who seemed to be made to walk only on soft Indian flowered carpets and be fanned with peacock's feathers, went down among roaring sailors, punch, tobacco-smoke, and bad music. When I again saw Minka she had changed her name to Katinka, and dwelt between Hamburg and Altona; she looked like the temple of Solomon after it had been destroyed by Nebuchadnezzar, and smelt of Assyrian Canaster; and as she told of Héloïse's death, she wept bitterly and tore her hair in despair, and fainted quite away; nor did she recover till she had swallowed a great glass of spirits.

And how the town itself was changed! And the Jungfernstieg! Snow lay on the roofs, and it seemed as if the houses had grown old and had white hair. The lime-trees of the Jungfernstieg were dead trees and dry boughs, which waved ghost-like in the cold wind. The sky was cutting blue, and soon grew dark. It was five o'clock on Sunday—the general hour for foddering—and the carriages rolled along. Gentlemen and ladies descended from them with frozen smiles upon their hungry lips. How horrible! At that instant I was thrilled with the awful thought that an unfathomable idiocy appeared in all these faces, and that all persons who passed by seemed bewildered in a strange delirium. Twelve years before, at the same hour, I had seen them with the same faces, like the puppets of a town hall clock, with the same gestures; and since then they had gone on in the same old way, reckoning and going on 'change and assisting one another, and moving their jawbones, and paying their *pourboires*, and counting up again: twice two is four. Horrible! I cried. Suppose that it should suddenly occur to one of these people while he sat on the office stool *that twice two is five!* and that he consequently has been multiplying wrongly all his life, and so wasted that life in an awful error. All at once a foolish delirium seized me, and, as I regarded the passers-by more nearly, it seemed to me as if they were themselves nothing but ciphers or Arabic numerals. There went a crook-footed Two by a fatal Three, his full-bosomed, enceinte spouse; behind them came Mr. Four on crutches, waddling along came a fatal Five, then with round belly and a little hood a well-known little Six, and the still better known Evil Seven; but as I looked more closely at the wretched Eight as it tottered past I recognized in it the insurance agent who once went adorned like a carnival ox, but who now looked like the leanest of Pharaoh's lean kine—pale, hollow cheeks, like an empty soup-plate; a cold, red nose, like a winter rose; a shabby black coat, which had a pitiful white shine; a hat into which Saturn with the scythe had cut air-holes; but his boots shone like looking-glasses, and he no longer seemed to think about devouring Héloïse and Minka for breakfast and supper, but to be longing very much for a good dinner of common beef. And I recognized many an old friend among the mere ciphers who rolled along. So these and the rest of the numerical folk drove by hurried and hungry, while more grimly droll a funeral passed not far off, past the houses of the Jungfernstieg. As a melancholy, masquerading show there walked on after the hearse, stilted on their little, thin, black silk legs, the well-known council servants, the privileged civic mourners, in a parodied old Burgundian costume, short black cloaks and black plumped breeches, white wigs and cravats, out of which the red mercenary faces stared comically, short steel rapiers on their hips, and green umbrellas on their arms.

But more uncanny and bewildering than these figures which went silently by were the sounds which rang in my ears from the other side. They were shrill, harsh, creaking, metallic tones, a crazy screeching, a painful splashing and despairing gulping, a gasping and tumbling, and groaning and bitter wailing—an indescribable ice-cold cry of pain. The basin of the Alster was frozen up, except that near the shore was a large square cut in the ice, and the terrible tones which I had heard came from the windpipes of the poor white creatures which swam round in it, and screeched in horrible agony; and oh, they were the same swans who once had cheered my heart so softly and merrily. Ah! the beautiful white swans! Their wings had been clipped to prevent them from flying in the autumn to the warm south, and now the north held them fast bound, fast banned in its dark, icy grave, and the waiter of the Pavilion said they were all right, in there, and that the cold was good for them. But it was not true; it is not good for anybody to be imprisoned, powerless, in a cold pool almost frozen, with the wings clipped so that one cannot fly away to the beautiful south, with its beautiful flowers, golden sunlight, and blue mountain lakes. Ah! with me it was little better, and I understood the suffering of these poor swans, as it ever grew darker and the stars came out bright above, the same stars who once so warm with love wooed the swans on fair summer nights, but who now looked down with frosty brilliance, and almost scornfully, on them. Ah! I now perceive that the stars are no living, sympathetic beings, but only gleaming phantasms of night, eternal delusions in a dreamed heaven—mere golden lies in dark blue Nothingness.

. . . .

You certainly know the fable of the *Flying Dutchman*. It is the story of an enchanted ship which can never arrive in port, and which since time immemorial has been sailing about at sea. When it meets a vessel, some of the unearthly sailors come in a boat and beg the others to take a packet of letters home for them. These letters must be nailed to the mast, else some misfortune will happen to the ship—above all if no Bible be on board, and no horse-shoe nailed to the foremast. The letters are always addressed to people whom no one knows, and who have long been dead, so that some late descendant gets a letter addressed to a far-away great-great-grandmother, who has slept for centuries in her grave. That timber spectre, that grim grey ship, is so called from the captain, a Hollander, who once swore by all the devils that he would get round a certain mountain, whose name has escaped me, in spite of a fearful storm, though he should sail till the Day of Judgment. The devil took him at his word, therefore he must sail for ever, until set free by a woman's truth. The devil in his stupidity has no faith in female truth, and allowed the enchanted captain to land once in seven years and get married, and so find opportunities to

save his soul. Poor Dutchman! He is often only too glad to
be saved from his marriage and his wife-saviour, and get again
on board.

The play which I saw in Amsterdam was based on this legend.
Another seven years have passed; the poor Hollander is more
weary than ever of his endless wandering; he lands, becomes
intimate with a Scottish nobleman, to whom he sells diamonds
for a mere song, and when he hears that his customer has a
beautiful daughter, he asks that he may wed her. This bargain
also is agreed to. Next we see the Scottish home; the maiden
with anxious heart awaits the bridegroom. She often looks with
strange sorrow at a great, time-worn picture which hangs in
the hall, and represents a handsome man in the Netherlandish-
Spanish garb. It is an old heirloom and, according to a legend
of her grandmother, is a true portrait of the Flying Dutchman
as he was seen in Scotland a hundred years before, in the time
of William of Orange. And with this has come down a warning
that the women of the family must beware of the original. This
has naturally enough had the result of deeply impressing the
features of the picture on the heart of the romantic girl. Therefore, when the man himself makes his appearance, she is startled,
but not with fear. He too is moved at beholding the portrait.
But when he is informed whose likeness it is, he with tact and
easy conversation turns aside all suspicion, jests at the legend,
laughs at the Flying Dutchman, the Wandering Jew of the
Ocean, and yet, as if moved by the thought, passes into a
pathetic mood, depicting how terrible the life must be of one
condemned to endure unheard-of tortures on a wild waste of
waters—how his body itself is his living coffin, wherein his soul
is terribly imprisoned—how life and death alike reject him,
like an empty cask scornfully thrown by the sea on the shore,
and as contemptuously repulsed again into the sea—how his
agony is as deep as the sea on which he sails—his ship without
anchor, and his heart without hope.

I believe that these are nearly the words with which the
bridegroom ends. The bride regards him with deep earnestness,
casting glances meanwhile at his portrait. It seems as if she
has penetrated his secret; and when he afterwards asks:
'Katherine, wilt thou be true to me?' she answers: 'True till
death.'

I remember that just then I heard a laugh, and that it came
not from the pit from but the gallery of the gods above. As I
glanced up I saw a wondrous lovely Eve in Paradise, who looked

seductively at me, with great blue eyes. Her arm hung over the gallery, and in her hand she held an apple, or rather an orange. But instead of symbolically dividing it with me, she only metaphorically cast the peel on my head. Was it done intentionally or by accident? That I would know! But when I entered Paradise to cultivate her acquaintance, I was not a little startled to find a white, soft creature, a wonderfully womanly, tender being, not languishing, yet delicately clear as crystal, a form of home-like propriety and fascinating amiability. Only there was something on the left upper lip which curved or twined like the tail of a slippery gliding lizard. It was a mysterious trait, something such as is not found in pure angels, and just as little in mere devils. This expression comes not from evil, but from the *knowledge* of good and evil—it is a smile which has been poisoned or flavoured by tasting the Apple of Eden. When I see this expression on soft, full, rosy, ladies' lips, then I feel in my own a cramp-like twitching—a convulsive yearning—to kiss those lips: it is our Affinity.

I whispered into the ear of the beauty:

'*Yuffrou*, I will kiss thy mouth.'

'*Bei Gott, Mynheer!* that is a good idea,' was the hasty answer, which rang with bewitching sound from her heart.

But—no. I will here draw a veil, and end the story or picture of which the Flying Dutchman was the frame. Thereby will I revenge myself on the prurient prudes who devour such narratives with delight, and are enraptured with them to their heart of hearts, *et plus ultra*, and then abuse the narrator, and turn up their noses at him in society, and decry him as immoral. It is a nice story, too, delicious as preserved pineapple or fresh caviare or truffles in Burgundy, and would be pleasant reading after prayers; but out of spite, and to punish old offences, I will suppress it. Here I make a long dash —————— which may be supposed to be a black sofa on which we sat as I wooed. But the innocent must suffer with the guilty, and I dare say that many a good soul looks bitterly and reproachfully at me. However, unto these of the better kind I will admit that I was never so wildly kissed as by this Dutch blonde, and that she most triumphantly destroyed the prejudice which I had hitherto held against blue eyes and fair hair. *Now* I understand why an English poet has compared such women to frozen champagne. In the icy crust lies hidden the strongest extract. There is nothing more piquant than the contrast between external cold and the inner fire which, Bacchante-like, flames up and irresistibly intoxicates the happy carouser. Ay, far more than in brunettes does the fire of passion burn in many a sham-calm holy image with golden-glory hair, and blue angel's eyes, and pious lily hands. I knew a blonde of one of the best families in Holland who at times left her beautiful chateau on the Zuyder-Zee and went incognito to Amsterdam, and there in the theatre threw orange-peel on the head of any one who pleased her, and gave herself up to the wildest debauchery, like a Dutch Messalina! . . .

When I re-entered the theatre, I came in time to see the last scene of the play, where the wife of the Flying Dutchman on a high cliff wrings her hands in despair, while her unhappy husband is seen on the deck of his unearthly ship, tossing on the waves. He loves her, and will leave her lest she be lost with him, and he tells her all his dreadful destiny, and the cruel curse which hangs above his head. But she cries aloud: 'I was ever true to thee, and I know how to be ever true unto death!'

Saying this she throws herself into the waves, and then the enchantment is ended. The Flying Dutchman is saved, and we see the ghostly ship slowly sink into the abyss of the sea.

The moral of the play is that women should never marry a Flying Dutchman, while we men may learn from it that one can, through women, go down and perish—under favourable circumstances!

. . . . .

When the food became very bad indeed, then we disputed as to the existence of God. But the beneficent Deity always had the majority. Only three of the table society were atheistically inclined, and even they gave way if we had at least good cheese for dessert. The most zealous Theist was one little Samson, and when he disputed with tall Van Pitter as to whether there was a personal God, he became at times wildly excited, and ran up and down the hall crying constantly: '*Bei Gott !* that isn't fair!' Tall Van Pitter, a lean Frisian, whose soul was as calm as the water in a Dutch canal, and whose words followed one another as leisurely as one canal boat after another, drew his arguments from the German philosophy which was at that time very much studied in Leyden. He ridiculed the narrow-minded men who attribute to God a particular private existence; he even accused them of blasphemy, because they gifted God with wisdom, justice, love, and other human qualities, which are utterly inappropriate, because these are relatively the negations or antitheses of human errors, such as stupidity, injustice, and hate. But when Van Pitter thus developed his own pantheistic views, there came forth against him the fat Fichtean, Dricksen of Utrecht, who stoutly confuted his vague conception of a God spread forth through all Nature—that is to say, existing only in space. Yes, he even declared it was blasphemy to so much as speak of the *existence* of God, since the very idea of existence involved that of space—in short, something substantial. Yes, it was blasphemy even to say of God, *He is*, because the purest or most abstract Being could not be conceived without limitations of sense, whereas, if man would think of God, he must abstract Him from all substance, and not think of Him as a form of extension, but as a series or order of developments, God not being an action *per se*, but only the principle of a cosmos beyond conception.

Hearing this, little Samson fairly raved, and ran up and down the hall, and cried ever more loudly: 'O God, O God! By God, that is not fair, O God!' I believe that he would, in honour of God, have beaten the fat Fichtean, had not his arms been too weak; but as it was he often attacked him, when the big and burly one would grasp him by his little arms, hold him fast, and without taking the pipe from his mouth, blow his airy arguments, mixed with tobacco smoke, into Samson's face, so that the little man was almost stifled with fume and fret, and wailed more and more pitifully: 'O God! O God!' but it availed him naught, though he defended His cause so valiantly.

Despite this divine indifference, despite this almost human unthankfulness, little Samson remained a staunch champion of Theism, as I believe from inborn inclination; for his father belonged to God's chosen folk, a race which God once very specially protected, and which, in consequence, has maintained till this day a great dependence on Him. Jews are ever the most devoted of Theists, especially those who, like little Samson, were born in the vicinity of Frankfort. These may be as republican as they please in political questions—yes, they may roll in the very mud of sansculottism—but the instant that religious ideas are involved they become the humblest servants of their Jehovah, the old fetish, who, however, will know nothing of the entire company, and who has newly baptized Himself into a divinely pure Spirit.

I believe that this divinely pure Spirit, this new ruler of heaven, who is now conceived as so moral, so cosmopolite and universal, takes it ill at heart that the poor Jews, who knew Him in His rude first form, remind Him every day in their synagogues of His early and obscure national relations. Perhaps the ancient Lord would fain forget that He was of Palestine origin, and once the God of Abraham, Isaac, and Jacob, and was in those times called JEHOVAH.

.   .   .   .   .   .

If the landlady of the 'Red Cow' had been an Italian she would have poisoned my victuals, but as she was a Dutchwoman she only cooked them as badly as possible. In fact, we experienced the very next day the result of her feminine revenge. The first dish was *no soup*. That was awful, especially for a man brought up decently as I was, who from youth upwards had had soup every day, and who had hitherto never imagined that there was a world where the sun never shone and man never knew soup. The second course was beef, as cold and hard as Myron's cow. Then followed fish, which had indeed an ancient and fish-like smell, and which went untouched in silence as it came. Then came a great, old spectre of a hen, which, far from satisfying our hunger, looked so wretchedly lean and hungry that we, out of sympathetic pity, could not touch it.

'And now, little Samson,' cried the burly Dricksen, 'dost thou still believe in God? *Is* this just? The Bandage-baggage visits Schnabelewopski in the dark watches of the night, and on that account we must starve by daylight!'

'O God, God!' sighed the little fellow, vilely vexed by such an atheistic outbreak, and perhaps by such a miserable meal. And his irritability increased as the tall Van Pitter let fly his arrows of wit against Anthropomorphists and praised the Egyptians who of yore worshipped oxen and onions; the first because they tasted so well when roasted, and the latter when stuffed.

But little Samson under such mockery became furious, and at last he shot forth his defence of Theism.

'God is for man what the sun is for the flowers. When the rays of his heavenly countenance fall on the flowers, then they grow and open out their calyxes, and unfold their most varied colours. By night, when the sun is gone, they stand sorrowful with closed petals, and sleep or dream of the kisses of the golden rays of the past. Those which are ever in the shadow lose colour and growth, shrink and grow pale, and wilt away, miserable and unfortunate. But those which grow entirely in the dark, in old castle vaults, under ruined cloisters, become ugly and poisonous; they twine like snakes; their very smell is un-healthy, evilly benumbing, deadly.'

'Oh, you need not spin out your Biblical parable any further,' said burly Dricksen, as he poured unto himself a great glass of Schiedam gin. 'Thou, little Samson, art a pious blossom that inhales in the sunshine of God the holy rays of virtue and love to such inspiration that thy soul blooms like a rainbow, while ours, turned away from God, fade colourless and hideous, if we don't indeed spread abroad a poisonous stink.'

'I once saw in Frankfort,' said little Samson, 'a watch which did not believe there was any watchmaker. It was of pinch-beck and went very badly.'

'I 'll show you anyhow that such a repeater knows how to strike,' replied Dricksen, who suddenly became silent and teased Samson no more.

As the latter, notwithstanding his weak little arms, was an admirable fencer, it was determined that the two should duel that day with rapiers. They went at it with great bitterness. The black eyes of little Samson gleamed as if of fire and greatly magnified, and contrasted the more strangely with his little arms, which came forth so pitifully from his rolled-up shirt-sleeves. He became more and more excited; he fought for the existence of God, the old Jehovah, the King of Kings. But He aided not in the least His champion, and in the sixth round the little man got a thrust in the lungs.

'O God!' he cried, and fell to the ground.

.   .   .   .

This scene excited me terribly. But all the fury of my feelings turned against the woman who had directly caused such disaster, and with a heart full of wrath and pain I stormed into the 'Red Cow.'

'Monster, why did you not serve us soup?' These were the words with which I addressed the landlady, who became deadly pale as I entered the kitchen. The porcelain on the chimney-piece trembled at the tone of my voice. I was as desperate as only that man can be who has had no soup, and whose best friend has just had a rapier through his lungs.

'Monster, why did you not serve us soup?' I repeated these words, while the consciously guilty woman stood as if frozen and speechless before me. But at last, as if from opened sluices, the tears poured from her eyes. They flooded her whole face, and ran down into the canal of her bosom. But this sight did not soften me, and with still greater bitterness, I cried: 'O ye women, I know that ye can weep, but are tears *soup*? Ye are created for our misery. Your looks are lies, and your breath is treason and deceit. Who first ate the apple of sin? Geese saved the Capitol, but a woman ruined Troy. O Troy, Troy! thou holy fortress of Priam, thou didst fall by a woman! Who cast Marcus Aurelius into destruction? By whom was Marcus Tullius Cicero murdered? Who demanded the head of John the Baptist? Who was the cause of Abelard's mutilation? A woman. History is replete, yea unto repletion, with the terrible examples of man's ruin caused by you. All your deeds are folly, and all your thoughts are ingratitude. We give you the highest, the holiest flame of our hearts, our love—and what do we get for it? Beef that the Devil would not eat, and worse poultry. Wretch and monster, why did you serve no soup?'

Myfrow began to stammer a series of excuses, and conjured me, by all the sweet memories of our love, to forgive her. She promised to provide better provender than before, and only charge six florins per head, though the Groote Dohlen landlord asked eight for his ordinary. She went so far as to promise oyster patties for the next day—yes, in the soft tone of her voice there was even a perfume as of truffles. But I remained firm. I was determined to break with her for ever, and left the kitchen with the tragic words: 'Farewell; between us two all is boiled to rags forever!'

In leaving I heard something fall. Was it a cooking-pot or Myfrow herself? I did not take the pains to look, and went straight to the Groote Dohlen to order six covers for the next day.

After this important business I hurried to little Samson's house and found him in evil case. He lay in an immense old-fashioned bed which had no curtains, and at the corners of which were great marbled wooden pillars which supported a richly gilt canopy. The face of the little fellow was pale from pain, and in the glance which he cast at me was so much grief, kindness, and wretchedness, that I was touched to the heart. The doctor had just left him, saying that his wound was serious. Van Moeulen, who alone had remained to watch all night, sat before his bed, and was reading to him from the Bible.

'Schnabelewopski,' sighed the sufferer, 'it is good that you came. You may listen, and 'twill do you good. That is a dear, good book. My ancestors bore it all over the world with them, and much pain, misfortune, cursing and hatred, yes, death itself, did they endure for it. Every page of it cost tears and blood: it is the written fatherland of the children of God; it is the holy inheritance of Jehovah.'

'Don't talk so much; it's bad for you,' said Van Moeulen.

'And indeed,' I added, 'don't talk of Jehovah, the most ungrateful of gods, for whose existence you have fought to-day.'

'O God!' sighed the little man, and tears fell from his eyes, 'Thou help'st our enemies.'

'Don't talk so much,' said Van Moeulen again. 'And thou, Schnabelewopski,' he whispered to me, 'excuse me if I bore thee; the little man would have it that I should read to him the history of his namesake Samson. We are at the fourteenth chapter—listen!

'"Samson went down to Timnath, and saw a woman in Timnath of the daughters of the Philistines."'

'No,' said the patient with closed eyes, 'we are at the sixteenth chapter. It is to me as if I were living in all that you read me, as if I heard the sheep bleating as they feed by Jordan, as if I myself had set fire to the tails of the foxes and chased them through the fields of the Philistines, and as if I had slain a thousand Philistines with the jawbone of an ass. Oh, the Philistines! they enslaved and mocked us, and made us pay toll like swine, and slung me out of doors from the ball-room of the "Horse," and kicked me at Bockenheim—kicked me out of doors from the "Horse"!—oh, by God, that was not fair.'

'He is feverish, and has wild fancies,' softly said Van Moeulen, and began the sixteenth chapter.

'"Then went Samson to Gaza, and saw there an harlot, and went in unto her.

'"And it was told the Gazites, saying, Samson is come hither. And they compassed him in, and laid wait for him all night in the gate of the city, and were quiet all the night, saying, In the morning, when it is day, we shall kill him."

'"And Samson lay till midnight, and arose at midnight, and took the doors of the gate of the city, and the two posts, and went away with them, bar and all, and put them upon his shoulders, and carried them up to the top of an hill that is before Hebron.

'"And it came to pass afterward, that he loved a woman in the valley of Sorek whose name was Delilah.

'"And the lords of the Philistines came up unto her and said unto her, Entice him and see wherein his great strength lieth, and by what means we may prevail against him, that we may bind him to afflict him: and we will give thee every one of us eleven hundred pieces of silver.

'"And Delilah said to Samson, Tell me, I pray thee, wherein thy great strength lieth, and wherewith thou mightest be bound to afflict thee.

'"And Samson said unto her, If they bind me with seven green withs that were never dried, than shall I be weak and be as another man.

'"Then the lords of the Philistines brought up to her seven green withs which had not been dried, and she bound him with them.

'"Now there were men lying in wait, abiding with her in the chamber. And she said, The Philistines be upon thee, Samson. And he brake the withs, as a thread of tow is broken when it toucheth the fire. So his strength was not known."'

'Oh, the fools of Philistines!' cried the little man, and smiled well pleased; 'and they wanted to take me up and put me in the constable's guard.'

Van Moeulen read on:

'"And Delilah said to Samson, Behold, thou hast mocked me, and told me lies: now tell me, I pray thee, wherewith thou mightest be bound.

'"And he said unto her, If they bind me fast with new ropes that never were occupied, then shall I be weak, and be as another man.

'"Delilah therefore took new ropes, and bound him therewith, and said unto him, The Philistines be upon thee, Samson. And there were liers in wait abiding in the chamber. And he brake them from off his arms like a thread."'

'Fools of Philistines,' cried the little man.

'"And Delilah said unto Samson, Hitherto thou hast mocked me, and told me lies: tell me wherewith thou mightest be bound? And he said unto her, If thou weavest the seven locks of my head with the web.

'"And she fastened it with the pin, and said unto him, The Philistines be upon thee, Samson. And he awaked out of his sleep, and went away with the pin of the beam, and with the web."'

The little man laughed. 'That was in the Eschenheimer Lane.' But Van Moeulen continued:

'"And she said unto him, How canst thou say, I love thee, when thine heart is not with me? thou hast mocked me these three times, and hast not told me wherein thy great strength lieth.

'"And it came to pass, when she pressed him daily with her words, and urged him, so that his soul was vexed unto death;

'"That he told her all his heart, and said unto her, There hath not come a razor upon mine head; for I have been a Nazarite unto God from my mother's womb; if I be shaven, then my strength will go from me, and I shall become weak, and be like any other man."'

'What folly!' sighed the little man.   Van Moeulen kept on:

'"And when Delilah saw that he had told her all his heart, she sent and called for the lords of the Philistines, saying, Come up this once, for he hath showed me all his heart. Then the lords of the Philistines came up unto her and brought money in their hand.

'"And she made him sleep upon her knees, and she called for a man and caused him to shave off the seven locks of his head; and she began to afflict him, and his strength went from him.

'"And she said, The Philistines be upon thee, Samson. And he woke out of his sleep, and said, I will go out as at other times before, and shake myself. And he wist not that the Lord was departed from him.

'"But the Philistines took him, and put out his eyes, and brought him down to Gaza, and bound him with fetters of brass; and he did grind in the prison house."'

'O God! God!' wailed and wept the sick man. 'Be quiet!' said Van Moeulen, and read on:

'"Howbeit the hair of his head began to grow again after he was shaven.

'"Then the lords of the Philistines gathered them together for to offer a great sacrifice unto Dagon their god, and to rejoice: for they said, Our god hath delivered Samson our enemy into our hand.

'"And when the people saw him, they praised their god: for they said, Our god hath delivered into our hands our enemy, and the destroyer of our country, which slew many of us.

'"And it came to pass, when their hearts were merry, that they said, Call for Samson, that he may make us sport: and they called for Samson out of the prison house; and he made them sport: and they set him between the pillars.

'"And Samson said unto the lad that held him by the hand, Suffer me that I may feel the pillars whereupon the house standeth, that I may lean upon them.

'"Now the house was full of men and women; and all the lords of the Philistines were there; and there were upon the roof about three thousand men and women, that beheld while Samson made sport.

"'And Samson called unto the Lord, and said, O Lord God, remember me, I pray thee, and strengthen me, 1 pray thee, only this once, O God, that I may be at once avenged of the Philistines for my two eyes.

"'And Samson took hold of the two middle pillars upon which the house stood, and on which it was borne up, of the one with his right hand, and of the other with his left.

"'And Samson said, Let me die with the Philistines. And he bowed himself with all his might; and the house fell upon the lords, and upon all the people that were therein. So the dead which he slew at his death were more than they which he slew in his life.'"

At this little Samson opened his eyes spectrally wide, raised himself spasmodically, seized with his slender arms the two pillars at the foot of his bed, and shook them, crying out in wrath: 'Let me die with the Philistines!' The strong columns remained immovable; but, exhausted and smiling sadly, the little man fell back on his pillow, while from his wound, the bandage of which was displaced, ran a red stream of blood.

JAN STEEN

In the house I lodged at in Leyden there once lived Jan Steen, the great Jan Steen, whom I hold to be as great as Raphael. Even as a sacred painter Jan was as great, and that will be clearly seen when the religion of sorrow has passed away, and the religion of joy has torn off the thick veil that covers the rose-bushes of the earth, and the nightingales dare at last to sing joyously out their long-concealed raptures.

But no nightingale will ever sing so joyously as Jan Steen painted. No one has understood so profoundly as he that there shall be an eternal festival on the earth; he comprehended that our life is only the pictured kiss of God, and he felt that the Holy Ghost is revealed most gloriously in light and in laughter.

His eye laughed into the light, and the light mirrored itself in his laughing eye. And Jan remained always a dear, good child. The stern old pastor of Leyden sat near him by the hearth, and delivered a lengthy discourse concerning his jovial life, his laughing, unchristian conduct, his love of drinking, his disorderly domestic affairs, his obdurate gaiety; and Jan listened quietly for two long hours, and betrayed not the slightest impatience at the lengthy sermon; only once he broke in with the words: 'Yes, Domine, that light is far better; yes, Domine, I beg of you to draw your stool a little nearer to the fire, so that the flame may cast its red gleam over your whole face, and leave the rest of the figure in shade——'

The Domine stood up wrathful and departed. But Jan seized his palette and painted the stern old man, just as in that sermon on vice he had unconsciously furnished a model. The picture is excellent, and hung in my bedroom at Leyden.

Now that I have seen so many of Jan Steen's pictures in Holland, I seem to know the whole life of the man. I know all his relations, his wife, his children, his mother, all his cousins, his enemies, his various connections—yes, I know them all by sight. These faces greet us out of all his pictures, and a collection of them would be a biography of the painter. He has often with a single stroke revealed the deepest secrets of his soul. As I think, his wife reproached him far too often about drinking too much. For in the picture which represents the Twelfth-night feast where Jan and his family are sitting at table, we see his wife with a large jug of wine in her hand, and eyes beaming like a Bacchante's. I am convinced, however, that the good lady never indulged in too much wine; only the rogue wanted us to believe that it was his wife, and not he, who was too fond of drinking. That is why he laughs so joyously out of the picture. He is happy; he sits in the midst of his family; his little son is king of the feast, and, with his tinsel crown, stands upon a stool; his old mother, with the happiest smirk of satisfaction in the wrinkles of her countenance, carries the youngest grandchild upon her arm; the musicians play their maddest dance melodies; and the frugal, sulky housewife is painted in, an object of suspicion to all posterity, as though she were inebriated.

How often, during my stay at Leyden, did I think myself back for whole hours into the household scenes in which the excellent Jan must have lived and suffered. Many a time I thought I saw him in the flesh, sitting at his easel, now and then grasping the great jug, 'reflecting and therewith drinking, and then again drinking without reflecting.' It was no gloomy Catholic spectre that I saw, but a modern bright spirit of joy, who after death still visited his old workroom to paint merry pictures and to drink. Only such ghosts will our children sometimes see, in the light of day, while the sun shines through the windows, and from the spire no black, hollow bells, but red, exulting trumpet tones, announce the pleasant hour of noon.

THE ROMANTIC SCHOOL

WHAT was the Romantic School in Germany?

It was nothing else than the reawakening of the poetry of the Middle Ages as it manifested itself in the poems, paintings, and sculptures, in the art and life of those times. This poetry, however, had been developed out of Christianity; it was a passion-flower which had blossomed from the blood of Christ. I know not if the melancholy flower which in Germany we call the passion-flower is known by the same name in France, and if the popular tradition has ascribed to it the same mystical origin. It is that motley-hued, melancholic flower in whose calyx one may behold a counterfeit presentment of the tools used at the crucifixion of Christ—namely, hammer, pincers, and nails. This flower is by no means unsightly, but only spectral: its aspect fills our souls with a dread pleasure, like those convulsive, sweet emotions that arise from grief. In this respect the passion-flower would be the fittest symbol of Christianity itself, whose most awe-inspiring charm consists in the voluptuousness of pain.

Although in France Christianity and Roman Catholicism are synonymous terms, yet I desire to emphasize the fact, that I here refer to the latter only. I refer to that religion whose earliest dogmas contained a condemnation of all flesh, and not only admitted the supremacy of the spirit over the flesh, but sought to mortify the latter in order thereby to glorify the former. I refer to that religion through whose unnatural mission vice and hypocrisy came into the world, for through the odium which it cast on the flesh the most innocent gratifications of the senses were accounted sins; and, as it was impossible to be entirely spiritual, the growth of hypocrisy was inevitable. I refer to that religion which, by teaching the renunciation of all earthly pleasures, and by inculcating abject humility and angelic patience, became the most efficacious support of despotism. Men now recognize the nature of that religion, and will no longer be put off with promises of a heaven hereafter; they know that the material world has also its good, and is not wholly given over to Satan, and now they vindicate the pleasures of the world, this beautiful garden of the gods, our inalienable heritage. Just because we now comprehend so fully all the consequences of that absolute spirituality, we are warranted in believing that the Christian-Catholic theories of the universe are at an end; for every epoch is a sphinx which plunges into the abyss as soon as its problem is solved.

We by no means deny the benefits which the Christian-Catholic theories effected in Europe. They were needed as a wholesome reaction against the terrible colossal materialism which was developed in the Roman Empire, and threatened the annihilation of all the intellectual grandeur of mankind. Just as the licentious memoirs of the last century form the *pièces justificatives* of the French Revolution; just as the reign of terror seems a necessary medicine when one is familiar with the confessions of the French nobility since the Regency; so the wholesomeness of ascetic spirituality becomes manifest when we read Petronius or Apuleius, books which may be considered as *pièces justificatives* of Christianity. The flesh had become so insolent in this Roman world that Christian discipline was needed to chasten it. After the banquet of a Trimalchio, a hunger-cure, such as Christianity, was required.

Or did, perhaps, the hoary sensualists seek by scourgings to stimulate the cloyed flesh to renewed capacity for enjoyment? Did ageing Rome submit to monkish flagellations in order to discover exquisite pleasure in torture itself, voluptuous bliss in pain?

Unfortunate excess! it robbed the Roman body-politic of its last energies. Rome was not destroyed by the division into two empires. On the Bosporus as on the Tiber, Rome was eaten up by the same Judaic spiritualism, and in both Roman history became the record of a slow dying-away, a death agony that lasted for centuries. Did perhaps murdered Judea, by bequeathing its spiritualism to the Romans, seek to avenge itself on the victorious foe, as did the dying centaur, who so cunningly wheedled the son of Jupiter into wearing the deadly vestment poisoned with his own blood? In truth, Rome, the Hercules among nations, was so effectually consumed by the Judaic poison that helm and armour fell from its decaying limbs, and its imperious battle tones degenerated into the prayers of snivelling priests and the trilling of eunuchs.

But that which enfeebles the aged strengthens the young. That spiritualism had a wholesome effect on the over-robust races of the north; the ruddy barbarians became spiritualized through Christianity; European civilization began. This is a praiseworthy and sacred phase of Christianity. The Catholic Church earned in this regard the highest title to our respect and admiration.   Through grand, genial institutions it controlled the bestiality of the barbarian hordes of the north, and tamed their brutal materialism.

The works of art in the Middle Ages give evidence of this mastery of matter by the spirit; and that is often their whole purpose. The epic poems of that time may be easily classified according to the degree in which they show that mastery. Of lyric and dramatic poems nothing is here to be said; for the latter do not exist, and the former are as much alike in all ages as are the songs of the nightingales in each succeeding spring.

Although the epic poetry of the Middle Ages was divided into sacred and secular, yet both classes were purely Christian in their nature; for if the sacred poetry related exclusively to the Jewish people and its history, which alone was considered sacred; if its themes were the heroes of the Old and the New Testaments, and their legends—in brief, the Church—still all the Christian views and aims of that period were mirrored in the secular poetry.   The flower of the German sacred poetry of the Middle Ages is, perhaps, *Barlaam and Josaphat*, a poem in which the dogma of self-denial, of continence, of renunciation, of the scorn of all worldly pleasures, is most consistently expressed.   Next in order of merit I would rank *Lobgesang auf den Heiligen Anno*, but the latter poem already evinces a marked tendency towards secular themes.   It differs in general from the former somewhat as an old German representation of a saint differs from a Byzantine image.   Just as in those Byzantine pictures, so also do we find in *Barlaam and Josaphat* the greatest simplicity; there is no perspective, and the long, lean, statue-like forms, and the grave, ideal countenances, stand severely outlined, as though in bold relief against a background of pale gold.   In the *Lobgesang auf den Heiligen Anno*, as in the old German pictures, the accessories seem almost more prominent than the subject; and, notwithstanding the bold outlines, every detail is most minutely executed, and one knows not which to admire most, the giantlike conception or the dwarflike patience of execution.   Ottfried's *Evangeliengedicht*, which is generally praised as the masterpiece of this sacred poetry, is far inferior to both of these poems.

In the secular poetry we find, as intimated above, first, the cycle of legends called the *Nibelungenlied*, and the *Book of Heroes*.

In these poems all the ante-Christian modes of thought and feelings are dominant; brute force is not yet moderated into chivalry; the sturdy warriors of the North stand like statues of stone, and the soft light and moral atmosphere of Christianity have not yet penetrated their iron armour. But dawn is gradually breaking over the old German forests, the ancient Druid oaks are being felled, and in the open arena Christianity and Paganism are battling: all this is portrayed in the cycle of traditions of Charlemagne; even the Crusades with their religious tendencies are mirrored therein. But now from this Christianized, spiritualized brute force is developed the peculiar feature of the Middle Ages, chivalry, which finally becomes exalted into a religious knighthood. The earlier knighthood is most felicitously portrayed in the legends of King Arthur, which are full of the most charming gallantry, the most finished courtesy, and the most daring bravery. From the midst of the pleasing, though bizarre, arabesques, and the fantastic, flowery mazes of these tales, we are greeted by the gentle Gawain, by the worthy Lancelot of the Lake, by the valiant, gallant, and honest, but somewhat tedious, Wigalois. By the side of this cycle of legends we find the kindred and connected legends of the Holy Grail, in which the religious knighthood is glorified, and in which are to be found the three grandest poems of the Middle Ages, *Titurel*, *Parcival*, and *Lohengrin*. In these poems we stand face to face, as it were, with the Muse of romantic poetry; we look deep into her large, sad eyes, and ere we are aware she has ensnared us in her network of scholasticism, and drawn us down into the weird depths of medieval mysticism. But farther on in this period we find poems which do not unconditionally bow down to Christian spirituality; poems in which it is even attacked, and in which the poet, breaking loose from the fetters of an abstract Christian morality, complacently plunges into the delightful realm of glorious sensuousness. Nor is it an inferior poet who has left us *Tristan and Isolde*, the masterpiece of this class. Verily, I must confess that Gottfried von Strassburg, the author of this, the most exquisite poem of the Middle Ages, is perhaps also the loftiest poet of that period. He surpasses even the grandeur of Wolfram von Eschenbach, whose *Parcival*, and fragments of *Titurel*, are so much admired. At present, it is perhaps permissible to praise Meister Gottfried without stint, but in his own time his book and similar poems, to which even *Lancelot* belonged, were considered godless and dangerous. Francesca da Polenta and her handsome friend paid dearly for reading together such a book—the greater danger, it is true, lay in the fact that they suddenly stopped reading.

All the poetry of the Middle Ages has a certain definite character, through which it differs from the poetry of the Greeks and Romans. In reference to this difference the former is called Romantic, the latter Classic. These names, however, are misleading, and have hitherto caused the most vexatious confusion, which is even increased when we call the antique poetry plastic as well as classic. In this, particularly, lies the germ of misunderstandings; for artists ought always to treat their subject-matter plastically. Whether it be Christian or pagan, the subject ought to be portrayed in clear contours. In short, plastic configuration should be the main requisite in the modern romantic as well as in antique art. And, in fact, are not the figures in Dante's *Divine Comedy* or in the paintings of Raphael just as plastic as those in Virgil or on the walls of Herculaneum?

The difference consists in this—that the plastic figures in antique art are identical with the thing represented, with the idea which the artist seeks to communicate. Thus, for example, the wanderings of the Odyssey mean nothing else than the wanderings of the man who was a son of Laertes and the husband of Penelope, and was called Ulysses. Thus, again, the Bacchus which is to be seen in the Louvre is nothing more than the charming son of Semele, with a daring melancholy look in his eyes, and an inspired voluptuousness on the soft arched lips. It is otherwise in romantic art: here the wanderings of a knight have an esoteric signification; they typify, perhaps, the mazes of life in general. The dragon that is vanquished is sin; the almond-tree, that from afar so encouragingly wafts its fragrance to the hero, is the Trinity, the God-Father, God-Son, and God-Holy-Ghost, who together constitute one, just as shell, fibre, and kernel together constitute the almond. When Homer describes the armour of a hero, it is naught else than good armour, which is worth so many oxen; but when a monk of the Middle Ages describes in his poem the garments of the Mother of God, you may depend upon it, that by each fold of those garments he typifies some special virtue, and that a peculiar meaning lies hidden in the sacred robes of the immaculate Virgin Mary; as her Son is the kernel of the almond, she is quite appropriately described in the poem as an almond-blossom. Such is the character of that poesy of the Middle Ages which we designate *romantic*.

Classic art had to portray only the finite, and its forms could be identical with the artist's idea. Romantic art had to represent, or rather to typify, the infinite and the spiritual, and therefore was compelled to have recourse to a system of traditional, or rather parabolic, symbols, just as Christ Himself had endeavoured to explain and make clear His spiritual meaning through beautiful parables. Hence the mystic, enigmatical, miraculous, and transcendental character of the art-productions of the Middle Ages. Fancy strives frantically to portray through concrete images that which is purely spiritual, and in the vain endeavour invents the most colossal absurdities; it piles Ossa on Pelion, Parcival on Titurel, to reach heaven.

Similar monstrous abortions of imagination have been produced by the Scandinavians, the Hindus, and the other races which likewise strive through poetry to represent the infinite; among them also do we find poems which may be regarded as romantic.

.   .   .   .

But human genius can transfigure deformity itself, and many painters succeeded in accomplishing the unnatural task beautifully and sublimely. The Italians, in particular, glorified beauty—it is true, somewhat at the expense of spirituality— and raised themselves aloft to an ideality which reached its perfection in the many representations of the Madonna. Where it concerned the Madonna, the Catholic clergy always made some concessions to sensuality. This image of an immaculate beauty, transfigured by motherly love and sorrow, was privileged to receive the homage of poet and painter, and to be decked with all the charms that could allure the senses. For this image was a magnet, which was to draw the great masses into the pale of Christianity. Madonna Maria was the pretty *dame du comptoir* of the Catholic Church, whose customers, especially the barbarians of the north, she attracted and held fast by her celestial smiles.

During the Middle Ages architecture was of the same character as the other arts; for, indeed, at that period all manifestations of life harmonized most wonderfully. In architecture, as in poetry, this parabolizing tendency was evident. Now, when we enter an old cathedral, we have scarcely a hint of the esoteric meaning of its stony symbolism. Only the general impression forces itself on our mind. We feel the exaltation of the spirit and the abasement of the flesh. The interior of the cathedral is a hollow cross, and we walk here amid the instruments of martyrdom itself. The variegated windows cast on us their red and green lights, like drops of blood and ichor; requiems for the dead resound through the aisles; under our feet are gravestones and decay; in harmony with the colossal pillars, the soul soars aloft, painfully tearing itself away from the body, which sinks to the ground like a cast-off garment. When one views from without these Gothic cathedrals, these immense structures, that are built so airily, so delicately, so daintily, as transparent as if carved, like Brabant laces made of marble, then only does one realize the might of that art which could achieve a mastery over stone, so that even this stubborn substance should appear spectrally etherealized, and be an exponent of Christian spiritualism.

But the arts are only the mirror of life; and when Catholicism disappeared from daily life, so also it faded and vanished out of the arts. At the time of the Reformation Catholic poetry was gradually dying out in Europe, and in its place we behold the long-buried Grecian style of poetry again reviving. It was, in sooth, only an artificial spring, the work of the gardener and not of the sun; the trees and flowers were stuck in narrow pots, and a glass sky protected them from the wind and cold weather.

In the world's history every event is not the direct consequence of another, but all events mutually act and react on one another. It was not alone through the Greek scholars who, after the conquest of Constantinople, immigrated over to us, that the love for Grecian art, and the striving to imitate it, became universal among us; but in art as in life, there was stirring a contemporary Protestantism. Leo X, the magnificent Medici, was just as zealous a Protestant as Luther; and as in Wittenberg protest was offered in Latin prose, so in Rome the protest was made in stone, colours, and *ottave rime*. For do not the vigorous marble statues of Michael Angelo, Giulio Romano's laughing nymph-faces, and the life-intoxicated merriment in the verses of Messer Ludovico, offer a protesting contrast to the old, gloomy, withered Catholicism? The painters of Italy combated priestdom more effectively, perhaps, than did the Saxon theologians. The glowing flesh in the paintings of Titian—all that is simple Protestantism. The limbs of his Venus are much more fundamental theses than those which the German monk nailed to the church door of Wittenberg. Mankind felt itself suddenly liberated, as it were, from the thraldom of a thousand years; the artists, in particular, breathed freely again when the Alplike burden of Christianity was rolled from off their breasts; they plunged enthusiastically into the sea of Grecian mirthfulness, from whose foam the goddess of beauty again rose to meet them; again did the painters depict the ambrosial joys of Olympus; again did the sculptors, with the olden love, chisel the heroes of antiquity from out the marble blocks; again did the poets sing of the house of Atreus and of Laius; a new era of classic poetry arose.

In France, under Louis XIV, this neo-classic poetry exhibited a polished perfection, and, to a certain extent, even originality. Through the political influence of the *grand monarque* this new classic poetry spread over the rest of Europe. In Italy, where it was already at home, it received a French colouring; the Anjous brought with them to Spain the heroes of French tragedy; it accompanied Princess Henrietta to England; and, as a matter of course, we Germans modelled our clumsy temple of art after the bepowdered Olympus of Versailles. The most famous high priest of this temple was Gottsched, that old periwigged pate, whom our dear Goethe has so felicitously described in his memoirs.

Lessing was the literary Arminius who emancipated our theatre from that foreign rule. He showed us the vapidness, the ridiculousness, the tastelessness, of those apings of the French stage, which itself was but an imitation of the Greek. But not only by his criticism, but also through his own works of art, did he become the founder of modern German original literature. All the paths of the intellect, all the phases of life, did this man pursue with disinterested enthusiasm. Art, theology, antiquarianism, poetry, dramatic criticism, history— he studied all these with the same zeal and with the same aim. In all his works breathes the same grand social idea, the same progressive humanity, the same religion of reason, whose John he was, and whose Messiah we still await. This religion he preached always, but alas! often quite alone and in the desert. Moreover, he lacked the skill to transmute stones into bread. The greater portion of his life was spent in poverty and misery —a curse which rests on almost all the great minds of Germany, and which probably will only be overcome by political emancipation. Lessing was more deeply interested in political questions than was imagined—a characteristic which we entirely miss in his contemporaries. Only now do we comprehend what he had in view by his description of the petty despotisms in *Emilia Galotti*. At that time he was considered merely a champion of intellectual liberty and an opponent of clerical intolerance; his theological writings were better understood. The fragments 'Concerning the Education of the Human Race,' which have been translated into French by Eugène Rodrigue, will perhaps suffice to give the French an idea of the wide scope of Lessing's genius. His two critical works which have had the most influence on art are his *Hamburger Dramaturgie* and his *Laocoön, or Concerning the Limits of Painting and Poetry*. His best dramatic works are *Emilia Galotti, Minna von Barnhelm,* and *Nathan the Wise*.

Gotthold Ephraim Lessing was born 22nd January 1729, at Kamenz, in Upper Lusatia, and died 15th February 1781, at Brunswick. He was a whole man, who, while with his polemics waging destructive battle against the old, at the same time created something newer and better. 'He resembled,' says a German author, 'those pious Jews, who, at the second building of the temple, were often disturbed by the attacks of their enemies, and with one hand would fight against the foe, while with the other hand they continued to work at the house of God.' This is not the place to discuss Lessing more fully, but I cannot refrain from saying that, in the whole range of literary history, he is the author whom I most love.

I desire here to call attention to another author, who worked in the same spirit and with the same aim, and who may be regarded as Lessing's most legitimate successor. It is true, a criticism of this author would be out of place here, for he occupies a peculiarly isolated place in the history of literature, and his relation to his epoch and contemporaries cannot even now be definitely pronounced. I refer to Johann Gottfried Herder, born in 1744, at Mohrungen, in East Prussia; died in 1803, at Weimar, in Saxony.

The history of literature is a great morgue, wherein each seeks the dead who are near or dear to him. And when, among the corpses of so many petty men, I behold the noble features of a Lessing or a Herder, my heart throbs with emotion. How could I pass you without pressing a hasty kiss on your pale lips?

But if Lessing effectually put an end to the servile apings of Franco-Grecian art, yet, by directing attention to the true art-works of Grecian antiquity, to a certain extent he gave an impetus to a new and equally silly species of imitation. Through his warfare against religious superstition he even advanced a certain narrow-minded jejune enlightenment, which at that time vaunted itself in Berlin; the sainted Nicolai was its principal mouthpiece, and the *German Encyclopaedia* its arsenal. The most wretched mediocrity began to raise its head, more disgustingly than ever. Imbecility, vapidity, and the commonplace distended themselves like the frog in the fable.

It is an error to believe that Goethe, who at that time had already appeared upon the scene, had met with general recognition. His *Goetz von Berlichingen* and his *Werther* were received with enthusiasm, but the works of the most ordinary bungler not less so, and Goethe occupied but a small niche in the temple of literature. It is true, as said before, that the public welcomed *Goetz* and *Werther* with delight, but more on account of their subject-matter than their artistic merits, which few were able to appreciate. Of these masterpieces, *Goetz von Berlichingen* was a dramatized romance of chivalry, which was the popular style at that time. In *Werther* the public saw only an embellished account of an episode in real life—namely, the story of young Jerusalem, a youth who shot himself from disappointed love, thereby creating quite a commotion in that dead-calm period. Tears were shed over his pathetic letters, and it was shrewdly observed that the manner in which Werther had been ostracized from the society of the nobility must have increased his weariness of life. The discussion concerning suicide brought the book still more into notice; a few fools hit upon the idea of shooting themselves in imitation of Werther, and thus the book made a marked sensation. But the romances of August Lafontaine were in equal demand, and as the latter was a voluminous writer, it followed that he was more famous than Wolfgang Goethe. Wieland was the great poet of that period, and his only rival was Herr Ramler of Berlin. Wieland was worshipped idolatrously, more than Goethe ever was. Iffland, with his lachrymose domestic dramas, and Kotzebue's farces, with their stale witticisms, ruled the stage.

It was against this literature that, in the closing years of the last century, there arose in Germany a new school, which we have designated the Romantic School. At the head of this school stand the brothers August Wilhelm and Friedrich Schlegel. Jena, where these two brothers, together with many kindred spirits, were wont to come and go, was the central point from which the new aesthetic dogma radiated. I advisedly say dogma, for this school began with a criticism of the art productions of the past, and with recipes for the art works of the future. In both of these fields the Schlegelian school has rendered good service to aesthetic criticism. In criticizing the art works of the past, either their defects and imperfections were set forth, or their merits and beauties illustrated. In their polemics, in their exposure of artistic shortcomings and imperfections, the Schlegels were entirely imitators of Lessing; they seized upon his great battle-sword, but the arm of August Wilhelm Schlegel was far too feeble, and the sight of his brother Friedrich too much obscured by mystic clouds; the former could not strike so strong, nor the latter so sure and telling a blow as Lessing. In reproductive criticism, however, where the beauties of a work of art were to be brought out clearly; where a delicate perception of the individualities was required; and where these were to be made intelligible, the Schlegels are far superior to Lessing. But what shall I say concerning their recipes for producing masterpieces? Here the Schlegels reveal the same impotency that we seem to discover in Lessing. The latter also, strong as he is in negation, is weak in affirmation; seldom can he lay down any fundamental principle, and even more rarely a correct one. He lacks the firm foundation of a philosophy, or a synthetic system. In this respect the Schlegels are still more woefully lacking. Many fables are rife concerning the influence of Fichtean idealism and Schelling's philosophy of nature upon the romantic school, and it is even asserted that the latter is entirely the result of the former. I can, however, at the most discover the traces of only a few stray thoughts of Fichte and Schelling, but by no means the impress of a system of philosophy. It is true that Schelling, who at that time was delivering lectures at Jena, had personally a great influence upon the romantic school. Schelling is also somewhat of a poet, a fact not generally known in France, and it is said that he is still in doubt whether he shall not publish his entire philosophical works in poetical, yes, even in metrical form. This doubt is characteristic of the man.

But if the Schlegels could give no definite, reliable theory for the masterpieces which they bespoke of the poets of their school, they atoned for these shortcomings by commending as models the best works of art of the past, and by making them accessible to their disciples. These were chiefly the Christian-Catholic productions of the Middle Ages. The translation of Shakespeare, who stands at the frontier of this art and with Protestant clearness smiles over into our modern era, was solely intended for polemical purposes, the present discussion of which space forbids. It was undertaken by A. W. Schlegel at a time when the enthusiasm for the Middle Ages had not yet reached its most extravagant height. Later, when this did occur, Calderon was translated and ranked far above Shakespeare. For the works of Calderon bear most distinctly the impress of the poetry of the Middle Ages—particularly of the two principal epochs of knight-errantry and monasticism. The pious comedies of the Castilian priest-poet, whose poetical flowers had been besprinkled with holy water and canonical perfumes, with all their pious *grandezza*, with all their sacerdotal splendour, with all their sanctimonious balderdash, were now set up as models, and Germany swarmed with fantastically-pious, insanely-profound poems, over which it was the fashion to work oneself into a mystic ecstasy of admiration, as in *The Devotion to the Cross*, or to fight in honour of the Madonna, as in *The Constant Prince*. Zacharias Werner carried the nonsense as far as it might be safely done without being imprisoned by the authorities in a lunatic asylum.

RELIGION AND PHILOSOPHY IN GERMANY

. . . There was one man at the Diet of Worms who, I am convinced, thought not of himself, but only of the sacred interests which he was there to champion. That man was Martin Luther, the poor monk whom Providence had selected to shatter the world-controlling power of the Roman Catholic Church, against which the mightiest emperors and most intrepid scholars had striven in vain. But Providence knows well on whose shoulders to impose its tasks; here not only intellectual but also physical strength was required. It needed a body steeled from youth through chastity and monkish discipline to bear the labour and vexations of such an office.

. . . Luther was not only the greatest, but also the most thoroughly German hero of our history. In his character are combined, on the grandest scale, all the virtues and all the faults of the Germans, so that, in his own person, he was the representative of that wonderful Germany. For he possessed qualities which we seldom find united, and which we usually even consider to be irreconcilably antagonistic. He was simultaneously a dreamy mystic and a practical man of action. His thoughts possess not only wings, but also hands; he could speak and could act. He was not only the tongue, but also the sword of his time. He was both a cold, scholastic word-caviller, and an enthusiastic, God-inspired prophet. When, during the day, he had wearily toiled over his dogmatic distinctions and definitions, then in the evening he took his lute, looked up to the stars, and melted into melody and devotion. The same man who could scold like a fish-wife could be as gentle as a tender maiden. At times he was as fierce as the storm that uproots oaks; and then again he was mild as the zephyr caressing the violets. He was filled with a reverential awe of God. He was full of the spirit of self-sacrifice for the honour of the Holy Ghost; he could sink his whole personality in the most abstract spirituality, and yet he could well appreciate the good things of this earth, and from his mouth blossomed forth the famous saying:

Who loves not wine, women, and song,
Will be a fool all his life long.

256

He was a complete man—I would say an absolute man, in whom spirit and matter were not antagonistic. To call him a spiritualist, would, therefore, be as erroneous as to call him a sensualist. How shall I describe him? He had in him something aboriginal, incomprehensible, miraculous.

. . . All praise to Luther! Eternal honour to the blessed man to whom we owe the salvation of our most precious possessions, and whose benefactions we still enjoy. It ill becomes us to complain of the narrowness of his views. The dwarf, standing on the shoulders of the giant, particularly if he puts on spectacles, can, it is true, see farther than the giant himself; but for noble thoughts and exalted sentiments a giant heart is necessary. It were still more unseemly of us to pass a harsh judgment on his faults, for those very faults have benefited us more than the virtues of thousands of other men. The refinement of Erasmus, the mildness of Melanchthon, could never have brought us so far as the godlike brutality of Brother Martin.

. . . From the day on which Luther denied the authority of the Pope, and publicly declared in the Diet 'that his teachings must be controverted through the words of the Bible itself, or with sensible reasons,' there begins a new era in Germany. The fetters with which Saint Boniface had chained the German Church to Rome are broken. This Church, which has hitherto formed an integral part of the great hierarchy, now splits into religious democracies. The character of the religion itself is essentially changed: the Hindu - Gnostic element disappears from it, and the Judaic-theistic element again becomes prominent. We behold the rise of evangelical Christianity. By recognizing and legitimizing the most importunate claims of the senses, religion becomes once more a reality. The priest becomes man, takes to himself a wife, and begets children, as God desires.

. . . If in Germany we lost through Protestantism, along with the ancient miracles, much other poetry, we gained manifold compensations. Men became nobler and more virtuous. Protestantism was very successful in effecting that purity of morals and that strictness in the fulfilment of duty which is generally called morality. In certain communities, indeed, Protestantism assumed a tendency which in the end became quite identical with morality, and the gospels remained as a beautiful parable only. Particularly in the lives of the ecclesiastics is a pleasing change now noticeable. With celibacy disappeared also monkish obscenities and vices. Among the

Protestant clergy are frequently to be found the noblest and most virtuous of men, such as would have won respect from even the ancient Stoics. One must have wandered on foot, as a poor student, through northern Germany, to learn how much virtue—and in order to give virtue a complimentary adjective, how much evangelical virtue—is to be found in an unpretentious-looking parsonage. How often of a winter's evening have I found there a hospitable welcome—I, a stranger, who brought with me no other recommendation save that I was hungry and tired! When I had partaken of a hearty meal, and, after a good night's rest, was ready in the morning to continue my journey, then came the old pastor, in his dressing-gown, and gave me a blessing on the way,—and it never brought me misfortune; and his good-hearted, gossipy wife placed several slices of bread-and-butter in my pocket, which I found not less refreshing; and silent in the distance stood the pastor's pretty daughters, with blushing cheeks and violet eyes, whose modest fire in the mere recollection warmed my heart for many a whole winter's day. . . . How strange! We Germans are the strongest and wisest of nations; our royal races furnish princes for all the thrones of Europe; our Rothschilds rule all the exchanges of the world; our learned men are pre-eminent in all the sciences; we invented gunpowder and printing—and yet if one of us fires a pistol he must pay a fine of three thalers; and if we wish to insert in a newspaper: 'My dear wife has given birth to a little daughter, beautiful as Liberty,' then the censor grasps his red pencil and strikes out the word 'Liberty.'

. . . I have said that we gained freedom of thought through Luther. But he gave us not only freedom of movement, but also the means of movement; to the spirit he gave a body; to the thought he gave words. He created the German language.

This he did by his translation of the Bible.

In fact, the Divine Author of that book seems to have known, as well as we others, that the choice of a translator is by no means a matter of indifference; and so He himself selected His trans-lator, and bestowed on him the wonderful gift to translate from a language which was dead and already buried, into another language that as yet did not exist.

. . . The knowledge of the Hebrew language had entirely disappeared from the Christian world. Only the Jews, who kept themselves hidden here and there in stray corners of the world, yet preserved the traditions of this language. Like a ghost keeping watch over a treasure which had been confided to it during life, so in its dark and gloomy ghettos sat this murdered nation, this spectre-people, guarding the Hebrew Bible.

. . . Luther's Bible is an enduring spring of rejuvenation for our language. All the expressions and phrases contained therein are German, and are still in use by writers. As this book is in the hands of even the poorest people, they require no special learned education in order to be able to express themselves in literary forms. When our political revolution breaks out, this circumstance will have remarkable results. Liberty will everywhere be gifted with the power of speech, and her speech will be biblical.

. . . More noteworthy and of more importance than his prose writings are Luther's poems, the songs which in battle and in trouble blossomed forth from his heart. Sometimes they resemble a floweret that grows on a rocky crag, then again a ray of moonlight trembling over a restless sea. Luther loved music, and even wrote a treatise on the art; hence his songs are particularly melodious. In this respect he merits the name, Swan of Eisleben. But he is nothing less than a wild swan in those songs wherein he stimulates the courage of his followers and inflames himself to the fiercest rage of battle. A true battle-song was that martial strain with which he and his companions marched into Worms. The old cathedral trembled at those unwonted tones, and the ravens, in their dark nests in the steeple, startled with affright. That song, the *Marseillaise* of the Reformation, preserves to this day its inspiriting power.

FLORENTINE NIGHTS

FIRST NIGHT

In the ante-room Maximilian found the doctor just as he was drawing on his black gloves. 'I am greatly pressed for time,' the latter hurriedly said to him. 'Signora Maria has not slept during the whole night; she has only just now fallen into a light slumber. I need not caution you not to wake her by any noise; and when she wakes on no account must she be allowed to talk. She must lie still, and not disturb herself; mental excitement will not be salutary. Tell her all kinds of odd stories, so that she must listen quietly.'

'Be assured, doctor,' replied Maximilian, with a melancholy smile. 'I have educated myself for a long time in chattering, and will not let her talk. I will narrate abundance of fantastic nonsense, as much as you require. But how long can she live?'

'I am greatly pressed for time,' answered the doctor, and slipped away.

Black Deborah, quick of hearing as she was, had already recognized the stranger's footstep, and softly opened the door. At a sign from him she left as softly, and Maximilian found himself alone with his friend. A single lamp dimly lighted the chamber. This cast now and then half timid, half inquisitive gleams upon the countenance of the sick lady, clothed entirely in white muslin, who lay stretched on a green sofa in calm sleep.

Silent, and with folded arms, Maximilian stood a little while before the sleeping figure, and gazed on the beautiful limbs which the light garments revealed rather than covered; and every time that the lamp threw a ray of light over the pale countenance, his heart quivered. 'For God's sake!' he said softly, 'what is this? What memories are awaking in me? Yes, now I know. This white form on the green ground, yes, now . . .'

At this moment the invalid awoke, and gazing out, as it were, from the depths of a dream, the tender dark-blue eyes rested upon him, asking, entreating . . . 'What were you thinking of, just now, Maximilian?' she said, in that awful, gentle voice so often found in consumptives, and wherein we seem to recognize the lisping of children, the twittering of birds, and the gurgle of the dying. 'What were you thinking of, just then, Maximilian?' she repeated again, and started up so hastily that the long curls, like roused snakes, fell in ringlets around her head.

'For God's sake!' exclaimed Maximilian, as he gently pressed her back on to the sofa, 'lie still, do not talk; I will tell you all I think, I feel, yes, what I myself do not know!

'In fact,' he pursued, 'I scarcely know what I was thinking and feeling just now. Dim visions of childhood were passing through my mind. I was thinking of my mother's castle, of the deserted garden there, of the beautiful marble statue that lay in the grass. . . . I said, "my mother's *castle*," but pray do not imagine anything grand and magnificent. To this name I have indeed accustomed myself; my father always laid a special emphasis on the words, "the castle," and accompanied them always with a singular smile. The meaning of that smile I understood later, when, a boy of some twelve years, I travelled with my mother to the castle. It was my first journey. We spent the whole day in passing through a thick forest; I shall never forget its gloomy horror; and only towards evening did we stop before a long cross-bar which separated us from a large meadow. Here we waited nearly half an hour before the boy came out of the wretched hut near by, removed the barrier, and admitted us. I say "the boy," because old Martha always called her forty-year-old nephew "the lad." To receive his gracious mistress worthily, he had assumed the livery of his late uncle; and it was in consequence of its requiring a little previous dusting that he had kept us waiting so long. Had he had time, he would have also put on stockings; the long red legs, however, did not form a very marked contrast with the glaring scarlet coat. Whether there were any trousers underneath I am unable to say. Our servant, Johann, who had likewise often heard of "the castle," put on a very amazed grimace as the boy led us to the little ruined building in which his master had lived. He was, however, altogether at a loss when my mother ordered him to bring in the beds. How could he guess that at the "castle" no beds were to be found and my mother's order that he should bring bedding for us he had either not heard or considered as superfluous trouble.

'The little house, only one story high, which in its best days contained, at the most, five habitable rooms, was a lamentable picture of transitoriness. Broken furniture, torn carpets, not one window-frame left entire, the floor pulled up here and there,

everywhere the hated traces of the wantonest military possession. "The soldiers quartered with us have always amused
themselves," said the boy, with a silly smile. My mother
signed that we should all leave her alone, and while the boy and
Johann were busying themselves, I went out to see the garden.
This also offered the most disconsolate picture of ruin. The great
trees were partly destroyed, partly broken down, and parasites
were scornfully spreading over the fallen trunks. Here and
there by the grown-up box-bushes the old paths might be
recognized. Here and there also stood statues, for the most
part wanting heads, or at all events noses. I remember a
Diana whose lower half the dark ivy grew round in a most
amusing way, as I also remember a Goddess of Plenty, out of
whose cornucopia mere malodorous weeds were blooming. Only
one statue had been spared by the malice of men and of time;
it had, indeed, been thrown from off its pedestal into the high
grass; but there it lay, free from mutilation, the marble goddess
with pure lovely features and the noble deep-cleft bosom, which
seemed, as it glowed out of the grass, like a Greek revelation.
I almost started when I saw it; this form inspired me with a
singular feeling, and bashfulness kept me from lingering long
near so sweet a sight.

'When I returned to my mother, she was standing at the
window, lost in thought, her head resting on her right arm,
and the tears were flowing over her cheeks. I had never seen
her weep so before. She embraced me with passionate tenderness, and asked my forgiveness, because, owing to Johann's
negligence, I should have no regular bed. "Old Martha," she
said, "is very ill, dear child, and cannot give up her bed to you;
but Johann will arrange the cushions out of the coach, so that you
will be able to sleep upon them, and he can also give you his
cloak for a covering. I shall sleep on the straw; this was my
dear father's bedroom; it was much better here once. Leave
me alone!" And the tears came still more impetuously.

'Whether it was owing to my unaccustomed place of rest or
to my disturbed heart, I could not sleep. The moonlight
streamed in through the broken window-panes, and seemed to
allure me out into the bright summer night. I might lie on the
right or the left side, close my eyes or impatiently open them
again—I could still think of nothing but the lovely marble
statue I had seen lying in the grass. I could not understand
the shyness which had come over me at the sight of it; I was
vexed at this childish feeling, and "To-morrow," I said softly

to myself, "to-morrow I will kiss you, you lovely marble face, kiss you just on that pretty corner of your mouth where the lips melt into such a sweet dimple!" An impatience I had never before felt was stirring through all my limbs; I could no longer rule the strange impulse, and I sprang up at last with audacious vivacity, exclaiming: "And why should I not kiss you to-night, you dear image?" Quietly, so that mother might not hear my steps, I left the house; with the less difficulty, since the entrance was furnished with an escutcheon indeed, but no longer with a door, and hastily worked my way through the abundant growth of the neglected garden. There was no sound; everything was resting silent and solemn in the still moonlight. The shadows of the trees seemed to be nailed on the earth. In the green grass lay the beautiful goddess, likewise motionless, yet no stony death, but only a quiet sleep, seemed to hold her lovely limbs fettered; and as I came near, I almost feared lest the least noise should awake her out of her slumber. I held my breath, as I leant over to gaze on the beautiful features; a shuddering pain thrust me back, but a boyish wantonness drew me again towards her; my heart was beating wildly, and at last I kissed the lovely goddess with such passion and tenderness and despair as I have never in this life kissed with again. And I have never been able to forget the fearful and sweet sensation which flowed through my soul as the blissful cool of those marble lips touched my mouth. . . . And so you see, Maria, that as I was just now standing before you, and saw you lying in your white muslin garments on the green sofa, your appearance suggested to me the white marble form in the green grass. Had you slept any longer my lips would not have been able to resist——'

'Max! Max!' she cried from the depth of her soul. 'Horrible! You know that a kiss from your mouth——'

'Oh, be silent; I know you think that something horrible. Do not look at me so imploringly. I do not misunderstand your feelings, although their causes are hidden from me. I have never dared to press my mouth on your lips.'

But Maria would not let him finish speaking; she seized his hand, covered it with passionate kisses, and then said, smiling: 'Please tell me more of your love affairs. How long did you adore the marble beauty that you kissed in your mother's castle garden?'

'We went away the next day,' Maximilian answered, 'and I have never seen the lovely statue again. It occupied my heart, however, for nearly three years. A wonderful passion for marble statues has since then developed in my soul, and this very day I have felt its transporting power. I was coming out of the Laurentian, the library of the Medici, and I wandered, I know not how, into the chapel where that most magnificent of Italian families built for itself a resting-place of jewels, and is quietly sleeping. For a whole hour I was absorbed in gazing on the marble figure of a woman, whose powerful body witnesses to the cunning strength of Michelangelo, while yet the whole form is pervaded by an ethereal sweetness which we are not accustomed to seek in that master. The whole dream-world, with its silent blisses, lives in that marble; a tender repose dwells in the lovely limbs, a soothing moonlight seems to course through the veins. It is the Night of Michelangelo Buonarotti. Oh, how willingly would I sleep the eternal sleep in the arms of that Night!

'Painted women forms,' Maximilian pursued, after a pause, 'have never so powerfully interested me as statues. Only once was I in love with a painting. It was a wondrously lovely Madonna that I learnt to know at a church in Cologne. I was at that time a very zealous church-goer, and my heart was absorbed in the mysticism of the Catholic religion. I would then have willingly fought like a Spanish knight, at the peril of my life, for the immaculate conception of Mary, the Queen of Angels, the fairest lady of heaven and earth! I was interested in all the members of the holy family at that time, and I took my hat off in an especially friendly manner whenever I passed near a picture of the holy Joseph. This disposition did not last long, however, and I deserted the Mother of God almost without any explanations, having become acquainted, in a gallery of antiquities, with a Grecian nymph, who for a long time held me enchained in marble fetters.'

'And you only loved sculptured or painted women?' said Maria, smiling.

'No, I have also loved dead women,' answered Maximilian, over whose face an expression of seriousness had spread. He failed to perceive Maria start and shrink at these words, and quietly proceeded:

'Yes, it is very strange that I once fell in love with a girl after she had been seven years dead. When I became acquainted with little Very I liked her extremely. For three days I occupied myself with this young person, and experienced the greatest pleasure in all that she said and did, and in every expression

of her charming wayward being, without being betrayed withal
into any over-tender emotion. And so I was not too deeply
grieved when a few months later I heard that a fever that had
seized her suddenly resulted in death. I forgot her entirely,
and I am convinced that from one year's end to another I had
not one thought of her. Seven years passed away, and I found
myself at Potsdam, to enjoy the beautiful summer in undisturbed solitude. My society was confined to the statues
in the garden of Sans-Souci. It happened there one day that
I recollected certain features, and a singular, lovely way of
speaking and moving, without being able to remember to whom
they belonged. Nothing is more annoying than such a drifting
into old memories, and I was therefore joyfully surprised when,
after some days, I recollected little Very, and discovered that
it was her dear, forgotten form that had hovered before me so
restlessly. Yes, I rejoiced at this discovery like one who un-
expectedly meets his most intimate friend; the pale hues gradually grew bright, and at last her sweet little person seemed to
stand bodily before me, smiling, pouting, witty, and prettier
than ever. From that time forth the sweet vision never left me,
it filled my whole soul; wherever I went or stood, it went
and stood at my side, spoke with me, laughed with me, always
gentle, and yet never over-tender. I was, however, more and
more fascinated with this vision, which daily gained more and
more reality for me. It is easy to raise ghosts, but it is difficult
to send them back again to their dark night; they look at us
then so imploringly, our own hearts lend them such powerful
intercession. I could not tear myself free, and fell in love with
little Very after she had been seven years dead. I lived thus
at Potsdam for six months, quite buried in this love. I guarded
myself more carefully than ever from any contact with the outer
world, and if any one in the street came at all near me, I
experienced the most miserable oppression. I cherished a deep
horror of every occurrence, such as, perhaps, the night-wandering spirits of the dead experience; for these, it is said, are terrified when they meet a living man, as much as a living man is
terrified when he meets a spectre. By chance a traveller came
at that time to Potsdam whom I could not escape—namely,
my brother. His appearance and his accounts of the latest news
woke me as from a deep dream, and I suddenly felt, with a
shudder, in what a frightful solitude I had been so long living.
In this condition I had not once noted the change of the seasons,
and I now gazed with wonder on trees, once leafless,

decked in their autumn mellowness. I immediately left Potsdam and little Very, and in another town, where important business was awaiting me, and by means of difficult circumstances and relations, I was soon again plunged into crude reality.

'The living women,' Maximilian pursued, while a sorrowful smile played on his upper lip, 'the living women with whom I then came into unavoidable contact, how they tormented me, tenderly tormented me with their pouting, jealousy, and constant sighs! At how many balls must I trot round with them, in how much gossip must I mix myself! What restless vanity, what delight in lying, what kissing treachery, what envenomed flowers! These women spoilt all pleasure and love for me, and I was for some time a misogynist, who damned the whole sex. It went with me almost as with the French officer, who, in the Prussian campaign, only saved himself with the greatest difficulty from the ice-pits of the Beresina, and since then retains such an antipathy to everything frozen, that now he thrusts away with disgust the sweetest and most delicious of Tortoni's ices. Yes, the remembrance of the Beresina of love that I passed through then spoilt for me, for a time, even the most charming ladies, women like angels, girls like vanilla sherbert.'

'Pray, do not abuse women,' exclaimed Maria. 'That is a worn-out commonplace among men. In the end, to be happy, you need women after all.'

'Oh,' sighed Maximilian, 'that is true, certainly. But women, unfortunately, have only one way of making us happy, while they have thirty thousand ways of making us unhappy.'

'Dear friend,' replied Maria, suppressing a little smile, 'I am speaking of the concord of two souls in unison. Have you never experienced this joy? But I see an unaccustomed blush spreading over your cheeks. Tell me, Max.'

'It is true, Maria, I feel as confused almost as a boy at confessing to you the happy love with which I was once infinitely blessed. That memory is not yet lost to me, and to its cool shades my soul often flies, when the burning dust and day's heat of life grow almost unbearable. Yet I am not able to give you a just idea of her. She was such an ethereal creature that she only seemed revealed to me in dreams. I think that you, Maria, have no vulgar prejudice against dreams; those nightly visions have, in truth, as much reality as the coarser shapes of day, which we can touch with our hands, and by which we are not seldom besmutched. Yes, it was in a dream that I knew that sweet being who has made me most happy on earth. I can say little of her outward appearance. I am not able to describe the form of her features with precision. It was a face that I had never seen before, and that I have never in my life seen since. So much I remember; it was not white and rosy, but all of one colour—a soft, warm, pale-yellow, transparent as crystal. The charm of this face was not in firm regularity of beauty, nor in interesting vivacity; its characteristic was, rather, a charming, enrapturing, almost terrible veracity. It was a face full of conscious fire and gracious goodness; it was more a soul than a face, and on that account I have never been able to make her outward form quite present to myself. The eyes were soft as flowers, the lips rather pale, but charmingly arched. She wore a silk dressing-gown of a cornflower blue colour, and in that consisted her entire clothing; neck and feet were naked, and through the thin delicate garment now and then peeped stealthily the slender tenderness of the limbs. Nor can I make plain the words we said to one another; I only know that we plighted our troth, and that we chatted with one another, gay and familiar and open-hearted, like bridegroom and bride, almost like brother and sister. Often we left off talking, and gazed into each other's eyes; we spent whole eternities so. What waked me I cannot say, but I revelled for a long time in the after-feeling of these love-blisses. I was long, as it were, intoxicated with ineffable delight, the pining depth of my heart was filled with bliss, a hitherto unknown joy seemed poured over all my emotions, and I remained glad and joyful, though I never saw the beloved form in my dreams again. But had I not enjoyed whole eternities in her gaze? and she knew me too well not to be aware that I do not like repetitions.'

'Truly,' exclaimed Maria, 'you are an *homme à bonne fortune*. But, tell me, was Mademoiselle Laurence a marble statue or a painting—was she dead or a dream?'

'Perhaps she was all these together,' answered Maximilian, very earnestly.

'I can imagine, dear friend, that this sweetheart was of very doubtful character. And when will you tell me the history?'

'To-morrow. It is too long, and I am tired to-night. I have just come from the opera, and have too much music in my ears.'

'You often go to the opera now, and I think, Max, you go there more to see than to hear.'

'You are not mistaken, Maria; I go to the opera, indeed, to look at the faces of the beautiful Italian women.

'How beautiful they are, these Italian women, when music illuminates their countenances! I say "illuminates," because the effect of the music, which I marked at the opera, on the faces of the beautiful women altogether resembled those light-and-shade effects which surprise us so when we look at statues by torchlight at night-time. These marble forms reveal to us then, with terrifying truth, their indwelling spirit and their horrible dumb secrets. In the same way the whole life of the fair Italian women becomes known to us when we see them at the opera; the changing melodies wake in their souls a succession of emotions, memories, wishes, scandals, which visibly speak in the movements of their features, in their blushes, in their pallors, and even in their eyes. He who knows how to read them may then see in their faces many very sweet and interesting things—histories as remarkable as Boccaccio's tales, emotions as tender as Petrarch's sonnets, caprices as full of adventure as Ariosto's *ottave rime*, sometimes, too, fearful treachery and sublime wickedness as poetic as Dante's *Inferno*. It is worth while to gaze at the boxes. If the men would only express their enthusiasm meanwhile with less frightful sounds! This mad noise in an Italian theatre often annoys me. But music is the soul of these men, their life, their national business. In other countries, certainly, there are musicians who equal the greatest Italian masters, but there is no other musical nation. Here, in Italy, music is not represented by individuals; it manifests itself in the whole population; music has become a nation. With us in the north it is quite different; there music only becomes a man, and is called Mozart or Meyerbeer; and when, moreover, they would accurately investigate what is the best that this northern music offers us, they find it in Italian sunshine and orange-perfume; and much rather than to our Germany those belong to fair Italy, the home of music. Yes, Italy will always be the home of music, even though her great *maestri* descend early into the grave or become dumb—even though Bellini dies and Rossini keeps silence.'

'Indeed,' remarked Maria, 'Rossini has preserved a very long silence. If I do not mistake, he has been silent for ten years.'

'Perhaps that is a joke on his part,' answered Maximilian. 'He wishes to show that the title, "Swan of Pesaro," which has been conferred upon him, is quite unsuitable. Swans sing at the end of their lives, but Rossini has left off singing in the middle of his life. And I believe that he has done well in that, and shown, even by that, that he is a genius. The artist who has only talent retains to the end of his life the impulse to exercise that talent; ambition stimulates him; he feels that he is constantly perfecting himself, and he is compelled to strive after the highest. But genius has already accomplished the highest; it is content; it contemns the world and small ambition, and goes home to Stratford-on-Avon, like William Shakespeare, or walks about the Boulevard des Italiens at Paris, and laughs and jokes, like Giacomo Rossini. If genius has a not altogether badly constituted body, it lives on in this way for a good while after it has given forth its masterpieces, or, as people express it, after it has fulfilled its mission. It is owing to a prepossession that people say that genius must die early; I think that from the thirtieth to the thirty-fourth year has been indicated as the most dangerous period for genius. How often have I bantered poor Bellini on this subject, and playfully prophesied that, being a genius, and having reached that dangerous age, he must soon die. Singular! in spite of the playful tone, he tormented himself about this prophecy; he called me his *jettature*, his evil eye, and always made the *jettature* sign. He so wished to live, he had an almost passionate hatred of death: he would hear nothing of dying; he was frightened of it as a child who is afraid to sleep in the dark. . . . He was a good, dear child, often rather naughty, but then one only needed to threaten him with an early death, and he would immediately draw in, and entreat, and make with his two raised fingers the *jettature* sign. Poor Bellini!'

'So you knew him personally? Was he handsome?'

'He was not ugly. You see, we cannot answer affirmatively when any one asks us such a question about our own sex. He had a tall, slender figure, which moved in an elegant, I might say a coquettish, manner; always *à quatre épingles*; a long, regular face, with a pale rosiness; very fair, almost golden, hair, put into small curls; very high noble brows, a straight nose, pale blue eyes, a beautifully-chiselled mouth, a round chin. His features had something vague and characterless; something like milk, and in this milk-face often mingled, half sweet, half bitter, an expression of sorrow. This expression of sorrow compensated for the want of soul in Bellini's face, but it was a sorrow without depth; it glistened in the eyes without poetry, it played passionless about his lips. The young *maestro* seemed anxious to make this flat, languid sorrow conspicuous in his whole person. His hair was curled in such a fanciful, melancholy way, his clothes sat so languidly about his frail body, he carried his little Spanish cane in so idyllic a way, that he always reminded me of the affected young shepherds with their be-ribboned sticks and bright-coloured jackets and pantaloons that we meet in our pastorals. And his gait was so young-ladylike, so elegaic, so ethereal. The whole man looked like a sigh *en escarpins*. . . .

Bellini's face, like his whole appearance, had that physical freshness, that bloom of flesh, that rosiness which makes a disagreeable impression on me—on me because I like much more what is deathlike and marble. Later on, when I had known him a long time, I felt some liking for Bellini. This arose after I had observed that his character was thoroughly noble and good. His soul was certainly pure and unspotted by any hateful contagion. And he was not wanting in that good-natured, child-like quality which we never miss in men of genius, even if they do not wear it as an outward show.

'Yes, I remember,' Maximilian pursued, sinking down on the chair, on the back of which he had been hitherto leaning—'I remember one moment when Bellini appeared in so amiable a light, that I gazed on him with pleasure, and resolved to become more intimately acquainted with him. But, unhappily, it was the last time I was to see him in this life. It was one evening after we had been dining together at the house of a great lady who had the smallest foot in Paris. We were very merry, and the sweetest melodies rang out from the piano. I see him still, the good-natured Bellini, as, at last, exhausted with the mad Bellinism that he chattered, he sank into a seat. . . . . It was a very low one, so that Bellini found himself sitting at the foot, as it were, of a beautiful lady, stretched on a sofa opposite, who gazed down on him with a sweet, malicious delight, as he worked off some French expressions to entertain her, and was compelled, as usual, to communicate what he had said in his Sicilian jargon to show that it was no *sottise*, but, on the contrary, the most delicate flattery. I think the fair lady paid little attention to Bellini's conversation. She had taken from his hand the little Spanish cane with which he often used to assist his weak rhetoric, and was making use of it for a calm destruction of the elegant curl-edifice on the young *maestro's* brows. But this wanton occupation was well repaid by the smile which gave her face an expression which I have seen on no other living human countenance. That face will never leave my memory! It was one of those faces which belong more to the kingdom of poetry than to the crude reality of life, contours which reminded one of Da Vinci—that noble oval, with the naïve cheek-dimples and the sentimental pointed chin of the Lombard school. The colouring was more soft and Roman, with the dull gleam of pearls, a distinguished pallor, *morbidezza*. In short, it was one of those faces which can only be found in early Italian portraits, which, perhaps, represent those great ladies with whom the Italian artists of the sixteenth century were in love when they created their masterpieces, of whom the poets of those days thought when they sang themselves immortal, and which kindled German and French heroes with desire when they girded on their swords and started across the Alps in search of great deeds. Yes, it was such a face, and on it played a smile of sweetest, malicious delight and most delicate wantonness, as she, the fair lady, with the point of the little Spanish cane destroyed the blonde curls on the good-natured Bellini's brows. At that moment Bellini seemed to me as if touched by an enchanted wand, as if transformed, and he was at once akin to my heart. His face shone with the reflection of that smile; it was, perhaps, the most joyful moment of his life. I shall never forget it. Fourteen days afterwards I read in the papers that Italy had lost one of her most famous sons!

'Strange! At the same time Paganini's death was announced. About his death I had no doubt, for the old, ash-coloured Paganini always looked like a dying man; but the death of the young, rosy Bellini seemed to me incredible. And yet the news of the death of the first was only a newspaper error; Paganini is safe and sound at Genoa, and Bellini lies in his grave at Paris!'

'Do you like Paganini?' asked Maria. 'He is the ornament of his country,' answered Maximilian, 'and deserves the most distinguished mentioned in speaking of the musical notabilities of Italy.'

'I have never seen him,' Maria remarked, 'but according to report his outward appearance does not altogether satisfy the sense of beauty. I have seen portraits of him.'

'Which are all different,' broke in Maximilian; 'they either make him uglier or handsomer than he is; they do not give his actual appearance. I believe that only one man has succeeded in putting Paganini's true physiognomy on to paper— a deaf painter, Lyser by name, who, in a frenzy full of genius, has, with a few strokes of chalk, so well hit Paganini's head that one is at the same time amused and terrified at the truth of the drawing. "The Devil guided my hand," the deaf painter said to me, chuckling mysteriously, and nodding his head with good-natured irony in the way he generally accompanied his genial

witticisms. This painter was, however, a wonderful old fellow;
in spite of his deafness he was enthusiastically fond of music,
and he knew how, when near enough to the orchestra, to read
the music on the musicians' faces, and to judge the more or less
skilful execution by the movements of their fingers; indeed, he
wrote critiques on the opera for an excellent journal at Hamburg.
And is that peculiarly wonderful? In the visible symbols
of the performance the deaf painter could see the sounds. There
are men to whom the sounds themselves are invisible symbols
in which they hear colours and forms.'

'You are one of those men!' exclaimed Maria.

'I am sorry that I no longer possess Lyser's little drawing;
it would perhaps have given you an idea of Paganini's outward
appearance. Only with black and glaring strokes could those
mysterious features be seized, features which seemed to belong
more to the sulphurous kingdom of shades than to the sunny
world of life. "Indeed, the Devil guided my hand," the deaf
painter assured me, as we stood before the Alster pavilion at
Hamburg on the day when Paganini gave his first concert there.
"Yes, my friend," he pursued, "it is true, as every one believes,
that he has sold himself to the Devil, body and soul, in order to
become the best violinist, to fiddle millions of money, and
principally to escape the damnable galley where he had already
languished many years. For, you see, my friend, when he was
chapel-master at Lucca he fell in love with a princess of the
theatre, was jealous of some little *abbate*, was perhaps deceived
by the faithless *amata*, stabbed her in approved Italian fashion,
came in the galley to Genoa, and, as I said, sold himself to the
Devil to escape from it, become the best violin-player, and impose
upon us this evening a contribution of two thalers each. But,
you see, all good spirits praise God; there in the avenue he comes
himself, with his suspicious famulus!"

'It was indeed Paganini himself, whom I then saw for the
first time. He wore a dark grey overcoat, which reached to
his feet, and made his figure seem very tall. His long black
hair fell in neglected curls on his shoulders, and formed a dark
frame round the pale, cadaverous face, on which sorrow, genius,
and hell had engraved their indestructible lines. Near him
danced along a little pleasing figure, elegantly prosaic—with
rosy, wrinkled face, bright grey little coat with steel buttons,
distributing greetings on all sides in an insupportably friendly
way, leering up, nevertheless, with apprehensive air at the
gloomy figure who walked earnest and thoughtful at his side.

It reminded one of Retzsch's representation of Faust and Wagner walking before the gates of Leipzig. The deaf painter made comments to me in his mad way, and bade me observe especially the broad, measured walk of Paganini. "Does it not seem," said he, "as if he had the iron cross-pole still between his legs? He has accustomed himself to that walk for ever. See, too, in what a contemptuous, ironical way he sometimes looks at his guide when the latter wearies him with his prosaic questions. But he cannot separate himself from him; a bloody contract binds him to that companion, who is no other than Satan. The ignorant multitude, indeed, believe that this guide is the writer of comedies and anecdotes, Harris from Hanover, whom Paganini has taken with him to manage the financial business of his concerts. But they do not know that the Devil has only borrowed Herr George Harris's form, and that meanwhile the poor soul of this poor man is shut up with other rubbish in a trunk at Hanover, until the Devil returns its flesh-envelope, when he perhaps will guide his master through the world in a worthier form—namely, as a black poodle."

'But if Paganini seemed mysterious and strange enough when I saw him walking in bright midday under the green trees of the Hamburg Jungfernstieg, how his awful bizarre appearance startled me at the concert in the evening! The Hamburg Opera House was the scene of this concert, and the art-loving public had flocked thither so early, and in such numbers, that I only just succeeded in obtaining a little place in the orchestra. Although it was post-day, I saw in the first row of boxes the whole educated commercial world, a whole Olympus of bankers and other millionaires, the gods of coffee and sugar by the side of their fat goddesses, Junos of Wandrahm and Aphrodites of Dreckwall. A religious silence reigned through the assembly. Every eye was directed towards the stage. Every ear was making ready to listen. My neighbour, an old furrier, took the dirty cotton out of his ears in order to drink in better the costly sounds for which he had paid two thalers. At last a dark figure, which seemed to have arisen from the underworld, appeared upon the stage. It was Paganini in his black costume—the black dress-coat and the black waist-coat of a horrible cut, such as is perhaps prescribed by infernal etiquette at the court of Proserpina; the black trousers anxiously hanging around the thin legs. The long arms appeared to grow still longer, as, holding the violin in one hand and the bow in the other, he almost touched the ground with them while

displaying to the public his unprecedented obeisances. In the
angular curves of his body there was a horrible woodenness,
and also something so absurdly animal-like that during these
bows one could not help feeling a strange desire to laugh; but
his face, which appeared still more cadaverously pale in the glare
of the orchestra lights, had about it something so imploring, so
simply humble, that a sorrowful compassion repressed one's
desire to laugh. Had he learnt these complimentary bows
from an automaton or a dog? Is that the entreating gaze of
one sick unto death, or is there lurking behind it the mockery
of a crafty miser? Is that a man brought into the arena at the
moment of death, like a dying gladiator, to delight the public
with his convulsions? Or is it one risen from the dead, a vampire with a violin, who, if not the blood out of our hearts, at
any rate sucks the gold out of our pockets?

'Such questions crossed our minds while Paganini was performing his strange bows, but all those thoughts were at once
still when the wonderful master placed his violin under his
chin and began to play. As for me, you already know my
musical second-sight, my gift of seeing at each tone a figure
equivalent to the sound, and so Paganini with each stroke of
his bow brought visible forms and situations before my eyes;
he told me in melodious hieroglyphics all kinds of brilliant
tales; he, as it were, made a magic-lantern play its coloured
antics before me, he himself being chief actor. At the first
stroke of his bow the stage scenery around him had changed;
he suddenly stood with his music-desk in a cheerful room,
decorated in a gay, irregular way after the Pompadour style;
everywhere little mirrors, gilded cupids, Chinese porcelain, a
delightful chaos of ribbons, garlands of flowers, white gloves,
torn lace, false pearls, diadems of gold leaf and spangles—such
tinsel as one finds in the room of a *prima donna*. Paganini's
outward appearance had also changed, and certainly most
advantageously; he wore short breeches of lily-coloured satin,
a white waistcoat embroidered with silver, and a coat of bright
blue velvet with gold buttons; the hair in little carefully curled
locks bordered his face, which was young and rosy, and gleamed
with sweet tenderness as he ogled the pretty little lady who stood
near him at the music-desk, while he played the violin.

'Yes, I saw at his side a pretty young creature, in antique
costume, the white satin swelled out below the waist, making
the figure still more charmingly slender; the piled-up hair
was powdered and curled, and the pretty round face shone out

all the more openly with its glancing eyes, its little rouged cheeks, its little beauty-patches, and the sweet impertinent little nose. In her hand was a roll of white paper, and by the movements of her lips as well as by the coquettish motion of her little upper lip she seemed to be singing; but none of her trills were audible to me, and only from the violin with which the young Paganini led the lovely child could I discover what she sang, and what he himself during her song felt in his soul. Oh, what melodies were those! Like the nightingale's notes, when the fragrance of the rose intoxicates her yearning young heart with desire, they floated in the evening twilight. Oh, what melting, languid delight was that! The sounds kissed each other, then fled away pouting, and then, laughing, clasped each other and became one, and died away in intoxicated harmony. Yes, the sounds carried on their merry game like butterflies, when one, in playful provocation, will escape from another, hide behind a flower, be overtaken at last, and then, wantonly joying with the other, fly away into the golden sunlight. But a spider, a spider can prepare a sudden tragical fate for such enamoured butterflies. Did the young heart anticipate this? A melancholy sighing tone, a foreboding of some slowly approaching misfortune, glided softly through the enrapturing melodies that were streaming from Paganini's violin. His eyes became moist. Adoringly he knelt down before his *amata*. But, alas! as he bowed down to kiss her feet, he saw under the bed a little *abbate*! I do not know what he had against the poor man, but the Genoese became pale as death, he seized the little fellow with furious hands, gave him sundry boxes on the ear, as well as a considerable number of kicks, flung him outside, drew a stiletto from its sheath, and buried it in the young beauty's breast.

'At this moment, however, a shout of "Bravo! Bravo!" broke out from all sides. Hamburg's enthusiastic sons and daughters were paying the tribute of their uproarious applause to the great artist, who had just ended the first part of his concert, and was now bowing with even more angles and contortions than before. And on his face the abject humility seemed to me to have become more intense. From his eyes stared a sorrowful anxiety like that of a poor malefactor. "Divine!" cried my neighbour the furrier as he scratched his ears; "that piece alone was worth two thalers."

'When Paganini began to play again a gloom came before my eyes. The sounds were not transformed into bright forms and colours; the master's form was clothed in gloomy shades, out of the darkness of which his music moaned in the most piercing tones of lamentation. Only at times, when a little lamp that hung above cast its sorrowful light over him, could I catch a glimpse of his pale countenance, on which the youth was not yet extinguished. His costume was singular, in two colours, yellow and red. Heavy chains weighed upon his feet. Behind him moved a face whose physiognomy indicated a lusty goat-nature. And I saw at times long hairy hands seize assistingly the strings of the violin on which Paganini was playing. They often guided the hand which held the bow, and then a bleating laugh of applause accompanied the melody, which gushed from the violin ever more full of sorrow and anguish. They were melodies which were like the song of the fallen angels who had loved the daughters of earth, and, being exiled from the kingdom of the blessed, sank into the underworld with faces red with shame. They were melodies in whose bottomless shallowness glimmered neither consolation nor hope. When the saints in heaven hear such melodies, the praise of God dies upon their pallid lips, and they cover their heads weeping. At times when the *obbligato* goat's laugh bleated in among the melodious pangs, I caught a glimpse in the background of a crowd of small women-figures who nodded their odious heads with wicked wantonness. Then a rush of agonizing sounds came from the violin, and a fearful groan and a sob, such as was never heard upon earth before, nor will be perhaps heard upon earth again; unless in the valley of Jehoshaphat, when the colossal trumpets of doom shall ring out, and the naked corpses shall crawl forth from the grave to abide their fate. But the agonized violinist suddenly made one stroke of the bow, such a mad despairing stroke, that his chains fell rattling from him, and his mysterious assistant and the other foul mocking forms vanished.

'At this moment my neighbour the furrier said: "A pity, a pity; a string has snapped—that comes from the constant *pizzicato*."

'Had a string of the violin really snapped? I do not know. I only observed the alteration in the sounds, and Paganini and his surroundings seemed to me again suddenly changed. I could scarcely recognize him in the monk's brown dress, which concealed rather than clothed him. With savage countenance half hid by the cowl, waist girt with a cord, and bare feet, Paganini stood, a solitary defiant figure, on a rocky prominence by the sea, and played his violin. But the sea became red and redder, and the sky grew paler, till at last the surging water looked like bright scarlet blood, and the sky above became of a ghastly, corpse-like pallor, and the stars came out large and threatening; and those stars were black, black as glooming coal. But the tones of the violin grew ever more stormy and defiant, and the eyes of the terrible player sparkled with such a scornful lust of destruction, and his thin lips moved with such a horrible haste, that it seemed as if he murmured some old accursed charms to conjure the storm and loose the evil spirits that lie imprisoned in the abysses of the sea. Often, when he stretched his long thin arm from the broad monk's sleeve, and swept the air with his bow, he seemed like some sorcerer who commands the elements with his magic wand; and then there was a wild wailing from the depth of the sea, and the horrible waves of blood sprang up so fiercely that they almost besprinkled the pale sky and the black stars with their red foam. There was a wailing and a shrieking and a crashing, as if the world were falling into fragments, and ever more stubbornly the monk played his violin. He seemed as if by the power of violent will he wished to break the seven seals wherewith Solomon sealed the iron vessels in which he had shut up the vanquished demons. The wise king sank those vessels in the sea, and I seemed to hear the voices of the imprisoned spirits while Paganini's violin growled its most wrathful bass. But at last I thought I heard the jubilee of deliverance, and out of the red billows of blood emerge i the heads of the fettered demons: monsters of legendary horror, crocodiles with bats' wings, snakes with stags' horns, monkeys with shells on their heads, seals with long patriarchal beards, women's faces with breasts in place of cheeks, green camels' heads, hermaphrodites of incomprehensible combination—all staring with cold, crafty eyes, and with long fin-like claws grasping at the fiddling monk. From the latter, however, in the furious zeal of his conjuration, the cowl fell back, and the curly hair, fluttering in the wind, fell round his head in ringlets, like black snakes.

'So maddening was this vision that, to keep my senses, I closed my ears and shut my eyes. When I again looked up the spectre had vanished, and I saw the poor Genoese in his ordinary form, making his ordinary bows, while the public applauded in the most rapturous manner.

'"That is the famous performance on the G string," remarked my neighbour; "I myself play the violin, and I know what it is to master that instrument." Fortunately, the pause was not considerable, or else the musical furrier would certainly have engaged me in a long conversation upon art. Paganini again quietly set his violin to his chin, and with the first stroke of his bow the wonderful transformation of melodies again also began. They no longer fashioned themselves so brightly and corporeally. The melody gently developed itself, majestically billowing and swelling like an organ chorale in a cathedral, and everything around, stretching larger and higher, had extended into a colossal space which, not the bodily eye, but only the eye of the spirit could seize. In the midst of this space hovered a shining sphere, upon which, gigantic and sublimely haughty, stood a man who played the violin. Was that sphere the sun? I do not know. But in the man's features I recognized Paganini, only ideally lovely, divinely glorious, with a reconciling smile. His body was in the bloom of powerful manhood, a bright blue garment enveloped his noble limbs, his shoulders were covered by gleaming locks of black hair; and as he stood there, sure and secure, a sublime divinity, and played the violin, it seemed as if the whole creation obeyed his melodies. He was the man-planet about which the universe moved with measured solemnity and ringing out beatific rhythms. Those great lights, which so quietly gleaming swept around, were they the stars of heaven, and that melodious harmony which arose from their movements, was it the song of the spheres, of which poets and seers have reported so many ravishing things? At times, when I endeavoured to gaze out into the misty distance, I thought I saw pure white garments floating around, in which colossal pilgrims passed muffled along with white staves in their hands, and, singular to relate, the golden knob of each staff was even one of those great lights which I had taken for stars. These pilgrims moved in large orbit around the great performer, the golden knobs of their staves shone ever brighter at the tones of the violin, and the chorale which resounded from their lips, and which I had taken for the song of the spheres, was only the dying echo of those violin tones. A holy, ineffable ardour dwelt in those sounds, which often trembled, scarce audible, in mysterious whisper on the water, then swelled out again with a shuddering sweetness, like a bugle's notes heard by moonlight, and then finally poured forth in unrestrained jubilee, as if a thousand bards had struck their harps and raised their voices in a song of victory. These were sounds which the ear never hears, which only the heart can dream when it rests at night on a beloved breast. Perhaps also the heart can grasp them in the bright light of day, when it loses itself with joy in the curves of beauty in a Grecian work of art. . . .'

SECOND NIGHT

'And why will you torment me with this horrible medicine, since I must die so soon?'

It was Maria who, as Maximilian entered, spoke these words. The doctor was standing before her with a medicine bottle in one hand and in the other a little glass in which a brownish liquor frothed nauseously. 'My dear fellow,' he exclaimed, turning to the newcomer, 'you have just come at the right time; try and persuade signora to swallow these few drops; I am in a hurry.'

'I entreat you, Maria!' whispered Maximilian, in that tender voice which one did not often observe in him, and which seemed to come from so wounded a heart that the patient, singularly touched, took the glass in her hand. Before she put it to her mouth, she said, smiling: 'Will you reward me with the story of Laurence?'

'All that you wish shall be done,' nodded Maximilian.

The pale lady then drank the contents of the glass, half smiling, half shuddering.

'I am in a hurry,' said the doctor, drawing on his black gloves. 'Lie down quietly, signora, and move as little as possible.'

Led by black Deborah, who lighted him, he left the room. When the two friends were left alone, they looked at each other for a long time in silence. In the souls of both thoughts were clamorous which each strove to hide from the other. The woman, however, suddenly seized the man's hand and covered it with glowing kisses.

'For God's sake,' said Maximilian, 'do not agitate yourself so, and lie back quietly on the sofa.'

As Maria fulfilled this wish, he covered her feet carefully with a shawl, which he previously touched with his lips. She probably noticed him, for her eyes winked with contentment, like a happy child's.

'Was Mademoiselle Laurence very beautiful?'

'If you will not interrupt me, dear friend, and promise to listen quite silently, I will tell you circumstantially all that you wish to know.' Smiling in response to Maria's affirmative glance, Maximilian seated himself on the chair which was beside the sofa, and began his story:

'It is now eight years since I travelled to London to become acquainted with the language and the people. Confound the people and their language too! There they take a dozen mono-syllables in their mouths, chew them, gnash them, spit them out again, and they call that speaking! Fortunately, they are by nature tolerably taciturn, and though they always gape at us with open mouths, they spare us long conversations.

'You can well imagine how my dissatisfaction increased in that country. Nothing, however, equalled the gloomy mood which once came over me as I stood on Waterloo Bridge towards evening and gazed on the water. It seemed to me as if my soul were mirrored there, and were gazing up out of the water at me with all its scars. The most sorrowful stories came to my recollection. I thought of the rose which was always watered with vinegar, and so lost its sweet fragrance and faded early. I thought of the strayed butterfly which a naturalist, who ascended Mount Blanc, saw fluttering amid the ice. I thought of the tame monkey who was so familiar with men, played with them, ate with them, but once at table recognized in the roast meat on the dish her own little monkey baby, quickly seized it, and hastened to the woods, never more to be seen among her human friends. Ah, I felt so sorrowful that the hot tears started from my eyes. My tears fell down into the Thames, and floated on to the great sea which has swallowed so many tears without noticing them.

'At this moment it happened that a singular music awoke me from my gloomy dreams, and looking round, I saw on the bank a crowd of people, who seemed to have formed a circle round some amusing display. I drew nearer, and saw a family of performers, consisting of the following four persons:

'Firstly, a short, thick-set woman, dressed entirely in black, who had a very little head and a very large, protuberant belly. Upon this belly was hung an immense drum, upon which she drummed away most unmercifully.

'Secondly, a dwarf, who wore an embroidered coat like an old French marquis. He had a large powdered head, but for the rest, had very thin contemptible limbs, and danced to and fro striking the triangle.

'Thirdly, a young girl of about fifteen years, who wore a short close-fitting jacket of blue-striped silk, and broad pantaloons also with blue stripes. She was an aerially-made figure. The face was of Grecian loveliness. A straight nose, sweet pouting lips, a dreamy, tender, rounded chin, the colour a sunny yellow, the hair of a gleaming black, wound round the brows. So she stood, slender and serious, yes, ill-humoured, and gazed upon the fourth person of the company, who was just then engaged in his performance.

'This fourth person was a learned dog, a very hopeful poodle, and to the great delight of the English public, he had just put together, from some wooden letters before him, the name of the Duke of Wellington, and joined to it a very flattering word —namely "Hero." Since the dog, as one might conclude from his witty expression, was no English beast, but had, like the other three persons, come from France, the sons of Albion rejoiced that their great general had at least obtained from the French dog that recognition which the other French creatures had so disgracefully denied.

'In fact, this company consisted of French people, and the dwarf, who now announced himself as Monsieur Turlutu, began to bluster in French, and with such vehement gestures, that the poor English opened their mouths and noses still wider than usual. Often, after a long phrase, he crowed like a cock, and these cock-a-doodle-doos, as also the names of many emperors, kings, and princes which he mixed up with his discourse, were probably the only sounds the poor spectators understood. Those emperors, kings, and princes he extolled as his patrons and friends. When only a boy of eight years, so he assured us, he had had an interview with His Most Sacred Majesty Louis XVI, who also, later on, always asked his advice on weighty matters. He escaped the storms of the Revolution, like many others, by flight, and he only returned under the Empire to his beloved country to take part in the glory of the great nation. Napoleon, he said, never loved him, whereas His Holiness Pope Pius VII almost idolized him. The Emperor Alexander gave him bonbons, and the Princess Wilhelm von Kyritz always placed him on her lap. His Highness Duke Charles of Brunswick often allowed him to ride on his dogs, and His Majesty King Ludwig of Bavaria read to him his sublime poems. The Princes of Reuss-Schleiz-Kreuz and of Schwarzburg-Sondershausen loved him as a brother, and always smoked the same pipe with him. Yes, from childhood up, he said, he had lived among sovereigns; the present monarchs, had, as it were, grown up with him; he looked upon them as equals, and he felt deep sorrow every time that one of them passed from the scene of life. After these solemn words he crowed like a cock.

'Monsieur Turlutu was, in fact, one of the most curious dwarfs

I ever saw; his wrinkled old face formed such a droll contrast with his scanty, childish little body, and his whole person again contrasted as comically with his performances. He threw himself into the most sprightly postures, and with thrusts of an inhumanly long rapier he transfixed the air, affirming all the while, on his honour, that no one could parry this *quarte* or that *tierce*; that, on the contrary, his own defence could be broken through by no mortal man; and he challenged any one to engage with him in the noble art. After the dwarf had carried this performance on for some time, and found no one who would resolve on open conflict with him, he bowed with old French grace, gave thanks for the applause which was bestowed upon him, and took the liberty of announcing to the very honourable public the most extraordinary performance ever displayed upon English ground. "You see this person," he exclaimed, after drawing on dirty kid gloves, and leading the young girl of the company with respectful gallantry into the middle of the circle: "this is Mademoiselle Laurence, the only daughter of the honourable Christian lady whom you see there with the drum, and who still wears mourning for the loss of her dearly-beloved husband, the greatest ventriloquist in Europe! Mademoiselle Laurence will now dance! Now, admire the dancing of Mademoiselle Laurence." After these words, he again crowed like a cock.

'The young girl appeared to care not the least either for these words or the gaze of the spectators; ill-humouredly absorbed in herself, she waited till the dwarf had spread a large carpet at her feet, and under the guidance of the great drum had again begun to play his triangle. It was strange music, a mixture of awkward humming and a delightful tinkling, and I caught a pathetic, foolish, melancholy, bold, bizarre melody of, nevertheless, the most singular simplicity. But I soon forgot the music when the young girl began to dance.

'Dance and dancer powerfully seized my attention. It was not the classical dance which we still see in our great ballets, where, just as in classical tragedy, only sprawling unities and artificialities reign; it was not those danced Alexandrines, those declamatory springs, those antithetic capers, that noble emotion which pirouettes round on one foot, so that one sees nothing except heaven and petticoats, ideality and lies! There is, indeed, nothing so odious to me as the ballet at the Paris grand opera, where the traditions of that classical dance are retained in their purest forms, while in the rest of the arts, in poetry, in music, and in painting, the French have overturned the classical system. It will be, however, difficult for them to bring about a similar revolution in the art of dancing; they will need, as in their political revolution, to have recourse to terrorism, and guillotine the legs of the obdurate dancers. Mademoiselle Laurence was no great dancer; the joints of her feet were not very supple, her legs were not exercised in all possible dislocations, she understood nothing of the art of dancing as Madame Vestris teaches it, but she danced as nature commands to dance: her whole being was in harmony with her *pas*; not only her feet but her whole body danced; her face danced—she was often pale, almost deathly pale, her eyes opened to an almost ghostly size, desire and pain quivered on her lips, and her black hair, which enclosed her brows in smooth oval, moved like a pair of fluttering wings. It was, indeed, no classical dance, but also no romantic dance, in the sense of a young Frenchman of the Eugène Renduel school. This dance had nothing medieval, nor Venetian, nor hump-backed, nor macabre about it; there was neither moonshine nor incest in it. It was a dance which did not seek to answer by outward movements, but the outward movements seemed words of a strange speech which strove to express strange things. But what did this dance express? I could not understand, however passionately this speech uttered itself. I only guessed sometimes that it spoke of something intensely sorrowful. I, who so easily seized the meaning of all appearances, was nevertheless unable to solve this danced riddle; and that I groped in vain for the sense of it was partly the fault of the music, which certainly pointed intentionally to false roads, cunningly sought to lead me astray, and always disturbed me. Monsieur Turlutu's triangle often tittered maliciously. Madame, however, beat upon her drum so wrathfully, that her face glowed forth from the black cloud of cap like a blood-red northern light.

'Long after the troupe had passed away, I remained standing at the same spot, considering what that dance might signify. Was it a national dance of the south of France or of Spain? In such a dance might appear the impetuosity with which the dancer swung her little body to and fro, and the wildness with which she often threw her head backward in the bold way of those Bacchantes whom we gaze at with amazement on ancient vases. There was an intoxicated absence of will about her dance, something gloomy and inevitable; it was like the dance of fate. Or was it a fragment of some venerable forgotten

pantomime? Or was she dancing her personal history? Often
the girl bent down to the earth with a listening ear, as though
she heard a voice which spoke up to her. She trembled then like
an aspen leaf, bent suddenly to another side, went through her
maddest, most unrestrained leaps, then again bent her ear to
the earth, listened more anxiously than before, nodded her head,
became red and pale by turns, shuddered, stood for a while
stiffly upright as if benumbed, and made finally a movement
as one who washes his hands. Was it blood that so long and
with such care, such horrible care, she was washing from her
hands? She threw therewith a sideward glance so imploring,
so full of entreaty, so soul-dissolving—and that glance fell by
chance upon me.

'All the following night I was thinking of that glance, of that
dance, of that strange accompaniment; and as, on the following
day, I sauntered as usual through the streets of London, I longed
to meet the pretty dancer again, and I constantly pricked my
ears in case I might somewhere hear the music of the drum and
the triangle. I had at last found something in London which
interested me, and I no longer wandered aimless through its
yawning streets.

'I had just come out of the Tower, after carefully examining
the axe which cut off Anne Boleyn's head, as well as the English
crown-diamonds and the lions, when in front of the Tower
I caught a glimpse, amid a crowd, of madame with the great
drum, and heard Monsieur Turlutu crowing like a cock. The
learned dog again scraped together the heroism of the Duke
of Wellington, the dwarf again showed his not-to-be-parried
tierces and *quartes*, and Mademoiselle Laurence again began her
wondrous dance. There were again the same enigmatic movements, the same speech which I could not understand, the same
impetuous throwing back of the beautiful head, the same leaning down to the earth, the anguish which sought to soothe
itself by ever madder leaps, and again the listening ear bent to
the earth, the trembling, the pallor, the benumbed stiffness;
then also the fearful mysterious washing of the hands, and at
last the imploring side-glance, which rested upon me this time
still longer than before.

'Yes, women, and young girls as well as women, immediately
observe when they have excited the attention of a man.
Although Madameoiselle Laurence, when she was not dancing,
gazed fixedly and ill-humouredly before her, and while she
was dancing often cast only one glance on the public, it was

now no mere chance that this glance fell upon me; and the oftener I saw her dance, the more significantly it gleamed, but also the more incomprehensibly. I was fascinated by this glance, and for three weeks, from morning till evening, I wandered about the streets of London, always remaining wherever Mademoiselle Laurence danced. In spite of the greatest confusion of sounds, I could catch the tones of the drum and the triangle at the farthest distance; and Monsieur Turlutu, as soon as he saw me hastening near, raised his most friendly crow. Although I never spoke a word to him or to Mademoiselle Laurence, or to madame, or to the learned dog, I seemed at last as if I belonged to the company. When Monsieur Turlutu made a collection, he always behaved with the most delicate tact as he drew near me, and looked in the opposite direction when I put a small coin in his little three-cornered hat. His demeanour was indeed most distinguished; he reminded one of the good manners of the past; one could tell that the little man had grown up with monarchs, and all the stranger was it when at times, altogether forgetting his dignity, he crowed like a cock.

'I cannot describe to you how vexed I became, when, after seeking for three days in vain for the little company through all the streets of London, I was forced to conclude that they had left the town. Ennui again took me in its leaden arms, and again closed my heart. At last I could endure it no longer; I said farewell to the four estates of the realm, i.e. the mob, the blackguards, the gentlemen, and the fashionables, and travelled back again to civilized terra firma, where I knelt in adoration before the white apron of the first cook I met. Here once more I could sit down to dinner like a reasonable being, and refresh my soul by gazing at good-natured, unselfish faces. But I could not forget Mademoiselle Laurence; she danced in my memory for a long time; at solitary hours I often reflected over the lovely child's enigmatic pantomime, especially over the listening ear bent to the earth. It was a long time, too, before the romantic melodies of the triangle and drum died away in my memory.'

'And is that the whole story?' cried out Maria, all at once, starting up eagerly.

Maximilian pressed her softly down, placed his finger significantly to his lips, and whispered: 'Still! still! do not talk! Lie down, good and quiet, and I will tell you the rest of the story. Only on no account interrupt me.'

Leaning slowly back in his chair, Maximilian pursued the story:

'Five years afterwards I came for the first time to Paris, and at a very noteworthy period. The French had just performed their July revolution, and the whole world was applauding. This piece was not so horrible as the earlier tragedies of the Republic and the Empire. Only some thousand corpses remained upon the stage. The political Romanticists were not very contented, and announced a new piece in which more blood would flow, and the executioner have more to do.

'Paris delighted me by the cheerfulness which prevails there, and which exercises its influence over the most sombre minds. Singular! Paris is the stage on which the greatest tragedies of the world's history are performed—tragedies at the recollection of which hearts tremble and eyes become moist in the most distant lands; but to the spectator of these tragedies it happens as it happened to me once at the Porte Saint-Martin Theatre, when I went to see the *Tour de Nesle* performed. I found myself sitting behind a lady who wore a hat of rose-red gauze, and this hat was so broad that it obstructed the whole of my view of the stage, and I saw all the tragedy only through the red gauze of this hat, and all the horror of the *Tour de Nesle* appeared in the most cheerful rose-light. Yes, there is such a rose-light in Paris, which makes all tragedies cheerful to the near spectator, so that his enjoyment of life is not spoilt there. In the same way all the terrible things that one may bring in his own heart to Paris there lose their tormenting horror. Sorrows are singularly soothed. In this air of Paris all wounds are healed quicker than anywhere else; there is in this air something as generous, as kind, as amiable as in the people themselves.

'What most pleased me in the people of Paris was their polite bearing and distinguished air. Sweet pineapple perfume of politeness! how beneficently thou refreshedst my sick soul, which had swallowed down in Germany so much tobacco smoke, sauerkraut odour, and coarseness! The simple words of apology of a Frenchman, who, on the day of my arrival, only gently pushed against me, rang in my ears like the melodies of Rossini. I was almost terrified at such sweet politeness, I, who was accustomed to German clownish digs in the ribs without apology. During the first week of my stay in Paris, I several times deliberately sought to be jostled, simply to delight myself with this music of apology. But the French people has for me a certain touch of nobility, not only on account of its politeness, but also on account of its language. For, as you know, with us in the north the French language is one of the attributes of high birth; from childhood I had associated the idea of speaking French with nobility. And a Parisian market-woman spoke better French than a German canoness with sixty-four ancestors.

'On account of this language, which lends a distinguished bearing to it, the French people has in my eyes something delightfully fabulous. This originated in another reminiscence of my childhood. The first book in which I learnt French was the *Fables* of La Fontaine; its naïve, sensible manner of speech impressed itself on my recollection ineffaceably, and as I now came to Paris and heard French spoken everywhere, I was constantly reminded of La Fontaine's *Fables*, I constantly imagined I was hearing the well-known animal voices; now the lion spoke, then the wolf, then the lamb, or the stork, or the dove, not seldom, I thought, I caught the voice of the fox, and often the words awoke in my memory—"Eh! bonjour, Monsieur du Corbeau! Que vous êtes joli! que vous me semblez beau!"

'Such reminiscences, however, awoke in my soul still oftener when at Paris I ascended to that higher region which is called "the world." This was the very world which gave the happy La Fontaine the types of his animal characters. The winter season began soon after my arrival at Paris, and I took part in the *salon* life in which that world more or less joyfully moves. What struck me as most interesting in this world was not so much the equality of good manners which reigned there as the variety of its ingredients. Often when I gazed round at the people gathered peacefully together in a large drawing-room I thought I was in one of those curiosity shops where relics of all ages lie beside each other, a Greek Apollo, a Chinese pagoda, a Mexican Vizlipuzli by a Gothic Ecce-Homo, Egyptian idols with little dogs' heads, holy caricatures made of wood, of ivory, of metal, and so on. There I saw old mousquetaires who had danced with Marie Antoinette, republicans who were deified in the National Assembly, Montagnards without spot and without mercy, former men of the Directory who were throned in the Luxembourg, great dignitaries of the Empire, before whom all Europe had trembled, ruling Jesuits of the Restoration—in short, mere faded, mutilated deities of olden times, in whom nobody believed any longer. The names seem to recoil from each other, but the men one may see standing peaceful and friendly together like the antiquities in the shops of the Quai Voltaire. In German countries, where the passions are not so easily disciplined, for such a heterogeneous mass of persons to live together in society would be quite impossible. And with us in the cold north the vivacity of speech is not so strong as in warmer France, where the greatest enemies, if they meet one another in a *salon*, cannot long observe a gloomy silence. In France, also, the desire to please is so great that people zealously strive to please not only their friends, but also their enemies. There is constant drapery and affectation, and the women here have the delightful trouble of excelling the men in coquetry; but they succeed, nevertheless.

'I do not mean anything wicked by this observation, certainly not as regards the French ladies, and least of all as regards the Parisian ladies. I am their greatest adorer, and I adore them on account of their failings still more than on account of their virtues. I know nothing more excellent than the legend that the Parisian women come into the world with all possible failings, but that a kind fairy has mercy upon them and lends to each fault a spell by which it works as a charm. That kind fairy is Grace! Are the Parisian women beautiful? Who can say? Who can see through all the intrigues of the toilet? Who can decipher whether what the tulle betrays is genuine, or what the swelling silk displays, false? And when the eye succeeds in piercing the shell, and we are at the point of finding the kernel, we discover that it is enclosed in a new shell, and after this again in another, and with this ceaseless change of fashions they mock masculine acuteness. Are their faces beautiful? Even this is difficult to find out. For all their features are in constant movement; every Parisian woman has a thousand faces, each more laughing, *spirituel*, gracious than the other, and puts to confusion those who seek to choose the loveliest face among them, or at all events, who wish to guess which is the true face. Are their eyes large? What do I know! We cease investigating the calibre of the cannon when the ball carries off our heads. And when their eyes do not hit, they at least blind us with the flash, and we are glad enough to get out of range. Is the space between nose and mouth broad or narrow? It is often broad when they wrinkle up their noses; it is often narrow when they give their upper lips an insolent little pout. Have they large or small mouths? Who can say where the mouth leaves off and where the smile begins? In order to give a just opinion, both the observer and the object of observation must be in a state of rest. But who can be quiet near a Parisian, and what Parisian woman is ever quiet? There are people who think that they can observe a butterfly quite accurately when they have stuck it on to paper with a pin. That is as foolish as it is cruel. The motionless transfixed butterfly is a butterfly no longer. One must observe the butterfly in his antics round the flowers, and one must observe the Parisian woman, not at home, when she is made fast by a pin through her breast, but in the *salon*, at soirées and balls, when she flutters about with her wings of gauze and silk beneath the gleaming chandeliers. Then is revealed in her an impetuous passion for life, a longing after a sweet stupor, a thirsting for intoxication, by which means she becomes almost horribly beautiful, and wins a charm which at the same time delights and terrifies our souls.

'This thirst to enjoy life, as if death were about to snatch them from the bubbling spring of enjoyment, or as if that spring were about to cease flowing, this haste, this fury, this madness of the Parisian women, especially as it shows itself at balls, reminds me always of the legend of the dead dancing-girls which we call *Willis*. These are young brides who died before the wedding-day, and the unsatisfied desire of dancing is preserved so powerfully in their hearts that they come every night out of their graves, assemble in bands on the high roads, and give themselves up at midnight to the wildest dances. Dressed in their wedding clothes, with garlands on their heads, and glittering rings on their pale hands, laughing horribly, irresistibly lovely, the *Willis* dance in the moonshine, and they dance ever more madly the more they feel that the hour of dancing, which has been granted them, is coming to an end, and that they must again descend to their cold graves.

'At a soirée once in the Chaussée d'Antin this idea moved my soul profoundly. It was a brilliant soirée, and none of the customary ingredients of social pleasure were wanting: enough light to illuminate us, enough mirrors to see ourselves in, enough people to heat us with the squeeze, enough *eau sucrée* to cool us. They began with music. Franz Liszt allowed himself to be drawn to the piano, pushed his hair over his genial brows, and waged one of his most brilliant battles. The keys seemed to bleed. If I am not mistaken, he played a passage from the *Palingenesis* of Ballanche, whose ideas he was translating into music, which was very useful for those who cannot read the works of that famous writer in the original. Afterwards he played Berlioz's *Marche au Supplice*, that excellent piece which the young musician, if I am not mistaken, composed on the morning of his wedding-day. Throughout the room pallid faces, heaving bosoms, deep-drawn breaths during the pauses, were succeeded at last by stormy applause. The women are always as it were intoxicated when Liszt plays anything for them. The *Willis* of the *salon* now gave themselves up to dancing with frantic delight, and I had difficulty in getting out of this confusion and escaping into the adjoining room. Here cardplaying was going on, and several ladies were resting in large chairs, looking on at the players, or at all events pretending to interest themselves in the play. As I passed one of these ladies and my arm touched her dress, I felt from hand to shoulder a slight quiver as from a very weak electric shock. A similar shock, but of the greatest force, went through my whole heart when I saw the lady's countenance. Was it she, or was it not? It was the same face, with the form and sunny colour of an antique, only it was no longer so marble pure and marble smooth as formerly. The acute observer might perceive on brow and cheeks several little flaws, perhaps smallpox marks, which here exactly resembled those delicate weather-flecks which may be seen on the faces of statues that have been standing some time in the rain. It was the same black hair which covered the brows in smooth oval like a raven's wings. As, however, her eyes met mine, and with that well-known side-glance, whose swift lightning had always shot so enigmatically through my soul, I doubted no longer—it was Mademoiselle Laurence.

'Stretched in a distinguished way on her chair, with a bouquet in one hand and the other placed on the arm of the chair, Mademoiselle Laurence sat not far from one of the tables, and seemed to devote her whole attention to the cards. Her dress of white satin was elegant and distinguished, but still quite simple. Except bracelets and brooches of pearl, she wore no jewels. An abundance of lace covered the youthful bosom, covered it almost puritanically up to the neck, and in this simplicity and modesty of clothing she formed a lovely and touching contrast with some elderly ladies, gaily adorned and glistening with diamonds, who sat near her, and displayed to view the ruins of former magnificence, the place where once Troy stood, in a state of melancholy nakedness. She had the same wondrous loveliness, the same enrapturing look of ill-humour, and I was irresistibly drawn towards her, till at last I stood behind her chair, burning with desire to speak to her, and yet held back by a trembling delicacy.

'I must have been standing silently behind her for some time, when she suddenly drew a flower from her bouquet and, without looking round, held it to me over her shoulder. The perfume of that flower was strong, and it exercised a peculiar enchantment over me. I felt myself freed from all social formality, and I seemed in a dream, where one does and says all kinds of things at which oneself wonders, and when one's words have an altogether childish, familiar, and simple character. Quiet, indifferent, negligent, as one does with old friends, I leant over the arm of the chair, and whispered in the youthful lady's ear: "Mademoiselle Laurence, where is, then, the mother with the drum?"

"'She is dead," answered she, in just the same tone—as quiet, indifferent, negligent.

'After a short pause, I again leant over the arm of the chair, and whispered in the youthful lady's ear: "Mademoiselle Laurence, where is the learned dog?"

"'He has run away into the wide world," she answered, in the same quiet, indifferent, negligent tone.

'And again, after a short pause, I leant over the arm of the chair, and whispered in the youthful lady's ear, "Mademoiselle Laurence, where, then, is Monsieur Turlutu, the dwarf?"

"'He is among the giants in the Boulevard du Temple," she answered. She had hardly spoken these words, and in just the same quiet, indifferent, negligent tone, when a serious old man, with a tall military figure, came towards her and announced that her carriage was ready. Slowly rising from her seat, she leant upon his arm, and without casting one glance back to me, left the company.

'When I inquired of the lady of the house, who had been standing all the evening at the entrance of the principal saloon, presenting her smiles to those who came or went, the name of the young lady who had just gone out with the old man, she laughed gaily in my face, and exclaimed: "Mon Dieu! who can know everybody! I know her as little——" She stopped, for she was about to say as little as myself, whom she had that evening seen for the first time. "Perhaps," I remarked, "your husband can give me some information; where shall I find him?"

"'At the hunt at Saint-Germain," answered the lady, with a yet louder laugh; "he went early yesterday morning, and will return to-morrow evening. But wait. I know somebody who has been talking a good deal with the lady you inquire after; I do not know his name, but you can easily find him out by inquiring after the young man whom M. Casimir Périer kicked, I don't know where."

'Although it is rather difficult to recognize any one by the fact of his having received a kick from a minister, I soon discovered my man, and I desired from him a more intimate knowledge of the singular creature who had so interested me, and whom I could describe to him clearly enough. "Yes," said the young man, "I know her very well; I have spoken to her at several soirées"—and he repeated to me a mass of meaningless things with which he had entertained her. What especially surprised him was her earnest look whenever he said anything complimentary to her. He also wondered not a little that she always declined his invitation to a *contre-danse*, assuring him that she was unable to dance. Of her name and condition he knew nothing. And nobody, much as I inquired, could give me any more distinct information on the subject. In vain I ran through all possible soirées; nowhere could I find Mademoiselle Laurence.'

'And that is the whole story?' exclaimed Maria, as she slowly turned round and yawned sleepily—'that is the whole memorable story? And you have never again seen either Mademoiselle Laurence, or the mother with the drum, or the dwarf Turlutu, or the learned dog?'

'Remain lying still,' replied Maximilian. 'I have seen them all again, even the learned dog. The poor rascal was certainly in a very sad state of necessity when I came across him at Paris. It was in the Quartier Latin. I had just passed the Sorbonne, when out of its gates rushed a dog, and behind him with sticks a dozen students, who were soon joined by two dozen old women, who all cried in chorus: "The dog is mad!" The animal looked almost human in his death agony, tears flowed from his eyes, and as he ran panting by and lifted his moist glance towards me, I recognized my old friend the learned dog, the Duke of Wellington's panegyrist, who had once filled the people of England with wonderment. Was he really mad? Had he been driven mad by sheer learning while pursuing his studies in the Quartier Latin? Or had he in the Sorbonne, by his growling and scratching, marked his disapprobation of the puffed-up charlatanry of some professor, who sought to free himself from his unfavourable hearer by proclaiming him to be mad? And, alas! the youths waste no time in investigating whether it is the wounded conceit of learning or envy that first called out: "The dog is mad!" and they strike with their thoughtless sticks, and the old women are ready with their howling, and cry down the voice of innocence and reason. My poor friend had to yield;

before my eyes he was miserably struck to death, insulted, and at last thrown on a dunghill! Poor martyr of learning!

'Not much more pleasant was the condition of the dwarf, Monsieur Turlutu, when I found him on the Boulevard du Temple. Mademoiselle Laurence had certainly told me that he had gone there, but whether I had not thought of actually seeing him there, or that the crowd had hindered me, it was some time before I noted the place where the giants were to be seen. When I entered I found two tall fellows lying idly on benches, who quickly sprang up and placed themselves in giant posture before me. They were, in truth, not as large as they boasted on the placards hanging outside. These two long fellows, who were dressed in pink *tricots*, had very black, perhaps false, whiskers, and brandished hollow wooden clubs over their heads. When I asked after the dwarf, whom the placards also announced, they replied that for four weeks he had not been exhibited on account of his increasing illness—that I could see him, however, on paying double the price of admission. How willingly one pays double admission-fee to see a friend again! And, alas, this was a friend who lay on his death-bed. This death-bed was properly a cradle, and the poor dwarf lay inside with his yellow shrivelled old face. A little girl of some fourteen years sat beside him, and rocked the cradle with her foot, and sang in a laughing, roguish tone:

'"Sleep, little Turlutu, sleep!"

'When the little fellow saw me, he opened his glassy pale eyes as wide as possible, and a melancholy smile played on his white lips; he seemed to recognize me again, stretched his shrunken little hand towards me, and gently rattled—"Old friend!"

'It was, in fact, a sad condition in which I found the man, who, in his eighth year, had had a long conversation with Louis XVI, whom the Czar Alexander had fed with bonbons, whom the Princess von Kyritz had taken on her lap, who had ridden on the Duke of Brunswick's dogs, whom the King of Bavaria had read his poems to, who had smoked out of the same pipe with German princes, whom the Pope had idolized, and Napoleon never loved! This last circumstance troubled him on his death-bed, or, as I said, in his death-cradle, and he wept over the tragic fate of the great Emperor, who had never loved him, but who died in such a sorrowful way at Saint Helena—"just as I am dying," he added, "solitary, misunderstood, forsaken by all kings and princes, a caricature of former magnificence!"

'Although I could not rightly understand how a dwarf who died among giants could compare himself with a giant who died among dwarfs, I was nevertheless moved by poor Turlutu's words and by his forsaken condition at the last moment. I could not help expressing my astonishment that Mademoiselle Laurence, who was now so grand, gave herself no trouble about him. I had scarcely uttered this name when the dwarf in the cradle was seized by the most fearful spasms, and he whispered with his white lips: "Ungrateful child! that I brought up, that I would elevate to be my wife, that I taught to move and behave among the great of this world, how to smile, how to bow at court, how to act—you have used my instructions well, and you are now a great lady, and you have a coach and footmen, and plenty of money, and plenty of pride, and no heart. You leave me here to die—to die alone and in misery, as Napoleon died at St. Helena! O Napoleon! you never loved me." What he added I could not catch. He raised his head, made some movements with his hand, as if fighting against somebody, perhaps against death. But that is an opponent whose scythe neither a Napoleon nor a Turlutu can withstand. No skill in fencing avails here. Faint, as if overcome, the dwarf let his head sink down again, looked at me a long time with an indescribable, ghostly stare, suddenly crowed like a cock, and expired.

'His death troubled me the more since he had been unable to give any more exact information about Mademoiselle Laurence. Where should I now find her again? I was not in love with her, nor did I feel my former inclination towards her; yet a mysterious desire spurred me to seek her everywhere. When I entered a drawing-room and examined the company, and could not find the well-known face, I soon lost all repose and was driven away. Reflecting over this feeling, I stood one day at a remote entrance to the Grand Opera, waiting for a carriage, and waiting with considerable annoyance, for it was raining very fast. But no carriage came, or, rather, only carriages which belonged to other people, who placed themselves comfortably inside, and the place around me became gradually solitary. 'Then you must come with me,' said at last a lady, who, concealed in her black mantilla, had stood for a little time near me, and was now on the point of getting into a carriage. The voice sent a quiver through my heart, the well-known side-glance again exercised its charm, and I was again as in a dream on finding myself beside Mademoiselle Laurence in a cosy warm carriage. We did not speak, indeed we could not have understood each other, as the carriage rattled noisily through the streets of Paris for a long time, till it stopped at last before a great gateway.

'Servants in gorgeous livery lighted us up the steps and through a succession of rooms. A lady's-maid met us with sleepy face, and stammering many excuses, said that there was only a fire in the red room. Motioning to the woman to go away, Laurence said, with a laugh: "Chance is leading you a long way to-night; there is only a fire in my bedroom."

'In this bedroom, in which we soon found ourselves alone, blazed a large open fire, which was the pleasanter since the room was of immense size and height. This large sleeping-room, which rather deserved the name of a sleeping-hall, had a similarly desolate appearance. Furniture and decoration, all bore the impress of a time whose brilliance seems to us now so bedimmed, its sublimity so jejune, that its remains raise a certain dislike within us, if not indeed a smile. I speak of the time of the Empire, of the time of the golden eagle, of high-flying plumes, of Greek coiffures, of glory, of great drum-majors, of military masses, of official immortality (conferred by the *Moniteur*), of continental coffee prepared from chicory, of bad sugar manufactured from beetroot, and of princes and dukes made from nothing at all. But it had its charm, though, that time of pathetic materialism. Talma declaimed, Gros painted, Bigottini danced, Grassini sang, Maury preached, Rovigo had the police, the Emperor read Ossian, Pauline Borghese let herself be moulded as Venus, and quite naked too, for the room was well warmed, like the bedroom in which I found myself with Mademoiselle Laurence.

'We sat by the fire chatting familiarly, and she told me with a sigh that she was married to a Bonopartist hero, who enlivened her every evening before going to bed with a description of one of his battles; a few days ago, before going away, he had fought for her the battle of Jena; he was very ill, and with difficulty survived the Prussian campaign. When I asked her how long her father had been dead, she laughed, and confessed that she had never known a father, and that her so-called mother had never been married.

'"Not married!" I exclaimed; "I saw her myself in London in the deepest mourning on account of her husband's death!"

'"Oh," replied Laurence, "for twelve years she had always dressed herself in black, to excite people's compassion as an unhappy widow, as well as to allure any donkey desirous of marrying, for she hoped to reach the haven of marriage quicker under the black flag. But only death had pity on her, and she died of a haemorrhage. I never loved her, for she always gave me plenty of beatings and little to eat. I should have died of starvation if Monsieur Turlutu had not often given me a little piece of bread on the sly; but the dwarf wished to marry me on that account, and when his hopes were frustrated he made common cause with my mother—I say 'mother' from custom—and both agreed to torment me. They always said that I was a superfluous creature, and that the learned dog was worth a thousand times more than I with my bad dancing. And then they praised the dog at my expense, extolled him to the skies, caressed him, fed him with cakes, and threw me the crumbs. The dog, they said, was their best support; he delighted the public, who were not in the least interested in me; the dog must support me by his work. I ate the bread of the dog. The cursed dog!"

'"Oh, do not curse him any more," I broke in upon her passion; "he is dead now; I saw him die."

'"Is the beast dead?" exclaimed Laurence, springing up with a red glow of joy over her face.

'"And the dwarf is also dead," I added.

'"Monsieur Turlutu?" cried Laurence, also with joy. But this joy gradually died from her face, and in a milder, almost melancholy tone, she added: "Poor Turlutu!"

'When I told her, without any concealment, that the dwarf had complained of her very bitterly on his death-bed, she became passionately disturbed, and assured me, with many protestations, that she had taken care to provide for him as well as possible, that she had offered him a pension if he would go and live quietly somewhere in the country. "But ambitious as he was," Laurence pursued, "he wished to stay in Paris, and even to live at my house; he could then, he thought, through my interposition, renew his connections in the Faubourg Saint-Germain, and again take his former brilliant position in society. When I flatly refused him this, he told me that I was a cursed ghost, a vampire, a death-child."

'Laurence suddenly stopped, shuddered violently, and said at last, with a deep sigh: "Ah, I wish they had left me in the grave with my mother!" As I pressed her to explain these mysterious words, a stream of tears flowed from her eyes, and, trembling and sobbing, she confessed to me that the black woman with the drum, who gave herself out as her mother, had once herself told her that the rumour which went about concerning her birth was no mere story. "For in the town where we lived," pursued Laurence, "they always called me the death-child! The old woman maintained that I was the daughter of a count who lived there, and who constantly ill-treated his wife, and when she died buried her very magnificently; she was, however, near her confinement, and only apparently dead, and when some churchyard thieves opened the grave to strip the richly-adorned corpse, they found the countess alive and in child-birth; and as she expired immediately after delivery, the thieves placed her again quietly in her grave, took away the child, and gave it to the receiver of the stolen goods, the great ventriloquist's sweetheart, to be brought up. This poor child, who had been buried before it was born, was everywhere called the death-child. Ah! you cannot understand how much sorrow I felt even as a little girl when any one called me by that name. While the great ventriloquist was alive, whenever he was discontented with me, he always called out: 'Cursed death-child, I wish you had never been taken out of the grave!' He was a skilful ventriloquist, and could so modulate his voice that it seemed to come up out of the earth, and he told me that that was the voice of my dead mother telling me her fate. He might well know that horrible fate, for he had been a valet of the count's. He took a cruel pleasure in the horrible fright which I, poor little girl, received from the words which seemed to ascend from the earth. These words, which seemed to ascend from the earth, mingled together fearful tales—tales which I never understood in their connection, and which later on I gradually forgot; but when I danced they would again come into my mind with living power. Yes, when I danced a singular remembrance seized me; I forgot myself, and I seemed to be quite another person, and as if all the sorrows and secrets of this person were poisoning me, and as soon as I left off dancing it was all extinguished in my memory."

'While Laurence said this, slowly and as if questioning, she stood before me at the fireplace, where the fire was burning pleasanter than ever; and I sat in the easy-chair, which was apparently the seat of her husband, where he told her his battles before going to bed of an evening. Laurence looked at me with her large eyes as if she were asking my advice; she moved her head to and fro in such a melancholy reflective way; she filled me with such a sweet compassion; she was so slender, so young, so lovely, this lily that had sprung out of the grave, this daughter of death, this ghost with the face of an angel and the body of a bayadère! I do not know how it came to pass; perhaps it was the influence of the easy-chair on which I was sitting, but it suddenly came into my mind that I was the old general who had described the battle of Jena yesterday from this place, and as if I must go on with my narrative, and I said: "After the battle of Jena all the Prussian fortresses yielded themselves up within a few weeks, almost without drawing a sword. First Magdeburg yielded; it was the strongest fortress, and had three hundred guns. Was not that disgraceful?"

'But Mademoiselle Laurence allowed me to say no more; the troubled mood had vanished from her face; she laughed like a child, and cried: "Yes, that was disgraceful, more than disgraceful! If I were a fortress and had three hundred guns, I would never yield myself!"

'But as Mademoiselle Laurence was not a fortress, and had not three hundred guns——'

At these words Maximilian suddenly stopped in his story, and, after a pause, asked gently: 'Are you asleep, Maria?'

'I'm asleep,' answered Maria.

'So much the better,' said Maximilian, with a smile; 'then I need not be afraid of wearying you if I describe the furniture of the room in which I found myself, as novelists are accustomed to do rather at length nowadays.'

'Say what you like, dear friend: I'm asleep.'

'It was,' continued Maximilian, 'a very magnificent bed. The feet, as in all the beds of the Empire, consisted of caryatides and sphinxes; it gleamed with richly-gilt eagles, billing like turtle-doves, perhaps an emblem of love under the Empire. The curtains of the bed were of red silk, and as the flames from the fireplace shone brightly through them, I found myself with Laurence in a fiery red illumination, and I seemed to be the god Pluto with the flames of hell blazing round him as he held the sleeping Proserpine in his arms. She was asleep, and in this condition I gazed on her sweet face, and sought in her features a clue to that sympathy which my soul felt for her. What was the meaning of this woman? What sense lurked under the symbolism of that beautiful form? I held the charming enigma in my arms now as my own property, and yet I could not find the solution of it.

'But is it not folly to wish to sound the inner meaning of any phenomenon outside us, when we cannot even solve the enigma of our own souls? We hardly know even whether outside phenomena really exist! We are often unable to distinguish reality from mere dream-faces. Was it a shape of my fancy, or was it horrible reality that I heard and saw on that night? I know not. I only remember that as the wildest thoughts were flowing through my heart, a singular sound came to my ear. It was a crazy melody, peculiarly soft. It seemed known to me, and at last I distinguished the tones of a triangle and a drum. This music, whirring and humming, seemed to come from afar, and yet as I looked up I saw near me in the middle of the room a well-known performance. It was Monsieur Turlutu the dwarf who played the triangle, and madame beating the great drum, while the learned dog was scratching about on the floor, as if searching for his wooden letters. The dog appeared to move with difficulty, and his skin was spotted with blood. Madame still wore her black mourning, but her belly was no longer so spaciously protuberant, but repulsively pendant. Her face, too, was no longer red, but pale. The dwarf, who still wore the embroidered coat of an old French marquis and a powdered *toupet*, appeared to have grown somewhat, perhaps because he was so horribly lean. He again exhibited his skill in fencing, and seemed to be again spinning off his old vaunts; but he spoke so softly that I was unable to understand a word, and only by the movements of his lips could I sometimes observe that he was again crowing like a cock.

'While this ludicrous, horrible caricature moved like a magic lantern with confused haste before my eyes, I felt Mademoiselle Laurence breathing more and more uneasily. A cold paroxysm froze her whole body, and her sweet limbs writhed as if with unbearable agony. At last, however, supple as an eel, she glided from my arms, stood suddenly in the middle of the room, and began to dance, while the mother with the drum and the dwarf with the triangle continued their deadened soft music. She danced just as formerly on Waterloo Bridge and in the squares of London. There were the same mysterious panto-mimes, the same outbreaks of passionate leaping, the same Bacchante-like throwing of the head backwards, often also the same leaning towards the earth, as if she wished to hear some-body speaking beneath, then also the trembling, the pallor, the benumbed stiffness, and again the listening with ear bent to the earth. Again also she rubbed her hands as if washing herself. At last she appeared again to cast her intense, sorrowful, imploring glance upon me, but now only in the features of her death-pale countenance could I recognize that glance—not in her eyes, for they were shut. In ever softer sounds the music died away; the mother with the drum and the dwarf, gradually growing pale and breaking like mist, vanished at last altogether; but Mademoiselle Laurence still stood and danced with closed eyes. This dance with closed eyes in the silent nocturnal chamber gave this sweet being so ghostly an appearance that a disagreeable feeling seized me; I shuddered, and was heartily glad when she finished her dance, and as easily as she had slipped away again glided into my arms.

'In truth, this scene was not pleasant to me. But we accustom ourselves to everything. And it is even possible that what was mysterious in this woman lent her a more peculiar charm, that an awful tenderness mingled with my emotions. In any case, after some weeks I ceased to wonder in the least when the low sounds of the drum and triangle were heard at night, and my dear Laurence suddenly started up and danced a solo with closed eyes. Her husband, the old Bonapartist, commanded in the neighbourhood of Paris, and his duties allowed him to pass the day only in the city. Of course he became my most intimate friend, and he wept when later on he bade me farewell. He travelled with his wife to Sicily, and I have seen neither of them again since.'

When Maximilian had finished this narrative, he hastily seized his hat and slipped out of the room.

DON QUIXOTE

THE first book that I read after I arrived at boyhood's years of discretion, and had tolerably mastered my letters, was *The Life and Deeds of the Sagacious Knight, Don Quixote de la Mancha*, written by Miguel Cervantes de Saavedra. Well do I remember the time, when, early in the morning, I stole away from home and hastened to the court-garden, that I might read *Don Quixote* without being disturbed. It was a beautiful day in May, the blooming Spring lay basking in the silent morning light, listening to the compliments of that sweet flatterer, the nightingale, who sang so softly and caressingly, with such a melting fervour, that even the shyest of buds burst into blossom, and the lusty grasses and the fragrant sunshine kissed more rapturously, and the trees and flowers trembled from very ecstasy. But I seated myself on an old moss-covered stone bench in the so-called Avenue of Sighs, not far from the waterfall, and feasted my little heart with the thrilling adventures of the valiant knight. In my childish simplicity I took everything in sober earnest; no matter how ridiculous the mishaps which fate visited upon the poor hero, I thought it must be just so, and imagined that to be laughed at was as much a part of heroism as to be wounded; and the former vexed me just as sorely as the latter grieved my heart. I was a child, and knew nothing of the irony God has interwoven into the world, and which the great poet has imitated in his miniature world;—and I wept most bitterly, when for all his chivalry and generosity the noble knight gained only ingratitude and cudgels. As I was unpractised in reading, I spoke every word aloud, and so the birds and the trees, the brooks and the flowers, could hear all I read, and as these innocent beings know as little as children of the irony of the world, they too took it all for sober earnest, and wept with me over the sorrows of the unfortunate knight; an old decrepit oak sobbed even; and the waterfall shook more vehemently his white beard, and seemed to scold at the wickedness of the world. We felt that the heroism of the knight was none the less worthy of admiration because the lion turned tail without fighting, and that if his body was weak and withered, his armour rusty, his steed a miserable jade, his deeds were all the more worthy of praise.

We despised the vulgar rabble who beat the poor hero so bar-
barously, and still more the rabble of higher rank, who were
decked in silk attire, gay courtly phrases, and grand titles, and
jeered at the man who was so far their superior in powers of
mind and nobility of soul. Dulcinea's knight rose ever higher
in my esteem, and my love for him grew stronger and stronger
the longer I read in that wonderful book, which I continued to
do daily in that same garden, so that when autumn came I had
reached the end of the story—and I shall never forget the day
when I read the sorrowful combat, in which the knight came to
so ignominious an end.

It was a gloomy day; dismal clouds swept over a leaden sky,
the yellow leaves fell sorrowfully from the trees, heavy tear-
drops hung on the last flowers that drooped down in a sad
faded way their dying little heads, the nightingales had long
since died away, from every side the image of transitoriness
stared at me—and my heart was ready to break as I read how
the noble knight lay on the ground, stunned and bruised, and
through his closed visor said, in tones faint and feeble, as if
he was speaking from the grave: 'Dulcinea is the fairest lady
in the world, and I the unhappiest knight on earth, but it is
not meet that my weakness should disown this truth—strike
with your lance, Sir Knight.'

Ah me! that brilliant knight of the silver moon, who vanquished the bravest and noblest man in the world, was a
disguised barber!

That was long ago. Many new springs have bloomed forth
since then, yet their mightiest charm has always been wanting,
for, alas! I no longer believe the sweet deceits of the nightingale, Spring's flatterer; I know how soon his magnificence fades,
and when I look at the youngest rosebuds I see them in spirit
bloom to a sorrowful red, grow pale, and be scattered by the
winds. Everywhere I see a disguised Winter.

In my breast, however, still blooms that flaming love, which
soared so ardently above the earth, to revel adventurously in
the broad yawning spaces of heaven, and which, pushed back
by the cold stars, and sinking home again to the little earth,
was forced to confess, with sighing and triumph, that there is
in all creation nothing fairer or better than the heart of man.
This love is the inspiration that fills me, always divine, whether
it does foolish or wise deeds.—And so the tears the little boy
shed over the sorrows of the silly knight were in no wise spent
in vain, any more than the later tears of the youth, as on many

a night he wept in the study over the deaths of the holy heroes
of freedom—over King Agis of Sparta, over Caius and Tiberius
Gracchus of Rome, over Jesus of Jerusalem, and over Robes-
pierre and Saint-Just of Paris. Now that I have put on the
toga virilis, and myself desire to be a man, the tears have come
to an end, and it is necessary to act like a man, imitating my
great predecessors; in the future, if God will, to be wept also
by boys and youths. Yes, upon these one can still reckon in
our cold age; for they can still be kindled by the breezes that
blow to them from old books, and so they can comprehend the
flaming hearts of the present. Youth is unselfish in its thoughts
and feelings, and on that account it feels truth most deeply,
and is not sparing, where a bold sympathy is wanted, with
confession or deed. Older people are selfish and narrow-
minded; they think more of the interest of their capital than of
the interest of mankind; they let their little boat float quietly
down the gutter of life, and trouble themselves little about the
sailor who battles with the waves on the open sea; or they creep
with clinging tenacity up to the heights of mayoralty or the
presidency of their club, and shrug their shoulders over the
heroic figures which the storm throws down from the columns
of fame; and then they tell, perhaps, how they themselves also
in their youth ran their heads against the wall, but that later
on they reconciled themselves to the wall, for the wall was the
absolute, existing by and for itself, which, because it was, was
also reasonable, on which account he is unreasonable who will
not endure a high, reasonable, inevitable, eternally-ordained
absolutism. Ah, these objectionable people, who wish to
philosophize us into a gentle slavery, are yet more worthy of
esteem than those depraved ones who do not even admit
reasonable grounds for the defence of despotism, but being
learned in history fight for it as a right of custom, to which
men in the course of time have gradually habituated themselves,
and which has so become incontestably valid and lawful.

Ah, well! I will not, like Ham, lift up the garment of my
father's shame; but it is terrible how slavery has been made
with us a matter for prating about, and how German philosophers
and historians have tormented their brains to defend despotism,
however silly or awkward, as reasonable and lawful. Silence
is the honour of slaves, says Tacitus; these philosophers and
historians maintain the contrary, and exhibit the badge of
slavery in their button-holes.

Perhaps, after all, you are right, and I am only a Don Quixote, and the reading of all sorts of wonderful books has turned my head, as it was with the Knight of La Mancha, and Jean Jacques Rousseau was my Amadis of Gaul, Mirabeau my Roland or Agramante; and I have studied too much the heroic deeds of the French Paladins and the round table of the National Convention. Indeed, my madness and the fixed ideas that I created out of books are of a quite opposite kind to the madness and the fixed ideas of him of La Mancha. He wished to establish again the expiring days of chivalry; I, on the contrary, wish to annihilate all that is yet remaining from that time, and so we work with altogether different views. My colleague saw windmills as giants; I, on the contrary, can see in our present giants only vaunting windmills. He took leather wine-skins for mighty enchanters, but I can see in the enchanters of to-day only leather wine-skins. He held beggarly pot-houses for castles, donkey-drivers for cavaliers, stable wenches for court ladies; I, on the contrary, hold our castles for beggarly pot-houses, our cavaliers for mere donkey-drivers, our court ladies for ordinary stable wenches. As he took a puppet-show for a state ceremony, so I hold our state ceremonies as sorry puppet-shows, yet as bravely as the brave Knight of La Mancha I strike out at the clumsy machinery. Alas! such heroic deeds often turn out as badly for me as for him, and like him I must suffer much for the honour of my lady. If I denied her from mere fear or base love of gain, I might live comfortably in this reasonably constructed world, and I should lead a fair Maritornes to the altar, and let myself be blessed by fat enchanters, and banquet with noble donkey-drivers, and engender harmless romances as well as other little slaves! Instead of that, wearing the three colours of my lady, I must strike through unspeakable opposition, and fight battles, every one of which costs me my heart's blood. Day and night I am in straits, for those enemies are so artful that many I struck to death still give themselves the appearance of being alive, changing themselves into all forms, and spoiling day and night for me. How many sorrows have I suffered by such fatal spectres! Where anything lovely bloomed for me then they crept in, those cunning ghosts, and blighted even the most innocent buds. Everywhere, and when I should least suspect it, I discovered on the ground the traces of their silvery slime, and if I took no care, I might have a dangerous fall even in the house of my love. You may smile and hold such anxieties for idle fancies like those of Don Quixote. But fancied pains hurt all the same; and if one fancies that one has drunk hemlock one may get into a consumption, and one certainly will not get fat. And the report that I have got fat is a calumny; at least I have not yet received any fat sinecure, even if I possess the requisite talents. I fancy that everything has been done to keep me lean; when I was hungry they fed me with snakes, when I was thirsty they gave me wormwood to drink; they poured hell into my heart, so that I wept poison and sighed fire; they crouched near me even in my dreams; and I see horrible spectres, noble lackey faces with gnashing teeth and threatening noses, and deadly eyes glaring from cowls, and white ruffled hands with gleaming knives.

And even the old woman who lives near me in the next room considers me to be mad, and says that I talk the maddest nonsense in my sleep; and the other night she plainly heard me calling out: 'Dulcinea is the fairest woman in the world, and I the unhappiest knight on earth; but it is not meet that my weakness should disown this truth. Strike with your lance, Sir Knight!'

GODS IN EXILE

. . . I am speaking here of that metamorphosis into demons which the Greek and Roman gods underwent when Christianity achieved supreme control of the world. The superstition of the people ascribed to those gods a real but cursed existence, coinciding entirely in this respect with the teaching of the Church. The latter by no means declared the ancient gods to be myths, inventions of falsehood and error, as did the philosophers, but held them to be evil spirits, who, through the victory of Christ, had been hurled from the summit of their power, and now dragged out their miserable existences in the obscurity of dismantled temples or in enchanted groves, and by their diabolic arts, through lust and beauty, particularly through dancing and singing, lured to apostasy unsteadfast Christians who had lost their way in the forest. . . . I will remind the reader that the perplexities into which the poor old gods fell at the time of the final triumph of Christendom—that is, in the third century—offer striking analogies to former sorrowful events in their god-lives; for they found themselves plunged into the same sad predicament in which they had once before been placed in that most ancient time, in that revolutionary epoch when the Titans broke loose from their confinement in Orcus, and piling Pelion on Ossa, scaled high Olympus. At that time the poor gods were compelled to flee ignominiously and conceal themselves under various disguises on earth. Most of them repaired to Egypt, where, as is well known, for greater safety, they assumed the forms of animals. And in a like manner, when the true Lord of the universe planted the banner of the cross on the heavenly heights, and those iconoclastic zealots, the black band of monks, hunted down the gods with fire and malediction and razed their temples, then these unfortunate heathen divinites were again compelled to take to flight, seeking safety under the most varied disguises and in the most retired hiding-places. Many of these poor refugees, deprived of shelter and ambrosia, were now forced to work at some plebeian trade in order to earn a livelihood. Under these circumstances several, whose shrines had been confiscated, became wood-choppers and day-labourers in Germany, and were compelled to drink beer instead of nectar. It appears that Apollo was reduced to this dire plight, and stooped so low as to accept service with cattle-breeders, and as once before he had tended the cows of Admetus, so now he lived as a shepherd in Lower Austria. Here, however, he aroused suspicion through the marvellous sweetness of his singing, and, being recognized by a learned monk as one of the ancient magic-working heathen gods, he was delivered over to the ecclesiastical courts. On the rack he confessed that he was the god Apollo. Before his execution he begged that he might be permitted for the last time to play the zither and sing to its accompaniment. But he played so touchingly and sang so enchantingly, and was so handsome in face and form, that all the women wept; and many of them indeed afterwards sickened. After some lapse of time, it was decided to remove his body from the grave under the impression that he was a vampire, and impale it upon a stake, this being an approved domestic remedy certain to effect the cure of the sick women; but the grave was found empty.

I have but little to communicate concerning the fate of Mars, the ancient god of war. I am not disinclined to believe that during the feudal ages he availed himself of the then prevailing doctrine that might makes right. Lank Schimmelpfennig, nephew of the executioner of Münster, once met Mars at Bologna, and conversed with him. Shortly before, he had served as a soldier under Frundsberg, and was present at the storming of Rome. Bitter thoughts must have filled his breast when he saw his ancient, favourite city, and the temples wherein he and his brother gods had been so revered, now ignominiously laid waste.

Better than either Mars or Apollo fared the god Bacchus at the great stampede, and the legends relate the following: In Tyrol there are very large lakes, surrounded by magnificent trees that are mirrored in the blue waters. Trees and water murmur so that one experiences strange feelings of awe when one wanders there alone. On the bank of such a lake stood the hut of a young fisherman, who lived by fishing, and who also acted as ferryman to any travellers who wished to cross the lake. He had a large boat, which was fastened to the trunk of an old tree not far from his dwelling. Here he lived quite alone. Once, about the time of the autumnal equinox, towards midnight, he heard a knocking at his window, and on opening the door he saw three monks, with their heads deeply muffled in their cowls, who seemed to be in great haste. One of them hurriedly asked him for the boat, promising to return it within a few hours. The monks were three, and the fisherman could not hesitate; so he unfastened the boat, and when they had embarked, and departed he went back to his hut and lay down. He was young, and soon fell asleep; but in a few hours he was awakened by the returning monks. When he went out to them, one of them pressed a silver coin into his hand, and then all three hastened away. The fisherman went to look at his boat, which he found made fast. Then he shivered, but not from the night air. A peculiarly chilling sensation had passed through his limbs, and his heart seemed almost frozen, when the monk who paid the fare touched his hand; the monk's fingers were cold as ice. For some days the fisherman could not forget this circumstance; but youth will soon shake off mysterious influences and the fisherman thought no more of the occurrence until the following year, when, again just at the time of the autumnal equinox, towards midnight, there was a knocking at the window of the hut, and again the three cowled monks appeared, and again demanded the boat. The fisherman delivered up the boat with less anxiety this time, but when after a few hours they returned, and one of the monks again hastily pressed a coin into his hand, he again shuddered at the touch of the icy cold fingers. This happened every year at the same time and in the same manner. At last, as the seventh year drew near, an irresistible desire seized on the fisherman to learn, at all costs, the secret that was hidden under these three cowls. He piled a mass of nets into the boat, so as to form a hiding-place into which he could slip while the monks were preparing to embark. The sombre expected travellers came at the accustomed time, and the fisherman succeeded in hiding himself under the nets unobserved. To his astonishment, the voyage lasted but a short time, whereas it usually took him over an hour to reach the opposite shore; and greater yet was his surprise when here, in a locality with which he had been quite familiar, he beheld a wide forest-glade which he had never before seen, and which was covered with flowers that, to him, were of quite strange kind. Innumerable lamps hung from the trees, and vases filled with blazing resin stood on high pedestals; the moon, too, was so bright that the fisherman could see all that took place, as distinctly as if it had been midday. There were many hundreds of young men and young women, most of them beautiful as pictures, although their faces were all as white as marble, and this circumstance, together with their garments, which consisted of white, very white, tunics with purple borders, girt up, gave them the appearance of moving statues. The women wore on their heads wreaths of vine leaves, either natural or wrought of gold and silver, and their hair was partly plaited over the brow into the shape of a crown, and partly fell in wild locks on their necks. The young men also wore wreaths of vine-leaves. Both men and women, swinging in their hands golden staffs covered with vine leaves, hastened joyously to greet the new-comers. One of the latter threw aside his cowl, revealing an impertinent fellow of middle age, with a repulsive, libidinous face, and pointed goat-ears, and scandalously extravagant sexuality. The second monk also threw aside his cowl, and there came to view a big-bellied fellow, not less naked, whose bald pate the mischievous women crowned with a wreath of roses. The faces of the two monks, like those of the rest of the assemblage, were white as snow. White as snow also was the face of the third monk, who laughingly brushed the cowl from his head. As he unbound the girdle of his robe, and with a gesture of disgust flung off from him the pious and dirty garment, together with crucifix and rosary, lo! there stood, robed in a tunic brilliant as a diamond, a marvellously beautiful youth with a form of noble symmetry, save that there was something feminine in the rounded hips and the slender waist. His delicately curved lips, also, and soft, mobile features gave him a somewhat feminine appearance; but his face expressed also a certain daring, almost reckless heroism. The women caressed him with wild enthusiasm, placed an ivy-wreath upon his head, and threw a magnificent leopard-skin over his shoulders. At this moment came swiftly dashing along, drawn by two lions, a golden two-wheeled triumphal chariot. Majestically, yet with a merry glance, the youth leaped on the chariot, guiding the wild steeds with purple reins. At the right of the chariot strode one of his uncassocked companions, whose lewd gestures and unseemly form delighted the beholders, while his comrade, with the bald pate and fat paunch, whom the merry women had placed on an ass, rode at the left of the chariot, carrying in his hand a golden drinking-cup, which was constantly refilled with wine. On moved the chariot, and behind it whirled the romping, dancing, vine-crowned men and women. At the head of the triumphal procession marched the orchestra; the pretty, chubby-cheeked youth, playing the double flute; then the nymph with the high-girt tunic, striking the jingling tambourine with her knuckles; then the equally gracious beauty, with the triangle; then the goat-footed trumpeters, with handsome but lascivious faces, who blew their fanfares on curious sea-shells and fantastically-shaped horns; then the lute players.

But, dear reader, I forgot that you are a most cultured and well-informed reader, and have long since observed that I have been describing a Bacchanalia and a feast of Dionysus. You have often seen on ancient bas-reliefs, or in the engravings of archaeological works, pictures of the triumphal processions held in honour of the god Bacchus; and surely, with your cultivated and classic tastes, you would not be frightened even if at dead of night, in the depths of a lonely forest, the lonely spectres of such a Bacchanalian procession, together with the customary tipsy personnel, should appear bodily before your eyes. At the most you would only give way to a slight voluptuous shudder, an aesthetic awe, at sight of this pale assemblage of graceful phantoms, who have risen from their monumental sarcophagi, or from their hiding-places amid the ruins of ancient temples, to perform once more their ancient, joyous, divine service; once more, with sport and merry-making, to celebrate the triumphal march of the divine liberator, the Saviour of the senses; to dance once more the merry dance of paganism, the *cancan* of the antique world—to dance it without any hypocritical disguise, without fear of the interference of the police of a spiritualistic morality, with the wild abandonment of the old days, shouting, exulting, rapturous. *Evoe Bacche!*

But alas, dear reader, the poor fisherman was not, like yourself, versed in mythology; he had never made archaeological studies; and terror and fear seized upon him when he beheld the *Triumphator* and his two strange acolytes emerge from their monks' garb. He shuddered at the immodest gestures and leaps of the Bacchantes, Fauns, and Satyrs, who, with their goats' feet and horns, seemed to him peculiarly diabolical, and he regarded the whole assemblage as a congress of spectres and demons, who were seeking by their mysterious rites to bring ruin on all Christians. His hair stood on end at sight of the reckless impossible posture of a Maenad, who, with flowing hair and head thrown back, only balanced herself by the weight of her thyrsus. His own brain seemed to reel as he saw the Corybantes in mad frenzy wounding their own bodies with short swords, seeking voluptuousness in pain itself. The soft and tender, yet so terrible, tones of the music seemed to penetrate to his very soul, like a burning, consuming, excruciating flame. But when he saw that infamous Egyptian symbol, of exaggerated size and smothered in flowers, borne upon a tall pole by an unashamed woman, then sight and hearing forsook the poor fisherman—and he darted back to the boat, and crept under the nets, with chattering teeth and trembling limbs, as though Satan already held him fast by the foot. Soon after, the three monks also returned to the boat and shoved off. When they had disembarked at the original starting-place, the fisherman managed to escape unobserved from his hiding-place, so that they supposed he had merely been behind the willows awaiting their return. One of the monks, as usual, with icy-cold fingers pressed the fare into the fisherman's hand, then all three hurried away.

For the salvation of his own soul, which he believed to be endangered, and also to guard other good Christians from ruin, the fisherman held it his duty to communicate a full account of the mysterious occurrence to the Church authorities; and as the superior of a neighbour Franciscan monastery was in great repute as a learned exorcist, the fisherman determined to go to him without delay. The rising sun found him on his way to the monastery, where, with modest demeanour, he soon stood before his excellency the superior, who received him seated in an easy-chair in the library, and with hood drawn closely over his face, listened meditatively while the fisherman told his tale of horror. When the recital was finished, the superior raised his head, and as the hood fell back, the fisherman saw, to his dismay, that his excellency was one of the three monks who annually sailed over the lake—the very one, indeed, whom he had the previous night seen as a heathen demon riding in the golden chariot drawn by lions. It was the same marble-white face, the same regular, beautiful features, the same mouth with its delicately curved lips. And these lips now wore a kindly smile, and from that mouth now issued the gracious and melodious words, 'Beloved son in Christ, we willingly believe that you have spent the night in company of the god Bacchus. Your fantastic ghost-story gives ample proof of that. Not that we would say aught unpleasant of this god: at times he is undoubtedly a care-dispeller, and gladdens the heart of man. But he is very dangerous for those who cannot bear much; and to this class you seem to belong. We advise you to partake in future very sparingly of the golden juice of the grape, and not again to trouble the spiritual authorities with the fantasies of a drunken brain. Concerning this last vision of yours, you had better keep a very quiet tongue in your head; otherwise the secular arm of our beadle shall measure out to you twenty-five lashes. And now, beloved son in Christ, go to the monastery kitchen, where brother butler and brother cook will set before you a slight repast.'

With this, the reverend father bestowed the customary benediction on the fisherman, and when the latter, bewildered, took himself off to the kitchen and suddenly came face to face with brother cook and brother butler, he almost fell to the earth in affright, for they were the same monks who had accompanied the superior on his midnight excursions across the lake. He recognized one by his fat paunch and bald head, and the other by his lascivious grin and goat-ears. But he held his tongue, and only in later years did he relate his strange story.

Several old chronicles which contain similar legends locate the scene near the city of Speyer, on the Rhine.

Along the coast of East Friesland an analogous tradition is found, in which the ancient conception of the transportation of the dead to the realm of Hades, which underlies all those legends, is most distinctly seen. It is true that none of them contain any mention of Charon, the steersman of the boat: this old fellow seems to have entirely disappeared from folk-lore, and is to be met with only in puppet-shows. But a far more notable mythological personage is to be recognized in the so-called forwarding agent, or dispatcher, who makes arrangements for the transportation of the dead, and pays the customary passage-money into the hands of the boatman; the latter is generally a common fisherman, who officiates as Charon. Notwithstanding his quaint disguise, the true name of this dispatcher may readily be guessed, and I shall therefore relate the legend as faithfully as possible.

The shores of East Friesland that border on the North Sea abound with bays, which are used as harbours, and are called fiords. On the farthest projecting promontory of land generally stands the solitary hut of some fisherman, who here lives, peaceful and contented, with his family. Here nature wears a sad and melancholy aspect. Not even the chirping of a bird is to be heard, only now and then the shrill screech of a sea-gull flying up from its nest among the sand-hills, that announces the coming storm. The monotonous plashings of the restless sea harmonize with the sombre, shifting shadows of the passing clouds. Even the human inhabitants do not sing here, and on these melancholy coasts the strain of a *Volkslied* is never heard. The people who live here are an earnest, honest, matter-of-fact race, proud of their bold spirit and of the liberties which they have inherited from their ancestors. Such a people are not imaginative, and are little given to metaphysical speculations. Fishing is their principal support, added to which is an occasional pittance of passage-money for transporting some traveller to one of the adjacent islands.

It is said that at a certain period of the year, just at midday, when the fisherman and his family are seated at table eating their noonday meal, a traveller enters and asks the master of the house to vouchsafe him an audience for a few minutes to speak with him on a matter of business. The fisherman, after vainly inviting the stranger to partake of the meal, grants his request, and they both step aside to a little table. I shall not describe the personal appearance of the stranger in detail, after the tedious manner of novel-writers: a brief enumeration of the salient points will suffice. He is a little man, advanced in years, but well preserved. He is, so to say, a youthful greybeard: plump, but not corpulent; cheeks ruddy as an apple; small eyes, which blink merrily and continually, and on his powdered little head is set a three-cornered little hat. Under his flaming yellow cloak, with its many collars, he wears the old-fashioned dress of a well-to-do Dutch merchant, such as we see depicted in old portraits—namely, a short silk coat of a parrot-green colour, a vest embroidered with flowers, black breeches, striped stockings, and shoes ornamented with buckles. The latter are so brightly polished that it is hard to understand how the wearer could trudge afoot through the slimy mud of the coast and yet keep them so clean. His voice is a thin, asthmatic treble, sometimes inclining to be rather lachrymose; but the address and bearing of the little man are as grave and measured as beseem a Dutch merchant. This gravity, however, appears to be more assumed than natural, and is in marked contrast with the searching, roving, swift-darting glances of the eye, and with the ill-repressed fidgetiness of the legs and arms. That the stranger is a Dutch merchant is evidenced not only by his apparel, but also by the mercantile exactitude and caution with which he endeavours to effect as favourable a bargain as possible for his employers. He is, as he says, a forwarding agent, and has received from some of his mercantile friends a commission to transport a certain number of souls, as many as can find room in an ordinary boat, from the coast of East Friesland to the White Island. In fulfilment of this commission, he adds, he wishes to know if the fisherman will this night convey in his boat the aforesaid cargo to the aforesaid island; in which case he is authorized to pay the passage-money in advance, confidently hoping that, in Christian fairness, the fisherman will make his price very moderate. The Dutch merchant (which term is, in fact, a pleonasm, since every Dutchman is a merchant) makes this proposition with the utmost nonchalance, as if it referred to a cargo of cheeses, and not to the souls of the dead. The fisherman is startled at the word 'souls,' and a cold chill creeps down his back, for he immediately comprehends that the souls of the dead are here meant, and that the stranger is none other than the phantom Dutchman, who has already entrusted several of his fellow-fishermen with the transportation of the souls of the dead, and paid them well for it, too.

These East Frieslanders are, as I have already remarked, a brave, healthy, practical people; in them is lacking that morbid imagination which makes us so impressible to the ghostly and supernatural. Our fisherman's weird dismay lasts but a moment; suppressing the uncanny sensation that is stealing over him, he soon regains his composure, and, intent on securing as high a sum as possible, he assumes an air of supreme indifference. But after a little chaffering the two come to an understanding, and shake hands to seal the bargain. The Dutchman draws forth a dirty leather pouch, filled entirely with little silver pennies of the smallest denomination ever coined in Holland, and in these tiny coins counts out the whole amount of the fare. With instructions to the fisherman to be ready with his boat at the appointed place about the midnight hour when the moon becomes visible, the Dutchman takes leave of the whole family, and, declining their repeated invitations to dine, the grave little figure, dignified as ever, trips lightly away.

At the time agreed upon the fisherman appears at the appointed place. At first the boat is rocked lightly to and fro by the waves; but by the time the full moon has risen above the horizon the fisherman notices that his bark is less easily swayed, and so it gradually sinks deeper and deeper in the stream, until finally the water comes within a hand's-breadth of the boat's gunwale. This circumstance apprises him that his passengers, the souls, are now aboard, and he pushes off from shore with his cargo. Although he strains his eyes to the utmost, he can distinguish nothing but a few vapoury streaks that seem to be swayed hither and thither, and to intermingle with one another, but assume no definite forms. Listen intently as he may, he hears nothing but an indescribably faint chirping and rustling.

Only now and then a sea-gull with a shrill scream flies swiftly over his head; or near him a fish leaps up from out the stream, and for a moment stares at him with a vacuous look. The night-winds sigh, and the sea-breezes grow more chilly. Everywhere only water, moonlight, and silence! and silent as all around him is the fisherman, who finally reaches the White Island and moors his boat. He sees no one on the strand, but he hears a shrill, asthmatic, wheezy, lachrymose voice, which he recognizes as that of the Dutchman. The latter seems to be reading off a list of proper names, with a peculiar, monotonous intonation, as if rehearsing a roll-call. Among the names are some which are known to the fisherman as belonging to persons who have died that year. During the reading of the list, the boat is evidently being gradually lightened of its load, and as soon as the last name is called it rises suddenly and floats free, although but a moment before it was deeply imbedded in the sand of the sea-shore. To the fisherman this is a token that his cargo has been properly delivered, and he calmly rows back to his wife and child, to his beloved home on the fiord.

. . . Notwithstanding this clever disguise, I have ventured to guess who the important mythological personage is that figures in this tradition. It is none other than the god Mercury, Hermes Psychopompos, the whilom conductor of the dead to Hades. Verily, under that shabby yellow cloak and prosaic tradesman's figure is concealed the youthful and most accomplished god of heathendom, the cunning son of Maia. On his little three-cornered hat not the slightest tuft of a feather is to be seen which might remind the beholder of the winged cap, and the clumsy shoes with steel buckles fail to give the least hint of the winged sandals. This grave and heavy Dutch lead is quite different from the mobile quicksilver, from which the god derived his very name. But the contrast is so exceedingly striking as to betray the god's design, which is the more effectually to disguise himself. Perhaps this mask was not chosen out of mere caprice. Mercury was, as you know, the patron god of thieves and merchants, and, in all probability, in choosing a disguise that should conceal him, and a trade by which to earn his livelihood, he took into consideration his talents and his antecedents.

. . . And thus it came to pass that the shrewdest and most cunning of the gods became a merchant, and, to adapt himself most thoroughly to his role, became the *ne plus ultra* of merchants—a Dutch merchant. His long practice in the olden time as Psychopompos, as conveyor of the dead to Hades, marks him out as particularly fitted to conduct the transportation of the souls of the dead to the White Island, in the manner just described.

The White Island is occasionally also called Brea, or Britannia. Does this perhaps refer to White Albion, to the chalky cliffs of the English coast? It would be a very humorous idea if England was designated as the land of the dead, as the Plutonian realm, as hell. In such a form, in truth, England has appeared to many a stranger.

In my essay on the Faust legend I discussed at full length the popular superstition concerning Pluto and his dominion. I showed how the old realm of shadows became hell, and how its old gloomy ruler became more and more diabolical. Neither Pluto, god of the nether regions, nor his brother Neptune, god of the sea, emigrated like the other gods. Even after the final triumph of Christendom they remained in their domains, their respective elements. No matter what silly fables concerning him were invented here above on earth, old Pluto sat by his Proserpine, warm and cosy down below.

Neptune suffered less from calumny than his brother Pluto, and neither church-bell chimes nor organ-strains could offend his ears in the depths of old ocean, where he sat peacefully by the side of his white-bosomed wife, Dame Amphitrite, surrounded by his court of dripping nereids and tritons. Only now and then, when a young sailor crossed the equator, he would dart up from the briny deep, in his hand brandishing the trident, his head crowned with seaweed, and his flowing, silvery beard reaching down to the navel. Then he would confer on the neophyte the terrible sea-water baptism, accompanying it with a long, unctuous harangue, interspersed with coarse sailor jests, to the great delight of the jolly tars. The harangue was frequently interrupted by the spitting of amber quids of chewed tobacco, which Neptune so freely scattered around him. A friend, who gave me a detailed description of the manner in which such a sea-miracle is performed, assured me that the very sailors that laughed most heartily at the droll antics of Neptune never for a moment doubted the existence of such a god, and sometimes when in great danger they even prayed to him.

Neptune, as we have seen, remained monarch of the watery realm; and Pluto, notwithstanding his metamorphosis into Satan, still continued to be prince of the lower regions. They fared better than did their brother Jupiter, who, after the overthrow of their father, Saturn, became ruler of heaven, and as sovereign of the universe resided at Olympus, where, surrounded by his merry troop of gods, goddesses, and nymphs-of-honour, he carried on his ambrosial rule of joy. But when the great catastrophe occurred,—when the rule of the cross, that symbol of suffering, was proclaimed,—then the great Kronides fled, and disappeared amid the tumults and confusion of the transmigration of races. All traces of him were lost, and I have in vain consulted old chronicles and old women: none could give me the least information concerning his fate. With the same purpose in view, I have ransacked many libraries, where I was shown the magnificent codices ornamented with gold and precious stones, true odalisques in the harem of science. To the learned eunuchs who, with such affability, unlocked for me those brilliant treasures, I here return the customary thanks. It appears as if no popular tradition of a medieval Jupiter exists; and all that I could gather concerning him consists of a story told me by my friend, Niels Andersen.

. . . 'The events that I am about to relate,' said Niels Andersen, 'occurred on an island, the exact situation of which I cannot tell. Since its discovery no one has been able again to reach it, being prevented by the immense icebergs that tower like a high wall around the island, and seldom, probably, permit a near approach. Only the crew of a Russian whaling-vessel, which a storm had driven so far to the north, ever trod its soil; and since then over a hundred years have elapsed. When the sailors had, by means of a small boat, effected a landing, they found the island to be wild and desolate. Sadly waved the blades of tall sedgy grass over the quicksands; here and there grew a few stunted fir-trees, or barren shrubs. They saw a multitude of rabbits hopping about, on which account they named it the Island of Rabbits. Only one miserable hut gave evidence that a human being dwelt there. As the sailors entered the hut they saw an old, very old man, wretchedly clad in a garment of rabbit-skins rudely stitched together. He was seated in a stone chair in front of the hearth, trying to warm his emaciated hands and trembling knees by the flaring brushwood fire. At his right side stood an immense bird, evidently an eagle, but which had been roughly treated by time, and shorn of all its plumage save the long bristly quills of its wings, that gave it a highly grotesque, and, at the same time, hideous appearance. At the old man's left, squatted on the earth, was an extraordinarily large hairless goat,

which seemed to be very old; although full milky udders, with
fresh, rosy nipples, hung at its belly.

'Among the sailors were several Greeks, one of whom, not
thinking that his words would be understood by the aged
inhabitant of the hut, remarked in the Greek language to a
comrade: "This old fellow is either a spectre or an evil demon."
But at these words the old man suddenly arose from his seat,
and to their great surprise the sailors beheld a stately figure,
which, in spite of its advanced age, raised itself erect with com-
manding, yes, with king-like dignity, his head almost touching
the rafters. The features, too, although rugged and weather-
beaten, showed traces of original beauty, they were so noble
and well proportioned. A few silvery locks fell over his brow,
which was furrowed by pride and age. His eyes had a dim
and fixed look, but occasionally they would still gleam piercingly;
and from his mouth were heard in the melodious and sonorous
words of the ancient Greek language: "You are mistaken,
young man; I am neither a spectre nor an evil demon; I am
an unhappy old man, who once knew better days. But who
are ye?"

'The sailors explained the accident which had befallen them,
and then inquired concerning the island. The information,
however, was very meagre. The old man told them that since
time immemorial he had inhabited this island, whose bulwark
of ice served him as a secure asylum against his inexorable foes.
He subsisted principally by catching rabbits, and every year,
when the floating icebergs had settled, a few bands of savages
crossed over on sleds, and to them he sold rabbit-skins, receiving
in exchange various articles of indispensable necessity. The
whales, which sometimes came swimming close to the island,
were his favourite company. But it gave him pleasure to hear
again his native tongue, for he too was a Greek. He entreated
his countrymen to give him an account of the present condition
of Greece. That the cross had been torn down from the battlements of Grecian cities apparently caused the old man a
malicious satisfaction; but it did not altogether please him when
he heard that the crescent had been planted there instead.
It was strange that none of the sailors knew the names of the
cities concerning which the old man inquired, and which, as
he assured them, had flourished in his time. In like manner
the names of the present cities and villages in Greece, which
were mentioned by the sailors, were unknown to him; at this
the old man would shake his head sadly, and the sailors looked

at one another perplexed. They noticed that he knew exactly all the localities and geographical peculiarities of Greece; and he described so accurately and vividly the bays, the peninsulas, the mountain-ridges, even the knolls and most trifling rocky elevations, that his ignorance of their towns was all the more surprising. With especial interest, with a certain anxiety even, he questioned them concerning an ancient temple, which in his time, he assured them, had been the most beautiful in all Greece; but none of his hearers knew the name, which he pronounced with a loving tenderness. But finally, when the old man had again described the site of the temple, with the utmost particularity, a young sailor recognized the place by the description.

'The village wherein he was born, said the young man, was situated hard by, and when a boy he had often tended his father's swine at the very place where there had been found ruins of an ancient structure, indicating a magnificent grandeur in the past. Now, only a few large marble pillars remained standing; some were plain, unadorned columns, others were surmounted by the square stones of a gable. From the cracks of the masonry the blooming honeysuckle-vines and red bell-flowers trailed downwards. Other pillars—among the number some of rose-coloured marble—lay shattered on the ground, and the costly marble capitals, ornamented with beautiful sculpture, representing foliage and flowers, were overgrown by rank creepers and grasses. Half buried in the earth lay huge marble blocks, some of which were squares, such as were used for the walls; others were three-cornered slabs for roof-pieces. Over them waved a large, wild fig-tree, which had grown up out of the ruins. Under the shadow of that tree, continued the young man, he had passed whole hours in examining the strange figures carved on the large marble blocks; they seemed to be pictorial representations of all sorts of sports and combats, and were very pleasing to look at, but, alas! much injured by exposure, and overgrown with moss and ivy. His father, whom he had questioned in regard to the mysterious signification of these pillars and sculptures, told him that these were the ruins of an ancient pagan temple, and had once been the abode of a wicked heathen god, who had here wantoned in lewd debauchery, incest, and unnatural vices. Notwithstanding this, the unenlightened heathen were accustomed to slaughter in his honour a hundred oxen at a time, and the hollowed marble block into which was gathered the blood of the sacrifices was yet in existence. It was, in fact, the very trough which they were in the habit of using as a receptable for refuse wherewith to feed the swine.

'So spoke the young sailor. But the old man heaved a sigh that betrayed the most terrible anguish. Tottering, he sank into his stone chair, covered his face with his hands, and wept like a child. The great, gaunt bird, with a shrill screech, flapped its immense wings, and menaced the strangers with claws and beak. The old goat licked its master's hands, and bleated mournfully as in consolation.

'At this strange sight an uncanny terror seized upon the sailors: they hurriedly left the hut, and were glad when they could no longer hear the sobbing of the old man, the screaming of the bird, and the bleating of the goat. When they were safely on board the boat, they narrated their adventure. Among the crew was a learned Russian, professor of philosophy at the University of Kazan; and he declared the matter to be highly important. With his forefinger held knowingly to the side of his nose, he assured the sailors that the old man of the island was undoubtedly the ancient god Jupiter, son of Saturn and Rhea. The bird at his side was clearly the eagle that once carried in its claws the terrible thunderbolts. And the old goat was, in all probability, none other than Althea, Jupiter's old nurse, who had suckled him in Crete, and now in exile again nourished him with her milk.'

This is the story as told to me by Niels Andersen; and I must confess that it filled my soul with a profound melancholy. Decay is secretly undermining all that is great in the universe, and the gods themselves must finally succumb to the same miserable destiny. The iron law of fate so wills it, and even the greatest of the immortals must submissively bow his head. He of whom Homer sang, and whom Phidias sculptured in gold and ivory, he at whose glance earth trembled, he the lover of Leda, Alcmena, Semele, Danaë, Callisto, Io, Leto, Europa, and the rest—even he is compelled to hide himself behind the icebergs of the North Pole, and in order to prolong his wretched existence must deal in rabbit-skins, like a shabby Savoyard!

I do not doubt that there are people who will derive a malicious pleasure from such a spectacle. They are, perhaps, the descendants of those unfortunate oxen who, in hecatombs, were slaughtered on the altars of Jupiter. Rejoice! avenged is the blood of your ancestors, those poor martyrs of superstition. But we, who have no hereditary grudge rankling in us, we are touched at the sight of fallen greatness, and withhold not our holiest compassion.

CONFESSIONS

A WITTY Frenchman—a few years ago these words would have been a pleonasm—once dubbed me an unfrocked Romanticist. I have a weakness for all that is witty; and spiteful as was this appellation, it nevertheless delighted me highly. Notwithstanding the war of extermination that I had waged against Romanticism, I always remained a Romanticist at heart, and that in a higher degree than I myself realized. After I had delivered the most deadly blows against the taste for Romantic poetry in Germany, there stole over me an inexpressible yearning for the blue flower in the fairyland of Romanticism, and I grasped the magic lyre and sang a song wherein I gave full sway to all the sweet extravagances, to all the intoxication of moonlight, to all the blooming, nightingale-like fancies once so fondly loved. I know it was 'the last free-forest song of Romanticism,' and I am its last poet. With me the old German lyric school ends; while with me, at the same time, the modern lyric school of Germany begins. Writers on German literature will assign to me this double role. It would be unseemly for me to speak at length on this subject, but I may with justice claim a liberal space in the history of German Romanticism. For this reason I ought to have included in my account of the Romantic School a review of my own writings. By my omission to do this, a gap has been left which I cannot easily fill. To write a criticism of oneself is an embarrassing, even an impossible task. I should be a conceited coxcomb to obtrude the good I might be able to say of myself, and I should be a great fool to proclaim to the whole world the defects of which I might also be conscious. And even with the most honest desire to be sincere, one cannot tell the truth about oneself. No one has as yet succeeded in doing it, neither Saint Augustine, the pious Bishop of Hippo, nor the Genevese Jean Jacques Rousseau—least of all the latter, who proclaimed himself the man of truth and nature, but was really much more untruthful and unnatural than his contemporaries.

. . . Rousseau, who in his own person also slandered human nature, was yet true to it in respect of our primitive weakness, which consists in always wishing to appear in the eyes of the world as something different from what we really are. His self-portraiture is a lie, admirably executed, but still only a brilliant lie.

I recently read an anecdote concerning the King of Ashanti, which illustrates in a very amusing manner this weakness of human nature. When Major Bowditch was dispatched by the English Governor of the Cape of Good Hope as resident ambassador to the court of that powerful African monarch, he sought to ingratiate himself with the courtiers, especially with the court-ladies, by taking their portraits. The king, who was astonished at the accuracy of the likenesses, requested that he also might be painted, and had already had several sittings, when the artist noticed in the features of the king, who had often sprung up to observe the progress of the picture, the peculiar restlessness and embarrassment of one who has a request on the tip of his tongue and yet hesitates to express it. The painter pressed His Majesty to tell his wish, until at last the poor African king inquired, in a low voice, if he could not be painted white.

And so it is. The swarthy negro king wishes to be painted white. But do not laugh at the poor African: every human being is such another negro king, and all of us would like to appear before the public in a different colour from that which fate has given us. Fully realizing this, I took heed not to draw my own portrait in my review of the Romantic School. But in the following pages I shall have ample occasion to speak of myself, and this will to a certain extent fill up the gap caused by the missing portrait; for I have here undertaken to describe, for the reader's benefit and enlightenment, the philosophical and religious changes which have taken place in the author's mind since my book on Germany was written.

Fear not that I shall paint myself too white and my fellow-beings too black. I shall always give my own colours with exact fidelity, so that it may be known how far my judgment is to be trusted when I draw the portraits of others.

. . . Madame de Staël's hatred of the Emperor is the soul of her book, De l'Allemagne, and, although his name is nowhere mentioned, one can see at every line how the writer squints at the Tuileries. I doubt not that the book annoyed the Emperor more than the most direct attack; for nothing so much irritates a man as a woman's petty needle-pricks. We are prepared for great sabre-strokes, and instead we are tickled at the most sensitive spots.

Oh, the women! we must forgive them much, for they love

much—and many. Their hate is, in fact, only love turned the wrong way. At times they try to injure us, but only because they hope thereby to please some other man. When they write, they have one eye on the paper and the other on a man. This rule applies to all authoresses, with the exception of Countess Hahn-Hahn, who has only one eye. We male authors have also our prejudices. We write for or against something, for or against an idea, for or against a party; but women always write for or against one particular man, or, to express it more correctly, on account of one particular man. We men will sometimes lie outright; women, like all passive creatures, seldom invent, but can so distort a fact that they can thereby injure us more surely than by a downright lie. I verily believe my friend Balzac was right when he once said to me, in a sorrowful tone: '*La femme est un être dangereux.*'

Yes, women are dangerous; but I must admit that beautiful women are not so dangerous as those whose attractions are intellectual rather than physical; for the former are accustomed to have men pay court to them, while the latter meet the vanity of men half-way, and through the bait of flattery acquire a more powerful influence than the beautiful women. I by no means intend to insinuate that Madame de Staël was ugly; but beauty is something quite different. She had single points which were pleasing; but the effect as a whole was anything but pleasing. To nervous persons, like the sainted Schiller, her custom of continually twirling between her fingers some fragment of paper or similar small article was particularly annoying. This habit made poor Schiller dizzy, and in desperation he grasped her pretty hand to hold it quiet. This innocent action led Madame de Staël to believe that the tender-hearted poet was overpowered by the magic of her personal charms. I am told that she really had very pretty hands and beautiful arms, which she always displayed. Surely the Venus of Milo could not show such beautiful arms! Her teeth surpassed in whiteness those of the finest steed of Araby. She had very large, beautiful eyes, a dozen amorets would have found room on her lips, and her smile is said to have been very sweet: therefore she could not have been ugly—no woman is ugly. But I venture to say that had fair Helen of Sparta looked so, the Trojan War would not have occurred, and the strongholds of Priam would not have been burned, and Homer would never have sung the wrath of Pelidean Achilles.

. . . In my Memoirs I relate with more detail than is

admissible here how, after the French Revolution of July 1830, I emigrated to Paris, where I have ever since lived quiet and contented. What I did and suffered during the Restoration will be told when the disinterestedness of such a publication is no longer liable to doubt or suspicion. I worked much and suffered much; and about the time that the sun of the July revolution arose in France, I had gradually become very weary, and needed recreation. Moreover, the air of my native land was daily becoming more unwholesome for me, and I was compelled to contemplate seriously a change of climate. I had visions: in the clouds I saw all sorts of horrible, grotesque faces, that annoyed me with their grimaces. It sometimes seemed to me as if the sun were a Prussian cockade. At night I dreamed of a hideous black vulture that preyed on my liver; and became very melancholy. In addition to all this, I had become acquainted with an old magistrate from Berlin who had spent many years in the fortress of Spandau, and who described to me how unpleasant it was in winter to wear iron manacles. I thought it very unchristian not to warm the irons a little, for if our chains were only warmed somewhat, they would not seem so very unpleasant, and cold natures could even endure them very well. The chains ought also to be perfumed with the essence of roses and laurels, as is the custom in France. I asked my magistrate if oysters were often served at Spandau. He answered no; Spandau was too far distant from the sea. Meat, also, he said, was seldom to be had, and the only fowls were the flies which fell into one's soup. About the same time I became acquainted with a commercial traveller of a French wine establishment, who was never tired of praising the merry life of Paris, —how the air was full of music, how from morning until night one heard the singing of the *Marseillaise* and *En avant, marchons !* and *Lafayette aux cheveux blancs*. He told me that at every street-corner was the inscription: 'Liberty, Equality, Fraternity.' He likewise recommended the champagne of his firm, and gave me a large number of business cards. He also promised to furnish me with letters of introduction to the best Parisian restaurants, in case I should visit Paris. As I really did need recreation, and as Spandau was at too great a distance from the sea to procure oysters, and as the fowl-soup of Spandau was not to my taste, and as, moreover, the Prussian chains were very cold in winter and could not be conducive to my health, I determined to go to Paris, the fatherland of champagne and the *Marseillaise*, there to drink the former, and to hear the latter sung, together with *En avant, marchons!* and *Lafayette aux cheveux blancs*.

I crossed the Rhine on 1st May 1831. I did not see the old river-god, Father Rhine, so I contented myself with dropping my visiting card into the water. I am told that he was sitting down below, conning his French grammar; for during the Prussian rule his French had grown rusty from long disuse, and now he wished to practise it anew, in order to be prepared for contingencies. I thought I could hear him, conjugating: '*J'aime, tu aimes, il aime; nous aimons*'—but what does he love? Surely not the Prussians!

I awoke at St. Denis from a sweet morning sleep, and heard for the first time the shout of the driver: 'Paris! Paris!' Here we already inhaled the atmosphere of the capital, now visible on the horizon. A rascally lackey tried to persuade me to visit the royal sepulchre at St. Denis; but I had not come to France to see dead kings. . . . In twenty minutes I was in Paris, entering through the triumphal arch of the Boulevard St. Denis, which was originally erected in honour of Louis XIV, but now served to grace my entry into Paris. I was surprised at meeting such multitudes of well-dressed people, tastefully arrayed like the pictures of a fashion-journal. I was also impressed by the fact that they all spoke French, which, in Germany, is the distinguishing mark of the higher classes; the whole nation are as noble as the nobility with us. The men were all so polite, and the pretty women all smiled so graciously. If someone accidentally jostled me without immediately asking pardon, I could safely wager that it was a fellow-countryman. And if a pretty woman looked a little sour, she had either eaten sauerkraut or could read Klopstock in the original. I found everything quite charming. The skies were so blue, the air so balmy, and here and there the rays of the sun of July were still glimmering. The cheeks of the beauteous Lutetia were still flushed from the burning kisses of that sun, and the bridal flowers on her bosom were not yet wilted. But at the street corners the words, *Liberté, égalité, fraternité*, had already been erased. Honeymoons fly so quickly!

I immediately visited the restaurants to which I had been recommended. The landlords assured me that they would have made me welcome even without letters of introduction, for I had an honest and distinguished appearance, which in itself was a sufficient recommendation. Never did a German landlord so address me, even if he thought it. Such a churlish fellow feels himself in duty bound to suppress all pleasant speeches, and his German bluntness demands that he shall tell only the most disagreeable things to our faces. In the manner, and even in the language, of the French, there is so much delicious flattery, which costs so little, and is yet so gratifying. My poor sensitive soul, which had shrunk with shyness from the rudeness of the fatherland, again expanded under the genial influence of French urbanity. God has given us tongues that we may say something pleasant to our fellow-men.

My French had grown rusty since the battle of Waterloo, but after half an hour's conversation with a pretty flower-girl in the Passage de l'Opéra it soon flowed fluently again. I managed to stammer forth gallant phrases in broken French, and explained to the little charmer the Linnaean system, in which flowers are classified according to their stamens. The little one practised a different system, and divided flowers into those which smelled pleasantly and those which smelled unpleasantly. I believe that she applied a similar classification to men. She was surprised that, notwithstanding my youth, I was so learned, and spread the fame of my erudition through the whole Passage de l'Opéra. I inhaled with rapturous delight the delicious aroma of flattery, and amused myself charmingly. I walked on flowers, and many a roasted pigeon came flying into my gaping mouth.

. . . Among the notabilities whom I met soon after my arrival in Paris was Victor Bohain; and I love to recall to memory the jovial, intellectual form of him who did so much to dispel the clouds from the brow of the German dreamer, and to initiate his sorrow-laden heart into the gaieties of French life. He had at that time already founded the *Europe Littéraire*, and, as editor, solicited me to write for his journal several articles on Germany, after the genre of Madame de Staël. I promised to furnish the articles, particularly mentioning, however, that I should write them in a style quite different from that of Madame de Staël. 'That is a matter of indifference to me,' was the laughing answer; 'like Voltaire, I tolerate every genre, excepting only the *genre ennuyeux*.' And in order that I, poor German, should not fall into the *genre ennuyeux*, friend Bohain often invited me to dine with him, and stimulated my brain with champagne. No one knew better than he how to arrange a dinner at which one should not only enjoy the best cuisine, but be most pleasantly entertained. No one could do the honours of host as well as he; and he was certainly justified in charging the stockholders of the *Europe Littéraire* with one hundred thousand francs as the expense of these banquets. Even his wooden leg contributed to the humour of the man, and when he hobbled around the table, serving out champagne to his guests, he resembled Vulcan performing the duties of Hebe's office amidst the uproarious mirth of the assembled gods. Where is Victor Bohain now? I have heard nothing of him for a long period. The last I saw of him was about ten years ago, at an inn at Granville. He had just come over from England, where he had been studying the colossal English national debt, in this occupation smothering the recollection of his own little personal debts, to this little town on the coast of Normandy, and here I found him seated at a table with a bottle of champagne and an open-mouthed, stupid-looking citizen, to whom he was earnestly explaining a business project by which, as Bohain eloquently demonstrated, a million could be realized. Bohain always had a great fondness for speculation, and in all his projects there was always a million in progress—never less than a million. His friends nicknamed him, on this account, Messer Millione.

. . . The founding of the *Europe Littéraire* was an excellent idea. Its success seemed assured, and I have never been able to understand why it failed. Only one evening before the day on which the suspension occurred, Victor Bohain gave a brilliant ball in the editorial *salons* of the journal, at which he danced with his three hundred stockholders, just like Leonidas with his three hundred Spartans the day before the battle of Thermopylae. Every time that I behold in the gallery of the Louvre the painting by David which portrays that scene of antique heroism, I am reminded of the last ball of Victor Bohain. Just like the death-defying king in David's picture, so stood Victor Bohain on his solitary leg; it was the same classic pose. Stranger, when thou strollest in Paris through the Chaussée d'Antin towards the Boulevards, and findest thyself in the low-lying, filthy street that was once called the Rue Basse du Rempart, know that thou standest at the Thermopylae of the *Europe Littéraire*, where Victor Bohain with his three hundred stockholders so heroically fell.

. . . In my articles on German philosophy I blabbed without reserve the secrets of the schools, which, draped in scholastic formulas, were previously known only to the initiated. My revelations excited the greatest surprise in France, and I remember that leading French thinkers naïvely confessed to me that they had always believed German philosophy to be a peculiar mystic fog, behind which divinity lay hidden as in a cloud, and that German philosophers were ecstatic seers, filled with piety and the fear of God. It is not my fault that German philosophy is just the reverse of that which until now we have called piety and fear of God, and that our latest philosophers have proclaimed absolute atheism to be the last word of German philosophy. Relentlessly and with bacchantic recklessness they tore aside the blue curtain from the German heavens, and cried: 'Behold! all the gods have flown, and there above sits only an old spinster with leaden hands and sorrowful heart—Necessity.'

Alas! what then sounded so strangely is now being preached from all the house-tops in Germany, and the fanatic zeal of many of these propagandists is terrible! We have now bigoted monks of atheism, grand-inquisitors of infidelity, who would have bound Voltaire to the stake because he was at heart an obstinate deist. So long as such doctrines remained the secret possession of an intellectual aristocracy, and were discussed in a select coterie-dialect which was incomprehensible to the lackeys in attendance, while we at our philosophical *petits soupers* were blaspheming, so long did I continue to be one of the thoughtless free-thinkers, of whom the majority resembled those *grands seigneurs* who, shortly before the Revolution, sought by means of the new revolutionary ideas to dispel the tedium of their indolent court-life. But as soon as I saw that the rabble began to discuss the same themes at their unclean symposiums, where instead of wax-candles and chandeliers gleamed tallow-dips and oil-lamps; when I perceived that greasy cobblers and tailors presumed in their blunt mechanics' speech to deny the existence of God; when atheism began to stink of cheese, brandy, and tobacco—then my eyes were suddenly opened, and that which I had not comprehended through reason, I now learned through my olfactory organs and through my loathing and disgust. Heaven be praised! my atheism was at an end.

To be candid, it was perhaps not disgust alone that made the principles of the godless obnoxious to me, and induced me to abandon their ranks. I was oppressed by a certain worldly apprehension which I could not overcome, for I saw that atheism had entered into a more or less secret compact with the most terribly naked, quite fig-leafless, communistic communism. My dread of the latter has nothing in common with that of the parvenu, who trembles for his wealth, or with that of well-to-do tradesmen who fear an interruption of their profitable business. No; that which disquiets me is the secret dread of the artist and scholar, who sees our whole modern civilization, the laboriously-achieved product of so many centuries of effort, and the fruit of the noblest works of our ancestors, jeopardized by the triumph of communism. Swept along by the resistless current of generous emotions, we may perhaps sacrifice the cause of art and science, even all our own individual interests, for the general welfare of the suffering and oppressed people. But we can no longer disguise from ourselves what we have to expect when the great, rude masses, which by some are called the people, by others the rabble, and whose legitimate sovereignty was proclaimed long ago, shall obtain actual dominion. The poet, in particular, experiences a mysterious dread in contemplating the advent to power of this uncouth sovereign. We will gladly sacrifice ourselves for the people, for self-sacrifice constitutes one of our most exquisite enjoyments—the emancipation of the people has been the great task of our lives; we have toiled for it, and in its cause endured indescribable misery, at home as in exile—but the poet's refined and sensitive nature revolts at every near personal contact with the people, and still more repugnant is the mere thought of its caresses, from which may Heaven preserve us! A great democrat once remarked that if a king had taken him by the hand, he would immediately have thrust it into the fire to purify it. In the same manner I would say, if the sovereign people vouchsafed to press my hand, I would hasten to wash it. The poor people is not beautiful, but very ugly; only that ugliness simply comes from dirt, and will disappear as soon as we open public baths, in which His Majesty may gratuitously bathe himself.

. . . It required no great foresight to foretell these terrible events so long before their occurrence. I could easily prophesy what songs would one day be whistled and chirped in Germany, for I saw the birds hatching that in after-days gave tone to the new school of song. I saw Hegel, with his almost comically serious face, like a sitting hen, brooding over the fatal eggs; and I heard his cackling; to tell the truth, I seldom understood him, and only through later reflection did I arrive at an understanding of his works. I believe he did not wish to be understood.

. . . One beautiful starlight night, Hegel stood with me at an open window. I, being a young man of twenty-two, and having just eaten well and drunk coffee, naturally spoke with enthusiasm of the stars, and called them abodes of the blest. But the master muttered to himself: 'The stars! Hm! hm! the stars are only a brilliant eruption on the firmament.' 'What!' cried I; 'then there is no blissful spot above, where virtue is rewarded after death?' But he, glaring at me with his dim eyes, remarked, sneering: 'So you want a *pourboire* because you have supported your sick mother and not poisoned your brother?' At these words he looked anxiously around, but was reassured when he saw that it was only Henry Beer.

. . . I was never an abstract thinker, and I accepted the synthesis of the Hegelian philosophy without examination, because its deductions flattered my vanity. I was young and arrogant, and it gratified my self-conceit when I was informed by Hegel that not, as my grandmother had supposed, He who dwelt in the heavens, but I myself, here on earth, was God. This silly pride had, however, by no means an evil influence on me. On the contrary, it awoke in me the heroic spirit, and at that period I practised a generosity and self-sacrifice which completely cast into the shade the most virtuous and distinguished deeds of the good *bourgeoisie* of virtue, who did good merely from a sense of duty and in obedience to the laws of morality. I was myself the living moral law, and the fountainhead of all right and all authority. I myself was morality personified; I was incapable of sin, I was incarnated purity. . . . I was all love, and incapable of hate. I no longer revenged myself on my enemies; for, rightly considered, I had no enemies; at least, I recognized none as such. For me there now existed only unbelievers who questioned my divinity. Every indignity that they offered me was a sacrilege, and their contumely was blasphemy. Such godlessness, of course, I could not always let pass unpunished; but in those cases it was not human revenge, but divine judgment upon sinners. Absorbed in this exalted practice of justice, I would repress with more or less difficulty all ordinary pity. As I had no enemies, so also there existed for me no friends, but only worshippers, who believed in my greatness, and adored me, and praised my works, those written in verse as well as those in prose. Towards this congregation of truly devout and pious ones I was particularly gracious, especially towards the young-lady devotees.

But the expense of playing the role of a god, for whom it were unseemly to go in tatters, and who is sparing neither of body nor of purse, is immense. To play such a role respectably, two things are above all requisite—much money and robust health. Alas! it happened that one day [in February 1848] both these essentials failed me, and my divinity was at an end. Luckily, the highly-respected public was at that time occupied with events so dramatic, so grand, so fabulous and unprecedented that the change in the affairs of so unimportant a personage as myself attracted but little attention. Unprecedented and fabulous were indeed the events of those crazy February days, when the wisdom of the wisest was brought to naught, and the chosen ones of imbecility were raised aloft in triumph. The last became the first, and the lowliest became the highest. Matter, like thought, was turned upside down, and the world was topsy-turvy. If in those mad days I had been sane, those events would surely have cost me my wits; but, lunatic as I then was, the contrary necessarily came to pass, and, strange to say, just in the days of universal madness I regained my reason! Like many other divinities of that revolutionary period, I was compelled to abdicate ignominiously, and to return to the lowly life of humanity. I came back into the humble fold of God's creatures. I again bowed in homage to the almighty power of a Supreme Being, who directs the destinies of this world, and who for the future shall also regulate my earthly affairs. The latter, during the time I had been my own Providence, had drifted into sad confusion, and I was glad to turn them over to a celestial superintendent, who with His omniscience really manages them much better. The belief in God has since then been to me not only a source of happiness, but it has also relieved me from all those annoying business cares which are so distasteful to me. This belief has also enabled me to practice great economies; for I need no longer provide either for myself or for others, and since I have joined the ranks of the pious I contribute almost nothing to the support of the poor. I am too modest to meddle, as formerly, with the business of Divine Providence. I am no longer careful for the general good; I no longer ape the Deity; and with pious humility I have notified my former dependants that I am only a miserable human being, a wretched creature that has nothing more to do with governing the universe, and that in future, when in need and affliction, they must apply to the Supreme Ruler, who dwells in heaven, and whose budget is as inexhaustible as His goodness—whereas I, a poor ex-god, was often compelled, even in the days of my godhead, to seek the assistance of the Devil. It was certainly very humiliating for a god to have to apply to the Devil for aid, and I am heartily thankful to be relieved from my usurped glory. No philosopher shall ever again persuade me that I am a god. I am only a poor human creature, who is not over well; who is, indeed, very ill. In this pitiable condition it is a true comfort to me that there is someone in the heavens above to whom I can incessantly wail out the litany of my sufferings, especially after midnight, when Mathilde has sought the repose that she often sadly needs. Thank God! in such hours I am not alone, and I can pray and weep without restraint; I can pour out my whole heart before the Almighty, and confide to Him some things which one is wont to conceal even from one's own wife.

After the above confession, the kindly-disposed reader will easily understand why I no longer found pleasure in my work on the Hegelian philosophy. I saw clearly that its publication would benefit neither the public nor the author. I comprehended that there is more nourishment for famishing humanity in the most watery and insipid broth of Christian charity than in the dry and musty spider-web of the Hegelian philosophy. I will confess all. Of a sudden I was seized with a mortal terror of the eternal flames. I know it is a mere superstition; but I was frightened. And so, on a quiet winter's night, when a glowing fire was burning on my hearth, I availed myself of the good opportunity, and cast the manuscript of my work on the Hegelian philosophy into the flames. The burning leaves flew up the chimney with a strange and hissing sound.

Thank God! I was rid of it! Alas! would that I could destroy in the same manner all that I have ever published concerning German philosophy! But that is impossible, and since I cannot prevent their republication, as I lately learned to my great regret, no other course remains but to confess publicly that my exposition of German philosophy contains the most erroneous and pernicious doctrines.

. . . It is strange! during my whole life I have been strolling through the various festive halls of philosophy, I have participated in all the orgies of the intellect, I have coquetted with every possible system, without being satisfied, like Messalina after a riotous night; and now, after all this, I suddenly find myself on the same platform whereon stands Uncle Tom. That platform is the Bible, and I kneel by the side of my dusky brother in faith with the same devotion.

What humiliation! With all my learning, I have got no farther than the poor ignorant negro who can hardly spell! It is even true that poor Uncle Tom appears to see in the holy book more profound things than I, who am not yet quite clear, especially in regard to the second part.

. . . But, on the other hand, I think I may flatter myself that I can better comprehend, in the first part of the holy book, the character of Moses. His grand figure has impressed me not a little. What a colossal form! I cannot imagine that Og, King of Bashan, could have looked more giant-like. How insignificant does Sinai appear when Moses stands thereon! That mountain is merely a pedestal for the feet of the man whose head towers in the heavens and there holds converse with God. May God forgive the sacrilegious thought! but sometimes it appears to me as if this Mosaic God were only the reflected radiance of Moses himself, whom He so strongly represents in wrath and in love. It were a sin, it were anthropomorphism, to assume such an identity of God and His prophet; but the resemblance is most striking.

I had not previously much admired the character of Moses, probably because the Hellenic spirit was predominant in me, and I could not pardon the lawgiver of the Jews for his hatred of the plastic arts. I failed to perceive that Moses, notwithstanding his enmity to art, was nevertheless himself a great artist, and possessed the true artistic spirit. Only, this artistic spirit with him, as with his Egyptian countrymen, was applied to the colossal and the imperishable. But not, like the Egyptians, did he construct his works of art from bricks and granite, but he built human pyramids and carved human obelisks. He took a poor shepherd tribe and from it created a nation which should defy centuries; a great, an immortal, a consecrated race, a God-serving people, who to all other nations should be as a model and prototype: he created Israel.

I have never spoken with proper reverence either of the artist or of his work, the Jews; and for the same reason—namely, my Hellenic temperament, which was opposed to Jewish asceticism. My prejudice in favour of Hellas has declined since then. I see now that the Greeks were only beautiful youths, but that the Jews were always men, strong, unyielding men, not only in the past, but to this very day, in spite of eighteen centuries of persecution and suffering. Since that time I have learned to appreciate them better, and, were not all pride of ancestry a silly inconsistency in a champion of the Revolution and its democratic principles, the writer of these pages would be proud that his ancestors belonged to the noble house of Israel, that he is a descendant of those martyrs who gave the world a God and a morality, and who have fought and suffered on all the battle-fields of thought.

The histories of the Middle Ages, and even those of modern times, have seldom enrolled on their records the names of such knights of the Holy Spirit, for they generally fought with closed visors. The deeds of the Jews are just as little known to the world as is their real character. Some think they know the Jews because they can recognize their beards, which is all they have ever revealed of themselves. Now, as during the Middle Ages, they remain a wandering mystery, a mystery that may perhaps be solved on the day which the prophet foretells, when there shall be but one shepherd and one flock, and the righteous who have suffered for the good of humanity shall then receive a glorious reward.

You see that I, who in the past was wont to quote Homer, now quote the Bible, like Uncle Tom. In truth, I owe it much. It again awoke in me the religious feeling; and this new birth of religious emotion suffices for the poet, for he can dispense far more easily than other mortals with positive religious dogmas.

. . . The silliest and most contradictory reports are in circulation concerning me. Very pious but not very wise men of Protestant Germany have urgently inquired if, now that I am ill and in a religious frame of mind, I cling with more devotion than heretofore to the Lutheran evangelic faith, which, until now, I have only professed after a lukewarm, official fashion. No, dear friends, in that respect no change has taken place in me, and if I continue to adhere to the evangelic faith at all, it is because now, as in the past, that faith does not at all inconvenience me. I will frankly avow that when I resided in Berlin, like several of my friends, I would have preferred to separate myself from the bonds of all denominations, had not the rulers there refused a residence in Prussia, and especially in Berlin, to any who did not profess one of the positive religions recognized by the State. As Henry IV once laughingly said: 'Paris vaut bien une messe,' so I could say, with equal justice: 'Berlin is well worth a sermon.' Both before and after, I could easily tolerate the very enlightened Christianity which at that time was preached in some of the churches of Berlin. It was a Christianity filtered from all superstition, even from the doctrine of the divinity of Christ, like mock-turtle soup without turtle. At that time I myself was still a god, and no one of the positive religions had more value for me than another. I could wear any of their uniforms out of courtesy, after the manner of the Russian Emperor, who, when he vouchsafes the King of Prussia the honour to attend a review at Potsdam, appears uniformed as a Prussian officer of the guard.

Now that my physical sufferings, and the reawakening of my religious nature, have effected in me many changes, does the uniform of Lutheranism in some measure express my true sentiments? How far has the formal profession become a reality? I do not propose to give direct answers to these questions, but I shall avail myself of the opportunity to explain the services which, according to my present views, Protestantism has rendered to civilization. From this may be inferred how much more I am now in sympathy with this creed.

At an earlier period, when philosophy possessed for me a paramount interest, I prized Protestantism only for its services in winning freedom of thought, which, after all, is the foundation on which in later times Leibniz, Kant, and Hegel could build. Luther, the strong man with the axe, must, in the very nature of things, have preceded these warriors, to open a path for them. For this service I have honoured the Reformation as being the beginning of German philosophy, which justified my polemical defence of Protestantism. Now, in my later and more mature days, when the religious feeling again surges up in me, and the shipwrecked metaphysician clings fast to the Bible—now I chiefly honour Protestantism for its services in the discovery and propagation of the Bible. I say 'discovery,' for the Jews, who had preserved the Bible from the great conflagration of the sacred temple, and all through the Middle Ages carried it about with them like a portable fatherland, kept their treasure carefully concealed in their ghettos. Here came by stealth German scholars, the predecessors and originators of the Reformation, to study the Hebrew language and thus acquire the key to the casket wherein the precious treasure was enclosed. Such a scholar was the worthy Reuchlin; and his enemies, the Hochstratens, in Cologne, who are represented as the party of darkness and ignorance, were by no means such simpletons. On the contrary, they were far-sighted inquisitors, who foresaw clearly the disasters which a familiar acquaintance with the Holy Scriptures would bring on the Church. Hence the persecuting zeal with which they sought to destroy the Hebrew writings, at the same time inciting the rabble to exterminate the Jews, the interpreters of these writings. Now that the motives of their actions are known, we see that, properly considered, each was in the right. This reactionary party believed that the spiritual salvation of the world was endangered, and that all means, falsehood as well as murder, were justifiable, especially against the Jews. The lower classes, pinched by poverty, and heirs of the primeval curse, were embittered against the Jews because of the wealth they had amassed; and what to-day is called the hate of the proletariat against the rich, was then called hate against the Jews. In fact, as the latter were excluded from all ownership of land and from every trade, and relegated to dealing in money and merchandise, they were condemned by law to be rich, hated, and murdered. Such murders, it is true, were in these days committed under the mantle of religion, and the cry was: 'We must kill those who once killed our God.' How strange! The very people who had given the world a God, and whose whole life was inspired by the worship of God, were stigmatized as deicides! The bloody parody of such madness was witnessed at the outbreak of the revolution in San Domingo, where a negro mob devasted the plantations with murder and fire, led by a negro fanatic who carried an immense crucifix, amid bloodthirsty cries of 'The whites killed Christ; let us slay all whites!'

Yes, to the Jews the world is indebted for its God and His word. They rescued the Bible from the bankruptcy of the Roman empire, and preserved the precious volume intact during all the wild tumults of the migration of races, until Protestantism came to seek it and translated it into the language of the land and spread it broadcast over the whole world. This extensive circulation of the Bible has produced the most beneficent fruits, and continues to do so to this very day. The propaganda of the Bible Society has fulfilled a providential mission, which will bring forth quite different results from those anticipated by the pious gentlemen of the British Christian Missionary Society. They expect to elevate a petty, narrow dogma to supremacy, and to monopolize heaven as they do the sea, making it a British Church domain — and lo, without knowing it, they are demanding the overthrow of all Protestant sects; for, as they all draw their life from the Bible, when the knowledge of the Bible becomes universal, all sectarian distinctions will be obliterated.

While by tricks of trade, smuggling, and commerce the British gain footholds in many lands, with them they bring the Bible, that grand democracy wherein each man shall not only be a king in his own house, but also bishop. They are demanding, they are founding, the great kingdom of the spirit, the kingdom of the religious emotions, and the love of humanity, of purity, of true morality, which cannot be taught by dogmatic formulas, but by parable and example, such as are contained in that beautiful, sacred, educational book for young and old—the Bible.

To the observant thinker it is a wonderful spectacle to view the countries where the Bible, since the Reformation, has been exerting its elevating influence on the inhabitants, and has impressed on them the customs, modes of thought, and temperaments which formerly prevailed in Palestine, as portrayed both in the Old and in the New Testament. In the Scandinavian and Anglo-Saxon sections of Europe and America, especially among the Germanic races, and also to a certain extent in Celtic countries, the customs of Palestine have been reproduced in so marked a degree that we seem to be in the midst of the ancient Judean life. Take, for example, the Scotch Protestants: are not they Hebrews, whose names even are biblical, whose very cant smacks of the Phariseeism of ancient Jerusalem, and whose religion is naught else than a pork-eating Judaism? It is the same in Denmark and in certain provinces of North Germany, not to mention the majority of the new sects of the United States, among whom the life depicted in the Old Testament is pedantically aped. In the latter, that life appears as if daguerreotyped: the outlines are studiously correct, but all is depicted in sad, sombre colours; the golden tints and harmonizing colours of the promised land are lacking. But the caricature will disappear sooner or later. The zeal for the imperishable and the true—that is to say, the morality—of ancient Judaism will in those countries bloom forth just as acceptably to God as in the old time it blossomed on the banks of Jordan and on the heights of Lebanon. One needs neither palm-trees nor camels to be good; and goodness is better than beauty.

The readiness with which these races have adopted the Judaic life, customs, and modes of thought is, perhaps, not entirely attributable to their susceptibility of culture. The cause of this phenomenon is, perhaps, to be sought in the character of the Jewish people, which always had a marked elective affinity with the character of the Germanic, and also to a certain extent with that of the Celtic races. Judea has always seemed to me like a fragment of the Occident misplaced in the Orient. In fact, with its spiritual faith, its severe, chaste, even ascetic customs—in short, with its abstract inner life—this land and its people always offered the most marked contrasts to the population of neighbouring countries, who, with their luxuriantly varied and fervent nature of worship, passed their existence in a Bacchantic dance of the senses.

At a time when, in the temples of Babylon, Nineveh, Sidon, and Tyre, bloody and unchaste rites were celebrated, the description of which, even now, makes our hair stand on end, Israel sat under its fig-trees, piously chanting the praises of the invisible God, and exercised virtue and righteousness. When we think of these surroundings we cannot sufficiently admire the early greatness of Israel. Of Israel's love of liberty, at a time when not only in its immediate vicinity, but also among all the nations of antiquity, even among the philosophical Greeks, the practice of slavery was justified and in full sway— of this I will not speak, for fear of compromising the Bible in the eyes of the powers that be. No Socialist was more of a terrorist than our Lord and Saviour. Even Moses was such a Socialist; although, like a practical man, he attempted only to reform existing usages concerning property. Instead of striving to effect the impossible, and rashly decreeing the abolition of private property, he only sought for its moralization by bringing the rights of property into harmony with the laws of morality and reason. This he accomplished by instituting the jubilee, at which period every alienated heritage, which among an agricultural people always consisted of land, would revert to the original owner, no matter in what manner it had been alienated. This institution offers the most marked contrast to the Roman statute of limitations, by which, after the expiration of a certain period, the actual holder of an estate could no longer be compelled to restore the estate to the true owner, unless the latter should be able to show that within the prescribed time he had, with all the prescribed formalities, demanded restitution. This last condition opened wide the door for chicanery, particularly in a state where despotism and jurisprudence were at their zenith, and where the unjust possessor had at command all means of intimidation, especially against the poor who might be unable to defray the expense of litigation. The Roman was both soldier and lawyer, and that which he conquered with the strong arm he knew how to defend by the tricks of law. Only a nation of robbers and casuists could have invented the law of prescription, the statute of limitations, and consecrated it in that detestable book which may be called the bible of the Devil—I mean the codex of Roman civil law, which, unfortunately, still holds sway.

I have spoken of the affinity which exists between the Jews and the Germans, whom I once designated as the two pre-eminently moral nations. While on this subject, I desire to direct attention to the ethical disapprobation with which the ancient German law stigmatizes the statute of limitations: this I consider a noteworthy fact. To this very day the Saxon peasant uses the beautiful and touching aphorism: 'A hundred years of wrong do not make a single year of right.'

The Mosaic law, through the institution of the jubilee year, protests still more decidedly. Moses did not seek to abolish the right of property; on the contrary, it was his wish that every one should possess property, so that no one might be tempted by poverty to become a bondsman and thus acquire slavish propensities. Liberty was always the great emanci-pator's leading thought, and it breathes and glows in all his statutes concerning pauperism. Slavery itself he bitterly, almost fiercely, hated; but even this barbarous institution he could not entirely destroy. It was rooted so deeply in the customs of that ancient time that he was compelled to confine his efforts to ameliorating by law the condition of the slaves, rendering self-purchase by the bondsman less difficult, and shortening the period of bondage.

But if a slave thus eventually freed by process of law declined to depart from the house of bondage, then, according to the command of Moses, the incorrigibly servile, worthless scamp was to be nailed by the ear to the gate of his master's house, and after being thus publicly exposed in this disgraceful manner, he was condemned to lifelong slavery. Oh, Moses! our teacher, Rabbi Moses! exalted foe of all slavishness! give me hammer and nails that I may nail to the gate of Brandenburg our complacent, long-eared slaves in liveries of black, red, and gold.

I leave the ocean of universal religious, moral, and historical reflections, and modestly guide my bark of thought back again into the quiet inland waters of autobiography, in which the author's features are so faithfully reflected.

In the preceding pages I have mentioned how Protestant voices from home, in very indiscreet questions, have taken for granted that with the reawakening in me of the religious feeling my sympathy for the Church has also grown stronger. I know not how clearly I have shown that I am not particularly enthusiastic for any dogma or for any creed; and in this respect I have remained the same that I always was. I repeat this statement in order to remove an error in regard to my present views, into which several of my friends who are zealous Catholics have fallen. How strange! at the same time that in Germany Protestantism bestowed on me the undeserved honour of crediting me with a conversion to the evangelic faith, another report was circulating that I had gone over to Catholicism. Some good souls went so far as to assert that this latter conversion had occurred many years ago, and they supported this statement by definitely naming time and place. They even mentioned the exact date; they designated by name the church in which I had abjured the heresy of Protestantism, and adopted the only true and saving faith, that of the Roman Catholic Apostolic Church. The only detail that was lacking was how many peals of the bell had been sounded at this ceremony.

From the newspapers and letters that reach me I learn how widely this report has won credence; and I fall into a painful embarrassment when I think of the sincere, loving joy which is so touchingly expressed in some of these epistles. Travellers tell me that the salvation of my soul has even furnished a theme for pulpit eloquence. Young Catholic priests seek permission to dedicate to me the first fruits of their pen. I am regarded as a shining light—that is to be—of the Church. This pious folly is so well meant and sincere that I cannot laugh at it. Whatever may be said of the zealots of Catholicism, one thing is certain; they are no egotists; they take a warm interest in their fellow-men—alas! often a little too warm an interest. I cannot ascribe that false report to malice, but only to mistake. The innocent facts were in this case surely distorted by accident only. The statement of time and place is quite correct. I was really in the designated church on the designated day, and I did there undergo a religious ceremony; but this ceremony was no hateful abjuration, but a very innocent conjugation. In short, after being married according to the civil law, I also invoked the sanction of the Church, because my wife, who is a strict Catholic, would not have considered herself properly married in the eyes of God without such a ceremony; and for no consideration would I shake this dear being's belief in the religion which she has inherited.

It is well, moreover, that women should have a positive religion. Whether there is more fidelity among wives of the evangelic faith, I shall not attempt to discuss. But the Catholicism of the wife certainly saves the husband from many annoyances. When Catholic women have committed a fault, they do not secretly brood over it, but confess to the priest, and as soon as they have received absolution they are again as merry and light-hearted as before. This is much pleasanter than spoiling the husband's good spirits or his soup by downcast looks or grieving over a sin for which they hold themselves in duty bound to atone during their whole lives by shrewish prudery and quarrelsome excess of virtue. The confessional is likewise useful in another respect. The sinner does not keep her terrible secret preying on her mind; and since women are sure, sooner or later, to babble all they know, it is better that they should confide certain matters to their confessor than that they should, in some moment of overpowering tenderness, talkativeness, or remorse, blurt out to the poor husband the fatal confession.

Scepticism is certainly dangerous in the married state, and, although I myself was a free-thinker, I permitted no word derogatory to religion to be spoken in my house. In the midst of Paris I lived like a steady, commonplace townsman; and therefore when I married I desired to be wedded under the sanction of the Church, although in this country the civil marriage is fully recognized by society. My free-thinking friends were vexed at me for this, and overwhelmed me with reproaches, claiming that I had made too great concessions to the clergy. Their chagrin at my weakness would have been still greater had they known the other concessions that I had made to the hated priesthood. As I was a Protestant wedding a Catholic, in order to have the ceremony performed by a Catholic priest it was necessary to obtain a special dispensation from the archbishop, who in these cases exacts from the husband a written pledge that the offspring of the marriage shall be educated in the religion of the mother. But, between ourselves, I could sign this pledge with the lighter conscience since I knew the rearing of children is not my speciality, and as I laid down my pen the words of the beautiful Ninon de Lenclos came into my mind: 'O, le beau billet qu'a Lechastre!'

. . . I will crown my confessions by admitting that, if at that time it had been necessary in order to obtain the dispensation of the archbishop, I would have bound over not only the children but myself. But the ogre of Rome, who, like the monster in the fairy tales, stipulates that he shall have for his services the future births, was content with the poor children who were never born. And so I remained a Protestant, as before—a protesting Protestant; and I protest against reports which, without being intended to be defamatory, may yet be magnified so as to injure my good name.

. . . There is not a particle of unkindly feeling in my breast against the poor ogre of Rome. I have long since abandoned all feuds with Catholicism, and the sword which I once drew in the service of an idea, and not from private grudge, has long rested in its scabbard. In that contest I resembled a soldier of fortune, who fights bravely, but after the battle bears no malice either against the defeated cause or against its champions.

Fanatical enmity towards the Catholic Church cannot be charged against me, for there was always lacking in me the self-conceit which is necessary to sustain such an animosity. I know too well my own intellectual calibre not to be aware that with my most furious onslaughts I could inflict but little injury on a colossus such as the Church of St. Peter. I could only be a humble worker at the slow removal of its foundation stones, a task which may yet require centuries. I was too familiar with history not to recognize the gigantic nature of that granite structure. Call it, if you will, the Bastille of intellect; assert, if you choose, that it is now defended only by invalids; but it is therefore not the less true that the Bastille is not to be easily captured, and many a young recruit will break his head against its walls.

As a thinker and as a metaphysician, I was always forced to pay the homage of my admiration to the logical consistency of the doctrines of the Roman Catholic Church, and I may also take credit to myself that I have never by witticism or ridicule attacked its dogmas or its public worship. Too much and too little honour has been vouchsafed me in calling me an intellectual kinsman of Voltaire. I was always a poet; and hence the poesy which blossoms and glows in the symbolism of Catholic dogma and culture must have revealed itself more profoundly to me than to ordinary observers, and in my youthful days I was often touched by the infinite sweetness, the mysterious, blissful ecstasy and awe-inspiring grandeur of that poetry. There was a time when I went into raptures over the blessed Queen of Heaven, and in dainty verse told the story of her grace and goodness. My first collection of poems shows traces of this beautiful Madonna period, which in later editions I weeded out with laughable anxiety.

The time for vanity has passed, and every one is at liberty to smile at this confession.

It will be unnecessary for me to say that, as no blind hate

against the Catholic Church exists in me, so also no petty spite against its priests rankles in my heart. Whoever knows my satirical vein will surely bear witness that I was always lenient and forbearing in speaking of the human weaknesses of the clergy, although by their attacks they often provoked in me a spirit of retaliation. But even at the height of my wrath I was always respectful to the true priesthood; for, looking back into the past, I remembered benefits which they had once rendered me; for it is Catholic priests whom I must thank for my first instruction; it was they who guided the first steps of my intellect.

Pedagogy was the speciality of the Jesuits, and although they sought to pursue it in the interest of their order, yet sometimes the passion for pedagogy itself, the only human passion that was left in them, gained the mastery; they forgot their aim, the repression of reason and the exaltation of faith, and, instead of reducing men to a state of childhood, as was their purpose, out of the children they involuntarily made men by their instruction. The greatest men of the Revolution were educated in Jesuit schools. Without the training there acquired, that great intellectual agitation would perhaps not have broken out till a century later.

Poor Jesuit fathers! You have been the bugbear and the scapegoat of the liberals. The danger that was in you was understood, but not your merits. I could never join in the denunciations of my comrades, who at the mere mention of Loyola's name would always become furious, like bulls when a red cloth is held before them. It is certainly noteworthy, and may perhaps at the assizes in the valley of Jehoshaphat be set down as an extenuating circumstance, that even as a lad I was permitted to attend lectures on philosophy. This unusual favour was exceptional in my case, because the rector Schallmeyer was a particular friend of our family. This venerable man often consulted with my mother in regard to my education and future career, and once advised her, as she afterwards related to me, to devote me to the service of the Catholic Church, and send me to Rome to study theology. He assured her that through his influential friends in Rome he could advance me to an important position in the Church. But at that time my mother dreamed of the highest worldly honours for me. Moreover, she was a disciple of Rousseau, and a strict deist. Besides, she did not like the thought of her son being robed in one of those long black cassocks, such as are worn by Catholic priests, and in which they look so plump and awkward. She knew not how differently, how gracefully, a Roman *abbate* wears such a cassock, and how jauntily he flings over his shoulders the black silk mantle, which in Rome, the ever-beautiful, is the uniform of gallantry and wit.

Oh, what a happy mortal is such a Roman *abbate*! He serves not only the Church of Christ, but also Apollo and the Muses, whose favourite he is. The Graces hold his inkstand for him when he indites the sonnets which, with such delicate cadences, he reads in the Accademia degli Arcadi. He is a connoisseur of art, and needs only to taste the lips of a young songstress in order to be able to foretell whether she will some day be a *celeberrima cantatrice*, a *diva*, a world-renowned *prima donna*. He understands antiquities, and will write a treatise in the choicest Ciceronian Latin concerning some newly-unearthed torso of a Grecian Bacchante, reverentially dedicating it to the supreme head of Christendom, to the Pontifex Maximus, for so he addresses him. And what a judge of painting is the Signor *Abbate*, who visits the painters in their ateliers and directs their attention to the fine points of their female models! The writer of these pages had in him just the material for such an *abbate*, and was just suited for strolling in delightful *dolce far niente* through the libraries, art galleries, churches, and ruins of the Eternal City, studying among pleasures, and seeking pleasure while studying. I would have read Mass before the most select audiences, and during Holy Week I would have mounted the pulpit as a preacher of strict morality—of course even then never degenerating into ascetic rudeness. The Roman ladies, in particular, would have been greatly edified, and through their favour and my own merit I would, perhaps, have risen eventually to high rank in the hierarchy of the Church. I would, perhaps, have become a monsignore, a violet-stocking; perhaps even a cardinal's red hat might have fallen on my head. The proverb says:

> There is no priestling, how small soe'er he be,
> That does not wish himself a Pope to be.

And so it might have come to pass that I should attain the most exalted position of all, for, although I am not naturally ambitious, I would yet not have refused the nomination for Pope, had the choice of the conclave fallen on me. It is, at all events, a very respectable office, and has a good income attached to it; and I do not doubt that I could have discharged the duties of my position with the requisite address. I would have seated myself composedly on the throne of St. Peter, presenting my toe for the kisses of all good Christians, the priests as well as the laity. With a becoming dignity I would have let myself be carried in triumph through the pillared halls of the great basilica, and only when it tottered very threateningly would I have clung to the arms of the golden throne, which is borne on the shoulders of six stalwart *camerieri* in crimson uniform. By their side walk bald-headed monks of the Capuchin order, carrying burning torches. Then follow lackeys in gala dress, bearing aloft immense fans of peacocks' feathers, with which they gently fan the Prince of the Church. It is all just like Horace Vernet's beautiful painting of such a procession. With a like imperturbable sacerdotal gravity—for I can be very serious if it be absolutely necessary—from the lofty Lateran I would have pronounced the annual benediction over all Christendom. Here, standing on the balcony, *in pontificalibus* and with the triple crown upon my head, surrounded by my scarlet-hatted cardinals and mitred bishops, priests in suits of gold brocade and monks of every hue, I would have presented my holiness to the view of the swarming multitudes below, who, kneeling and with bowed heads, extended farther than the eye could reach; and I could composedly have stretched out my hands and blessed the city and the world.

But, as thou well knowest, gentle reader, I have not become a Pope, nor a cardinal, nor even a papal nuncio. In the spiritual as well as in the worldly hierarchy I have attained neither office nor rank; I have accomplished nothing in this beautiful world; nothing has become of me—nothing but a poet.

But no, I will not feign a hypocritical humility, I will not depreciate that name. It is much to be a poet, especially to be a great lyric poet, in Germany, among a people who in two things—in philosophy and in poetry—have surpassed all other nations. I will not with a sham modesty—the invention of worthless vagabonds—depreciate my fame as a poet. None of my countrymen have won the laurel at so early an age; and if my colleague, Wolfgang Goethe, complacently writes that 'the Chinese with trembling hand paints Werther and Lotte on porcelain,' I can, if boasting is to be in order, match his Chinese fame with one still more legendary, for I have recently learned that my poems have been translated into the Japanese language.

. . . But at this moment I am as indifferent to my Japanese

fame as to my renown in Finland. Alas! fame, once sweet as sugared pine-apple and flattery, has for a long time been nauseous to me; it tastes as bitter to me now as wormwood. With Romeo, I can say: 'I am the fool of fortune.' The bowl stands filled before me, but I lack a spoon. What does it avail me that at banquets my health is pledged in the choicest wines, and drunk from golden goblets, when I, myself, severed from all that makes life pleasant, may only wet my lips with an insipid potion? What does it avail me that enthusiastic youths and maidens crown my marble bust with laurel-wreaths, if meanwhile the shrivelled fingers of an aged nurse press a blister of Spanish flies behind the ears of my actual body. What does it avail me that all the roses of Shiraz so tenderly glow and bloom for me? Alas! Shiraz is two thousand miles away from the Rue d'Amsterdam, where, in the dreary solitude of my sick-room, I have nothing to smell, unless it be the perfume of warmed napkins. Alas! the irony of God weighs heavily upon me! the great Author of the Universe, the Aristophanes of Heaven, wished to show the petty, earthly, so-called German Aristophanes that his mightiest sarcasms are but feeble banter compared with His, and how immeasurably He excels me in humour and in colossal wit.

Yes, the mockery which the Master has poured out over me is terrible, and horribly cruel is His sport. Humbly do I acknowledge His superiority, and I prostrate myself in the dust before Him. But, although I lack such supreme creative powers, yet in my spirit also the eternal reason flames brightly, and I may summon even the wit of God before its forum, and subject it to a respectful criticism. And here I venture to offer most submissively the suggestion that the sport which the Master has inflicted on the poor pupil is rather too long drawn out: it has already lasted over six years, and after a time becomes monotonous. Moreover, if I may take the liberty to say it, in my humble opinion the jest is not new, and the great Aristophanes of Heaven has already used it on a former occasion, and has, therefore, been guilty of plagiarism on His own exalted self. In order to prove this assertion, I will quote a passage from the Chronicle of Lüneburg. This chronicle is very interesting for those who seek information concerning the manners and customs of Germany during the Middle Ages. As in a fashion-journal, it describes the wearing-apparel of both sexes which was in vogue at each particular period. It also imparts information concerning the popular ballads of the day, and quotes the opening lines of several of them. Among others, it records that during the year 1480 there were whistled and sung throughout all Germany certain songs, which for sweetness and tenderness surpassed any previously known in German lands. Young and old, and the women in particular, were quite bewitched by these ballads, which might be heard the livelong day. But these songs, so the chronicle goes on to say, were composed by a young priest who was afflicted with leprosy, and lived a forlorn, solitary life, secluded from all the world. You are surely aware, dear reader, what a horrible disease leprosy was during the Middle Ages, and how the wretched beings afflicted with this incurable malady were driven out from all society and from the abodes of men, and were forbidden to approach any human being. Living corpses, they wandered to and fro, muffled from head to foot, a hood drawn over the face, and carrying in the hand a bell, the Lazarus-bell, as it was called, through which they were to give timely warning of their approach, so that every one could get out of the way in time. The poor priest whose fame as a lyric poet the chronicle praised so highly was such a leper; and while all Germany, shouting and jubilant, sang and whistled his songs, he, a wretched outcast, in the desolation of his misery sat sorrowful and alone.

Oh, that fame was the old, familiar scorn, the cruel jest of God, the same as in my case, although there it appears in the romantic garb of the Middle Ages. The *blasé* king of Judea said rightly: There is no new thing under the sun. Perhaps that sun itself, which now beams so imposingly, is only an old warmed-up jest.

Sometimes among the gloomy phantasms that visit me at night I seem to see before me the poor priest of the Lüneburg Chronicle, my brother in Apollo, and his sorrowful eyes stare strangely out of his hood; but almost at the same moment it vanishes, and, faintly dying away, like the echo of a dream, I hear the jarring tones of the Lazarus-bell.

LUTETIA

The Paris newspapers of to-day give a communication from the Imperial-Royal Austrian consul in Damascus to the Imperial-Royal consul-general in Alexandria in relation to the Jews of Damascus, whose martyrdom recalls the darkest times of the Middle Ages. While we in Europe use such tales as material for poetry, and delight ourselves with such terribly naïve stories, with which our forefathers tormented themselves not a little; while we only know from poems and romances of those witches, were-wolves, and Jews who need the blood of pious Christian children for their satanic rites; while we laugh and forget, they begin in the East to recall very sadly the ancient superstition, and make very serious faces—faces of gloomy anger and the despairing agony of death! Meanwhile the executioner tortures, and on the bench of martyrdom the Jew confesses that as he needed some Christian blood wherein to dip his dry Easter bread at the approaching Passover festival, he had for this purpose slaughtered an old Capuchin! The Turk is stupid and vile, and gladly places his apparatus of bastinado and torture at the service of Christians against the accursed Jews; for he hates both sects, regarding them as dogs, and calls them by this honourable name, and he doubtless rejoices when the Christian Giaour gives him an opportunity of maltreating the Jewish Giaour with some pretence of justice. Wait till it shall be to the pasha's advantage, when he need no longer fear the armed intervention of Europeans, and then he will listen to the circumcised dogs, and then these will accuse our Christian brethren —the Lord knows who or which—to-day anvil, to-morrow hammer!

But for the friend of humanity such deeds must ever be a bitter pain. Events of this kind are disasters whose consequences are beyond computation. Fanaticism is an infectious evil, which spreads under the most varied forms, and finally rages against them all. The French consul in Damascus, Count Ratti-Menton, has brought evil things to pass, which have here excited a general cry of horror. He it is who inoculated the East with the Western superstition, and disseminated among the mob of Damascus a work in which Jews were accused of murdering Christians. This writing, which snorts with hatred, which Count Menton received from his spiritual friends for dissemination, was originally taken from the *Bibliotheca Prompta a Lucio Ferrario*, and it is distinctly asserted in it that the Jews in celebrating the feast of the Passover used the blood of a Christian. The noble count, however, guarded against repeating the story connected with it in the Middle Ages, that the Jews for the same purpose stole the consecrated wafers and pierced them with needles till blood ran from them —an evil deed, which came to light not only through sworn witnesses, but also by a clear flame being seen over the house in which the stolen host was thus crucified by the Jews. No; the unbelievers, the Mahommedans, would never have believed that, so that Count Menton must, in the interests of his mission, take refuge in less miraculous tales. I say in the interests of his *mission*, and submit these words to the fullest consideration. The count has not been long in Damascus; six months ago he was seen here in Paris, the workshop of all progressive, but also of all retrograde associations. The present Minister of Foreign Affairs, M. Thiers, who lately attempted to appear not only as a man of humanity but also as a son of the Revolution, has shown as regards the occurrences in Damascus a singular indifference. According to the *Moniteur* of to-day a vice-consul has already gone to Damascus to investigate the conduct of the French consul there. A vice-consul! Certainly some subordinate person from a neighbouring place, a man without name and without any guarantee of impartial independence.

PARIS, 20 *May* 1840.

The French, apart from all republican peculiarities, are by nature altogether Bonapartist. They are wanting in simplicity, in self-content, in inner and external repose; they love war for its own sake; even in peace their life is all battle and noise; old and young are gay and happy in the roll of drums and gunpowder-smoke and explosions of every kind.

PARIS, 13 *February* 1841.

They attack every question directly, and worry at it until it is either solved or else thrown aside as insoluble. That is the character of the French, and their history, for this reason, develops itself like a judicial trial. What a logical and systematic consequence do all the events of the French Revolution present! In this madness there was really method, and the writers of history, who, after the example of Mignet, attaching but little importance to chance and human passions, represent the most extravagant deeds since 1789 as a result of the sternest necessity—this so-called fatalistic school is in France quite in place, and its works are as true as they are easy to understand. The methods of seeing and of representing of these writers applied to Germany would, however, result in very erroneous and ill-digested works of history; for the German, for fear of any innovation whose results cannot be clearly ascertained, avoids every important question of politics as long as possible, or endeavours to find in detours a proper adjustment of difficulties, the questions meanwhile collecting and entangling themselves till they form an inextricable knot, which at last perhaps, like the Gordian, can only be cut by the sword. Heaven forbid that I hereby cast reproach upon the great German people! Do I not know that this embarrassment is the result of a virtue which is wanting to the French? The more ignorant a nation is, the more readily, the more recklessly it hurls itself headlong into the stream of action; but the more erudite, cultivated, and reflecting, the longer does it sound the flood, which it then wades with careful steps, if it does not delay and stay altogether on the bank for fear of hidden depths, or wet which gives colds and might cause a great national catarrh. And after all, it makes little difference that we advance slowly or, by standing still, lose a few centuries, for the future belongs to the German people, and, in fact, a very long and significant future. The French act so quickly and manage the present with such haste, because they perhaps foresee that the twilight of their day is drawing near, and so they haste that their day's work may be done. But their role is still attractive and beautiful enough, and the other nations are still only the honourable public which forms the audience which beholds the French comedy of State and People. It is true that this public has sometimes a fancy to express its approbation or dissatisfaction very energetically, and even to climb on the stage and take part in the play; but the French are always the chief actors in the great drama of the world, whether people throw laurels or rotten apples at their heads. 'All is over with France!' With such words a German correspondent here runs about prophesying the fall of the present Jerusalem, but he maintains his own pitiful existence by reporting what these fallen French daily act and do, and his own employers, the German editors, would, without letters from Paris, be unable to fill their columns for three weeks. No, France is not yet finished, but, like all nations and humanity itself, it is not eternal; it has perhaps outlived its glorious age, and it is now undergoing a transformation which cannot be denied; wrinkles are stealing over its smooth brow; grey hairs begin to appear on its heedless head, which sinks as if full of care and busy with to-morrow—for it no longer thinks only of to-day.

PARIS, 31 *March* 1841.

It is not the American negotiations alone which impel the English to settle the Egyptian question of inheritance as soon as possible, and thereby to put French diplomacy into a condition to take part in the councils and conclusions of the great Powers of Europe. The question of the Dardanelles stands threateningly before the door, crying for prompt decision, and here the English rely on the support of the French Cabinet in conferences, whose interests on this occasion, as opposed to those of Russia, coincide with their own.

Yes, the so-called question of the Dardanelles is of the greatest importance, not only for the great European Powers, but for all of us, for the least as well as the greatest, for Reuss-Schleitz-Greiz and Back-Pomerania, as much as for all-mighty Austria, for the smallest cobbler as for the greatest manufacturer of leather; for the destiny of the world is here at stake, and this question must be solved on the Dardanelles, no matter how. So long as this remains in doubt, Europe will suffer with a secret malady which will permit no repose, and must finally break out in a form which will be more terrible the longer it is delayed. The Dardanelles question is only a symptom of the Eastern question itself, of the Turkish question of inheritance, of this fundamental evil with which we are tainted, of the material basis of disease which ferments in the European bodies of state, and which, unfortunately, can only be cut out— perhaps with the sword. Even when we speak of other things, all the great monarchs have an eye on the Dardanelles, on the Sublime Porte, old Byzantium, Stamboul, Constantinople —the affliction has many names. If the principle of popular sovereignty were sanctioned in European states, the collapse of the Ottoman empire would not be so dangerous for the rest of the world, since then in the separated provinces the single races would soon elect their own regents, and be governed on as well as they could. But the doctrine of absolutism prevails as yet in the greater portion of Europe, according to which land and people are the property of the prince—property which one can acquire by the right of the strongest, by the *ultima ratio regis*, or the cannon-law. It is no wonder that none of the great Powers will permit the Russians to seize on this great inheritance, and that every one will have his slice of the Oriental cake—every one would feel keen appetite, seeing the barbarians at their feast, and the smallest German duodecimo-prince will ask at least for a *pourboire*. Such are human impulses, and the real reason why the fall of Turkey would endanger the world. The political reasons why England, France, and Austria cannot permit Russia to settle in Constantinople are evident to every schoolboy.

The outbreak of a war, which is in the nature of things, is, however, for the time delayed. Short-sighted politicians, who have only recourse to palliatives, feel tranquillized, and hope for undisturbed days of peace. Our financiers especially see everything in the loveliest light of hope. Even the greatest among them seems to yield to such a delusion, though not at all times. M. de Rothschild, who for some time appeared to be ill, is now quite restored and looks sound and well. The augurs of the Bourse, who perfectly understand deciphering the physiognomy of the great baron, assure us that the swallows of peace nestle in his smiles, that every anxiety as to war has vanished from his face, that there are no electric sparks foreboding storm visible in his eyes, and therefore it is clear that the terrible cannon-thunder-weather, which threatened the world is now dissipated. He even sneezes peace. It is true that the last time when I had the honour to make my call of respect on Herr von Rothschild, he gleamed with enraptured delight, and his rosy humour almost burst forth into poetry; for, as I once related, in such merry moments the Herr Baron lets his stream of oratory foam and sparkle in rhymes. I found that this time he succeeded marvellously well at rhyming, but he stopped at *Constantinople*, and scratched his head, as all poets do when rhymes are wanting. As I am myself something of a poet, I permitted myself to ask the Herr Baron whether a Russian *Zobel* (sable) would not rhyme to Constantinople. But this rhyme seemed to displease him greatly; he declared that England would never permit it, and that from it a European war might arise, which would cost the world much blood and many tears, and himself a great deal of money.

Herr von Rothschild is, in fact, the best political thermometer; I will not say weather-frog, because the word is not sufficiently respectful. And certes! one must have respect for this man, be it only for the respect which he inspires in others. I like best to visit him in his banking-house, where I can as a philosopher observe how people, and not only God's chosen, but all other kinds, bow and duck before him. There you may behold such a twisting and bending of backbones as the best acrobat could hardly equal. I have seen people who, when they drew near the great baron, shrank up as if they had touched an electric battery. Even while approaching the door of his cabinet many experience a thrill of awe such as Moses felt on Mount Horeb when he saw that he stood on holy ground, and even as Moses took off his shoes, so more than one courtier or broker would fain remove his boots before entering the private cabinet of M. de Rothschild. That private cabinet is indeed a remarkable place, which inspires sublime thoughts and feelings, as does the sight of the sea or of the starry heavens. We see here how small man is and how great is God! For gold is the God of our time and Rothschild is his prophet.

Some years ago, when I was about to call on Herr von Rothschild, a servant in livery crossed the corridor carrying the chamber-pot of the latter, while a speculator on the Bourse who was passing at the instant most respectfully took off his hat before the mighty pot. So far extends—with reverence be it said!—the devotion of certain people. I noted the name of that devoted man, and am sure that in time he will become a millionaire. When I one day told Monsieur —— that I had lunched with Baron Rothschild in the inner apartments of his bureaux, he clasped his hands in amazement, declaring that I had enjoyed an honour which had hitherto only been granted to a Rothschild of the blood or to a few sovereign princes, and that he would give half of his nose for such an honour. I will here remark that the nose of Monsieur —— would be quite large enough even if diminished by half.

The *comptoir* of M. de Rothschild is very extensive; it is a labyrinth of halls, a barrack of wealth. The room in which the baron works from morning to night—he has naught else to do save work—has been of late very much beautified. On the chimney-piece there is at present the marble bust of the Emperor of Austria, with whom the House of Rothschild has done the most business. The Herr Baron will, moreover, out of deep regard, have the busts made of all the European princes who have contracted loans through his firm, and this collection of marble busts will form a Valhalla which will be far greater than that of Regensburg. Whether Herr Rothschild will celebrate his Valhalla-contemporaries in rhymes or in un-rhymed royal Bavarian lapidary style, I know not.

PARIS, 12 *July* 1842.

You will have seen the result of the elections in the news-papers. Here in Paris there is indeed no need of looking into them—you can see it clearly written in every face. Yesterday they all had a hot and sultry look, and people's minds betrayed an excitement such as is only to be seen in great crises. The birds prophetic of storm, well known to us of yore, whirred invisibly through the air, and the sleepiest heads were suddenly awakened from their two years of repose. I confess that I myself, feeling the wind of these terrible wings, experienced a dire beating of my heart. I am always afraid at first when I see the demons of confusion and subversion unbridled, but after a while I become very cool and determined, and the maddest apparitions cannot inquiet or surprise me, because I have foreseen them. What would be the end of this movement for which Paris has, as usual, given the signal? It would be a war, the most terrible war of destruction, which—more's the pity!—will call the noblest races of civilization into the arena, to their joint destruction. I mean Germany and France. England, the great sea-serpent, which can always glide back into its watery nest, and Russia, which in its vast forests of firs, steppes, and ice-fields has also the securest lairs—these two cannot be utterly destroyed in a common political war, even by the most decided defeats; but Germany is, in such a case, in far greater danger, and even France may suffer terribly in her political existence. But this would be, so to speak, only the first act or prologue to the grand drama. The second will be the European or the world Revolution, the gigantic battle of the disinherited with the inheritors of fortune, and in that there will be no question of nationality or of religion, for there will be but one fatherland, the Earth, and but one religion, that of happiness in *this* life. Will the religious doctrines of the past in every country unite to a desperate resistance, and thus form a third act in the great play? Or will the old Absolute tradition enter again on the stage, but this time in a new costume and with new watchwords to incite and goad? How will this drama end? I do not know, but I think that at last the head

of the great water-snake will be crushed, and the skin pulled over
the head of the bear of the North. And then perhaps there will
be only *one* flock and *one* shepherd—a free shepherd with an
iron crook—and one great herd of men all shorn and all bleating
alike. Wild and gloomy times come roaring on, and the prophet
who would write a new Apocalypse must imagine new beasts,
and those so terrible that the old symbols of St. John as compared
to them will seem like soft doves and amorets. The gods hide
their faces out of pity to the sons of mankind, their nurslings
for so many years, and perhaps out of fear as to their own fate.
The future has an odour as of Russian leather, blood, blasphemy,
and much beating with the knout. I advise our descendants
to come into the world with thick skins.

To-day people are calmer than yesterday. The Conservatives
have recovered from a first fright, and the Opposition perceives
that it has only gained hopes, but that victory is as far off as
ever. The Ministry may still hold its own, although with a
very small, miserably needy majority. In the beginning of
next month, at the Presidential election, what is most absolutely
certain to happen will be known. It is perhaps an advantage
for the Government that so many decided Legitimists have
been elected. The Radicals will be morally weakened by these
new allies, and the Ministry strengthened in public opinion,
should it, in order to combat with the Legitimist Opposition,
necessarily arm itself from the old arsenal of the Revolution.
But the flame is again being blown—blown in Paris, the centre
of civilization, the furnace which sends sparks over the whole
world. So now the French rejoice at what they've done;
perhaps to-morrow they'll repent it sore. Despair treads on
the heels of arrogance.

PARIS, *August* 1854

Yes, I have spoken the word. It was the foolish pride of
the German poet which kept me even *pro forma* from becoming
a Frenchman. It was an ideal whim from which I could not
free myself. As regards that which we call patriotism, I was
always a free-thinker, but I could never free myself from a
certain dread when I should do anything which might seem even
only half-way to breaking loose from my native land. Even in
the mind of the most enlightened there remains a little mandrake
root of the old superstition which will not be banned away.
One does not like to speak thereof, but it sends its folly
into the most secret corner of our soul. The alliance which I

contracted with our dear Frau Germania, the blonde savage, was never happy. I can well remember certain moonlight nights when she tenderly pressed me against her vast breasts with their virtuous nipples; but there was only a certain number of these sentimental nights, and towards morning there came over us an unpleasant gaping coolness, and then began no end of quarrelling. And we lived apart at bed and table; yet it never came to a real separation. I never could bring my heart to really separate from my domestic trouble. Every desertion is hateful to me, and I never could part from a German cat or dog, however intolerable I found its fleas and fidelity. The smallest sucking-pig of my fatherland cannot complain of me as to this. Among the aristocratic and brilliant sows of Périgord who discovered truffles and feed thereon, I never denied the modest little grunters who at home in the Teutobergian forest grub on native acorns from a plain wooden trough, as their pious ancestors did when Arminius slew Varus. I have not lost a bristle of my Germanism, not a bell from my cap, and I have always the right to fasten on it the black-red-gold cockade. And I still have the right to say to Massmann: 'We German donkeys.' Had I let myself be naturalized in France, Massmann might have replied: 'I am still a German ass, but thou art one no longer'—and then he would have thrown a scornful, mocking somersault which would have broken my heart. No, I have never exposed myself to such disgrace. Naturalization may do for other people; a tipsy lawyer from Zweibrücken, a silly fellow with iron brow and copper nose, may, to get a place as schoolmaster, give up a native land which nothing knows of him, and nothing will ever know; but that will not do for a German poet who has written the most beautiful German poems. It would be a horrible and mad thought for me to have to say that I am a German poet and also a naturalized Frenchman. I should seem to myself like one of those monsters with two heads which are exhibited in fairs. It would annoy me terribly in writing poetry when I thought that one head began to scan in French turkey-cock pathos the most unnatural Alexandrines, while the other poured forth its feelings in the inborn, true natural metres of the German language. And oh! just as repulsive to me as the measures are the verses of the French—that perfumed dirt! I can hardly bear their altogether scentless better poets. When I study that so-called *poésie lyrique* of the French, then I recognize the grandeur and glory of German poetry, and then I dare imagine that I may boast of having gained my laurels in this field. We will not yield a single laurel-leaf, and the mason, when he is called on to decorate our tombstone with an inscription, will find no one to protest when he engraves the words: 'Here lies a German poet.'

PARIS, 15 *June* 1843.

If I had lived as a private gentleman in Rome during the time of the Emperor Nero, and had acted as correspondent for the *Daily Post* of Boeotia or for the unofficial *State Journal* of Abdera, my colleagues would often have rallied me on this, that I never mentioned the state intrigues of the imperial mother, Agrippina, nor described the magnificent dinners with which the King of Judea or Agrippa regaled the diplomatic body of Rome every Saturday, while I, on the contrary, constantly spoke of those Galileans, of that obscure little handful, consisting chiefly of slaves and of old women, dreaming away their foolish lives in conflicts and visions, and who were even disavowed by the Jews. My well-informed colleagues would have certainly laughed at me if I had had nothing more to say of the court festival of Caesar, at which His Majesty in his own grand person played the guitar, than that some of those Galileans had been covered with pitch and fired, and so served to illuminate the gardens of the Golden House. It was indeed a very significant illumination, and it was a bitter-cruel, truly Roman joke to make the so-called Obscurants serve as lights in the joyous solemnities of the antique world, intoxicated with sensual pleasure. Now the joke has been turned to shame; those torches threw out sparks of faith by which the old decayed Roman world and all its glory was consumed; the number of that handful became legion; in battling with them the legions of Caesar had to lay down their arms; and now *all* the empire by land or sea belongs to the Galileans.

PARIS, 7 *August* 1846.

Living is very bad here, but all the dearer for that. Breakfast and the noonday meal are brought to the boarders in tall baskets by rather sticky girls, just as in Göttingen. Ah! that I had the youthful academic appetite with which I once masticated the leanest and driest roast-veal of Georgia Augusta! Life itself is as wearisome here as on the flowery banks of the Leine. I must admit, however, that I have enjoyed two charming balls, where the dancers all appeared without crutches. There were not wanting a few daughters of

Albion, who were remarkable for beauty and awkwardness
—they danced as if riding on asses. Among the French
damsels shone the daughter of the famed Cellarius, who—
what an honour for little Barèges!—danced the polka on
her own feet. There were also several of the young dancing
fairies of the Grand Opera of Paris, who are generally
known as *rats*. Among these the silver-footed Mademoiselle
Lelhomme whirled her *entrechats*, and at the sight I thought
vividly of my dear Paris, where I could no longer endure the
endless dancing and music, and yet for which my heart doth
ever yearn. Marvellous mad enchantment! What with sheer
amusement and gaiety, Paris at last becomes so insupportable,
wearisome, and oppressive, all its joys being allied to such
exhausting exertion, that one is wild with happiness at escaping
from this galley of pleasure; and yet, ere he has been absent a
few months, the air of a waltz or the mere suspicion of a dancing-
girl's leg awakes in him the deepest yearning and home-sickness
for Paris. This is the case, however, only with the mossy-
heads or old *habitués* of this sweet bagnio, and not with
the young students of our native association, who, after a
short six months' university session, complain that it is not
so gently calm there as yon side the Rhine, where the cell
system of solitary reflection has been introduced; that one
cannot there calmly collect oneself as in Magdeburg or Spandau;
that their moral consciousness is lost in the billows of pleasure
which break over them; that the distraction is there too great.
Yes, it is indeed too great, for while we distract and divert
ourselves, our money is also diverted from us.

Ah, the money! It knows how to scatter and divert itself
from us, even here in Barèges, wearisome as this nest of health
may be. It passes all conception how expensive it is: it costs
twice as much here as in the other bathing-places in the Pyrenees.
And what greed among these mountaineers, whom we praise as
a kind of children of Nature and the relics of a race of innocents!
They adore money with a passion which borders on fanaticism,
and it is their true national religion. And yet is not gold the
god of the whole world—a god whom the most hardened atheist
cannot deny for three days, since without his divine aid the
baker would not give him the smallest roll?

Within a few days, during the great heat, there came whole
swarms of English to Barèges, red and hearty beefsteak-fed
faces, which contrasted almost insultingly with the pale community of the bathing visitors. The most important of these

arrivals is an enormously wealthy and tolerably well-known
member of Parliament of the Tory clique. This gentleman did
not seem to like the French, but, on the contrary, honoured us
Germans with the greatest esteem. He specially praised our
honesty and truth. Nor will he have in Paris, where he pro-
poses to pass the winter, any French, but only German servants.
I thanked him for the confidence which he had in us, and
recommended to him several fellow-countrymen of the
historical school.

FRAGMENTS

GOD was always the beginning and the end of all my thoughts. If now I ask: What is God? what His nature? even as a small child I already asked: What is God like? what does He look like? And at that time I could spend whole days looking up at the sky, and in the evening I was quite disconsolate, that I had never glimpsed the most holy countenance of God, but had only seen the silly grimaces of the grey clouds. I grew entirely confused by all the information learned from astronomy, which subject even the smallest child was not spared in that period of enlightenment. I could not get over the wonder of it, that all these thousands of millions of stars were great and beautiful globes, like our own, and that one simple God ruled over all these gleaming myriads of worlds. Once in a dream, I remember, I saw God, in the farthest distance of the high heavens. He was gazing contentedly out of a little window of heaven, a pious old face with a little Jewish beard; He was scattering handfuls of seeds, which as they fell from heaven opened out, as it were, in the immeasurable space, and grew to tremendous size, until they finally became bright, flourishing, inhabited worlds, each one as large as our own. I have never been able to forget this face; I often saw this cheerful old man in my dreams again, scattering the seeds of worlds out of His tiny window: I once even saw Him cluck with his lips, just as our maid used to do when she gave the hens their barley. I could only see the falling seeds, always expanding to vast shining globes: but the great hens, which were possibly lying in wait somewhere with wide-open beaks, to be fed with these world-spheres, those I could never see.

FROM LETTERS TO MOSER

HEINE ON HIS BAPTISM

As you may imagine, the question of baptism is much discussed here. No one of the family is against it except myself. And this self is a very obstinate person. You know enough of my ways of thinking to be able to infer that baptism to me is an act of indifference, that I set no great store by it as a symbol, and that the power to defend the rights of my unhappy brethren is likely to weigh more with me. Notwithstanding, I consider it a degradation and a stain on my honour to submit to baptism in order to qualify myself for state employment in Prussia. I really don't know how I shall get out of this fatal dilemma. I shall end by turning Catholic in desperation, and hanging myself. We are living in evil times; rogues take the lead, and our leaders must turn rogues. I understand the words of the Psalmist: 'Give me my daily bread that I may not blaspheme Thy name.' . . . It's plaguy to think that in my case the whole man is ruled by considerations of the budget. My principles are not in the least influenced by the thought of wealth or poverty, but my actions unfortunately are. Yes, great Moser, Heinrich Heine is very small. In fact, little Markus is greater than I. This is no jest, but my soberest, grimmest earnest. I cannot repeat it to you too often, in order that you may not measure me by the standard of your own great soul.

I recommend to your notice Golowin's *Travels in Japan.* You'll learn from them that the Japanese are the most civilized and polite people in the world; I should add the most Christian, if I had not read to my astonishment that no other people regard Christianity with such hatred and abhorrence as these. I shall turn Japanese. They hate nothing so much as the cross. I shall turn Japanese. Perhaps I shall send you to-day another poem from the *Rabbi,* in which I unfortunately have been interrupted. I entreat you not to communicate the poem, or anything else I tell you of my private affairs, to any one. A young Spanish Jew, at heart a Jew, but who for the sake of ease and luxury has been baptized, is in correspondence with Jehuda Abarbanel, and sends him the poem translated from the Moorish. Perhaps it will seem to you not very noble behaviour to write to his friend without reserve; still he sends him the poem. Think no more of it.

I know not what to say to you. Cohen assures me that Gans is preaching the gospel and trying to convert the children of Israel. If he is doing so from conviction, he is a fool; if from hypocrisy, he is a blackguard. True, I shall not cease to love him, yet I confess to you I'd sooner have heard that Gans had stolen silver spoons. That you, dear Moser, hold with

Gans I cannot believe, though Cohen assures me that it is so, and that he has it from your own lips. I should be very sorry if I thought that you looked on my own baptism in a favourable light. I assure you that if the law had permitted the stealing of silver spoons I should not have been baptized. Last Saturday I was in the synagogue, and had the pleasure of hearing with my own ears Dr. Salomon launching forth against baptized Jews, and in particular inveighing against the way in which they allowed themselves to be seduced to abjure the faith of their fathers in the bare hope of getting a post (I 'm quoting his very words). Indeed, it was a very good sermon, and I intend to call on the doctor to-day. If I had time I would write Dr. Zunz's wife a Hebrew *billet-doux*. I 'm becoming a regular Christian—I sponge on the rich Jews.

That was a good time when *Ratcliffe* and *Almansor* were being published by Dümmler. You, dear Moser, used to admire the fine passages, and wrap yourself in your mantle, and make heart-stirring speeches like Marquis Posa. It was winter then, and the thermometer had fallen to Auerbach, and Dithmar froze in spite of his nankeen trousers; and yet it seems to me that it was warmer then than on this 23rd of April, when the Hamburgers are beginning to appear abroad with their spring feelings, their bunches of violets, etc. It was much warmer then. Gans, if I mistake not, was not then baptized, and wrote long speeches for the *Verein*, and took his motto *Victrix causa deis placuit sed victa Catoni*. I remember that the psalm, 'By the waters of Babylon,' was then your favourite, and you would recite it so beautifully, so grandly, so movingly, that even now I feel inclined to weep, and not only by reason of the psalm. Then, too, you had some very wise notions on Judaism, on the Christian ignominiousness of proselytizing, the ignominy of Jews who get baptized with the object, not only of escaping difficulties, but of thereby gaining something good, picking up some plum, and other wise notions which you ought to write down on some occasion. You are independent enough not to mind doing it for fear of Gans, and as for myself you need not fash yourself on my account. Solon said that no man should be counted happy before his death, and he may add that no one before he dies should be reckoned an honest man. I am glad that old Friedländer and Bendavid are old and will soon die, so that they at least are safe, and our times will not be open to the reproach that they have not produced one blameless character.

Forgive me my ill-humour, most of it is directed against myself.
I often get up at night and stand before the looking-glass and
rail at myself. Now it would seem I am taking my friend's
heart for my glass. . . . Greet for me our 'extraordinary'
friend, and tell him that I love him. This is the truth, the whole
truth, and nothing but the truth. His image is dear to me as
ever, though it is no sacred image, still less an adorable and
miracle-working image. I often think of him because I do not
care to think of myself. Thus, last night, I thought to myself:
With what face would Gans appear before Moses if Moses were
suddenly to reappear on earth? And yet Moses is the greatest
jurist that ever lived, for his legislation has lasted till the present
day. I dreamed, too, that Gans and Mordecai Noah met in
Straulau, and, marvellous to relate, Gans was mute as a fish.
Zunz stood by with a sarcastic smile, and said to his wife:
'Look there, ducky!' I think that Lehmann made a long discourse, in his fullest tones, and spiced with 'enlightenment,'
'change of circumstances,' 'progress of the world-spirit,' a long
discourse which, instead of sending me to sleep as usual,
awoke me.

HEINE ON GOETHE

IF I 've told you nothing about Goethe, my interview with him
at Weimar, and his kindness and condescension, you have, I
assure you, lost nothing. All that is left is the building where
beauty once grew, and it was this thought alone which made
me take interest in him. He made me feel quite melancholy, and
I 've come to like him better since he has moved my sympathies.
At bottom, however, Goethe and I are opposite and mutually
repellent natures. He is essentially an easy-going man of the
world, who looks on enjoyment as the highest good, and though
he has at times glimpses and passing intuitions of the ideal life
which he expresses in his poems, yet he has never conceived it
deeply, still less lived it. I, on the contrary, am essentially
an enthusiast, i.e. inspired by the idea and ready to sacrifice
myself for it, and always goaded to lose myself in the idea.
At the same time, however, I have a keen sense of the
enjoyments of life; hence the violent struggle between my
common sense, which approves the enjoyment of life, and
rejects all exalted self-sacrifice as folly, and my enthusiastic
impulse, which often crops up unawares, and lays violent hands
on me, and will perchance some day drag me down to her ancient

realms—drag me up, I ought perhaps to say, for it is still an open question whether the enthusiast who sacrifices his life for the idea, does not in a single moment live more, aye, live happier than Herr von Goethe in the whole of his seventy-six years of comfortable egotism.

BIOGRAPHY

Baxter, Richard (1615–91).
THE AUTOBIOGRAPHY OF RICHARD BAXTER.   868

Boswell, James (1740–95). *See* Johnson.

Brontë, Charlotte (1816–55).
LIFE, 1857. By *Mrs Gaskell*. Introduction by *May Sinclair*. (*See also* Fiction.) 318

Burns, Robert (1759–96).
LIFE, 1828. By *J. G. Lockhart* (1794–1854). With Introduction by *Prof. James Kinsley*, M.A., PH.D.   (*See also* Poetry and Drama.) 156

Byron, Lord (1788–1824).
LETTERS. Edited by *R. G. Howarth*, B.LITT., and with an Introduction by *André Maurois*.   (*See also* Poetry and Drama.) 931

Canton, William (1845–1926).
A CHILD'S BOOK OF SAINTS, 1898.   (*See also* Essays.) 61

Cellini, Benvenuto (1500–71).
THE LIFE OF BENVENUTO CELLINI, written by himself. Translated by *Anne Macdonell*. Introduction by *William Gaunt*.   51

Cowper, William (1731–1800).
SELECTED LETTERS. Edited, with Introduction, by *W. Hadley*, M.A.   774
(*See also* Poetry and Drama.)

Dickens, Charles (1812–70).
LIFE, 1874. By *John Forster* (1812–76). Introduction by *G. K. Chesterton*. 2 vols.
(*See also* Fiction.) 781–2

Evelyn, John (1620–1706).
DIARY. Edited by *William Bray*, 1819. Intro. by *G. W. E. Russell*. 2 vols.   220–1

Fox, George (1624–91).
JOURNAL, 1694. Revised by *Norman Penney*, with Account of Fox's last years. Introduction by *Rufus M. Jones*.   754

Franklin, Benjamin (1706–90).
AUTOBIOGRAPHY, 1817. With Introduction and Account of Franklin's later life by *W. Macdonald*. Reset new edition (1949), with a newly compiled Index.   316

Goethe, Johann Wolfgang von (1749–1832).
LIFE, 1855. By *G. H. Lewes* (1817–78). Introduction by *Havelock Ellis*. Index.
(*See also* Poetry and Drama.) 269

Hudson, William Henry (1841–1922).
FAR AWAY AND LONG AGO, 1918. Intro. by *John Galsworthy*.   956

Johnson, Samuel (1709–84).
LIVES OF THE ENGLISH POETS, 1781. Introduction by *Mrs L. Archer-Hind*. 2 vols.
(*See also* Essays, Fiction.) 770–1
BOSWELL'S LIFE OF JOHNSON, 1791. A new edition (1949), with Introduction by *S. C. Roberts*, M.A., LL.D., and a 30-page Index by Alan Dent. 2 vols.   1–2

Keats, John (1795–1821).
LIFE AND LETTERS, 1848. By *Lord Houghton* (1809–85). Introduction by *Robert Lynd*. Note on the letters by Lewis Gibbs.   (*See also* Poetry and Drama.) 801

Lamb, Charles (1775–1834).
LETTERS. New edition (1945) arranged from the Complete Annotated Edition of the Letters. 2 vols.   (*See also* Essays and Belles-Lettres, Fiction.) 342–3

Napoleon Buonaparte (1769–1821).
HISTORY OF NAPOLEON BUONAPARTE, 1829. By *J. G. Lockhart* (1794–1854).   3
(*See also* Essays and Belles-Lettres.)

Nelson, Horatio, Viscount (1758–1805).
LIFE, 1813. By *Robert Southey* (1774–1843).   (*See also* Essays.) 52

Outram, General Sir James (1803–63), 'the Bayard of India.'
LIFE, 1903. Deals with important passages in the history of India in the nineteenth century. By *L. J. Trotter* (1827–1912).   396

Pepys, Samuel (1633–1703).
DIARY. Newly edited (1953), with modernized spelling, **by** *John Warrington*, from the edition of Mynors Bright (1875–9). 3 vols.   53–5

Plutarch (46?–120).
LIVES OF THE NOBLE GREEKS AND ROMANS. Dryden's edition, 1683–6. Revised, with Introduction, by *A. H. Clough* (1819–61). 3 vols.   407–9

Rousseau, Jean Jacques (1712–78).
CONFESSIONS, 1782. 2 vols. Complete and unabridged English translation. New Introduction by *Prof. R. Niklaus*, B.A., PH.D., of Exeter University.   859–60
(*See also* Essays, Theology and Philosophy.)

Scott, Sir Walter (1771–1832).
LOCKHART'S LIFE OF SCOTT. An abridgement by *J. G. Lockhart* himself from the original 7 volumes. New Introduction by *W. M. Parker*, M.A.   39

CLASSICAL

ESSAYS AND BELLES-LETTRES

Manzoni, Alessandro (1785–1873).

THE BETROTHED (*I Promessi Sposi*, 1840, rev. ed.). Translated (1951) from the Italian by *Archibald Colquhoun*, who also adds a preface. 999

Marryat, Frederick (1792–1848).

MR MIDSHIPMAN EASY. New Introduction by *Oliver Warner*. 82
THE SETTLERS IN CANADA, 1844. Introduction by *Oliver Warner*. 370

Maugham, W. Somerset (*b.* 1874).

CAKES AND ALE, 1930. The finest novel of the author's inter-war period. 932

Maupassant, Guy de (1850–93).

SHORT STORIES. Translated by *Marjorie Laurie*. Intro. by *Gerald Gould*. 907

Melville, Herman (1819–91).

MOBY DICK, 1851. Intro. by *Prof. Sherman Paul*. 179
TYPEE, 1846; and BILLY BUDD (*published* 1924). South Seas adventures. New Introduction by *Milton R. Stern*. 180

Meredith, George (1828–1909).

THE ORDEAL OF RICHARD FEVEREL, 1859. Introduction by *Robert Sencourt*. 916

Mickiewicz, Adam (1798–1855).

PAN TADEUSZ, 1834. Translated into English prose, with Introduction, by *Prof. G. R. Noyes*. Poland's epic of Napoleonic wars. 842

Modern Short Stories. Selected by *John Hadfield*. Twenty stories. 954

Moore, George (1852–1933).

ESTHER WATERS, 1894. The story of Esther Waters, the servant girl who 'went wrong.' Introduction by *C. D. Medley*. 933

Mulock [Mrs Craik], Maria (1826–87).

JOHN HALIFAX, GENTLEMAN, 1856. Introduction by *J. Shaylor*. 123

Pater, Walter (1839–94).

MARIUS THE EPICUREAN, 1885. Introduction by *Osbert Burdett*. 903

Poe, Edgar Allan (1809–49).

TALES OF MYSTERY AND IMAGINATION. Introduction by *Padraic Colum*. 336
(*See also* Poetry and Drama.)

Priestley, J. B. (*b.* 1894).

ANGEL PAVEMENT, 1931. A finely conceived novel of London. 938

Quiller-Couch, Sir Arthur (1863–1944).

HETTY WESLEY, 1903. Introduction by the author. (*See also* Essays.) 864

Radcliffe, Mrs Ann (1764–1823).

THE MYSTERIES OF UDOLPHO, 1794. Intro. by *R. A. Freeman*. 2 vols. 865–6

Reade, Charles (1814–84).

THE CLOISTER AND THE HEARTH, 1861. Introduction by *Swinburne*. 29

Richardson, Samuel (1689–1761).

PAMELA, 1740. Introduction by *George Saintsbury*. 2 vols. 683–4
CLARISSA, 1747–8. Introduction by *Prof. W. L. Phelps*. 4 vols. 882–5

Russian Short Stories. Translated, with Introduction, by *Rochelle S. Townsend*. Stories by Pushkin, Gogol, Tolstoy, Korolenko, Chehov, Chirikov, Andreyev, Kuprin, Gorky, Sologub. 758

Scott, Sir Walter (1771–1832).

The following Waverley Novels each contain an Introduction, biographical and bibliographical, based upon Lockhart's *Life*:
THE ANTIQUARY, 1816. Introduction by *W. M. Parker*, M.A. 126
THE BRIDE OF LAMMERMOOR, 1819. A romance of life in East Lothian, 1695. New Introduction by *W. M. Parker*, M.A. 129
GUY MANNERING, 1815. A mystery story of the time of George III. New Introduction by *W. M. Parker*, M.A. 133
THE HEART OF MIDLOTHIAN, 1818. Period of the Porteous Riots, 1736. New Introduction by *W. M. Parker*, M.A. 134
IVANHOE, 1820. A romance of the days of Richard I. 16
KENILWORTH, 1821. The tragic story of Amy Robsart, in Elizabeth I's time. New Preface and Glossary by *W. M. Parker*, M.A. 135
OLD MORTALITY, 1817. Battle of Bothwell Bridge, 1679. New Introduction by *W. M. Parker*, M.A. 137
QUENTIN DURWARD, 1823. A tale of adventures in fifteenth-century France. New Introduction by *W. M. Parker*, M.A. 140
REDGAUNTLET, 1824. A tale of adventure in Cumberland, about 1763. New Introduction by *W. M. Parker*, M.A. 141
ROB ROY, 1818. A romance of the Rebellion of 1715. 142
THE TALISMAN, 1825. Richard Cœur-de-Lion and the Third Crusade, 1191. New Preface by *W. M. Parker*, M.A. (*See also* Biography.) 144

Shchedrin (M. E. Saltykov, 1826–92).

THE GOLOVLYOV FAMILY. Translated by *Natalie Duddington*. Introduction by *Edward Garnett*. 908

Shelley, Mary Wollstonecraft (1797–1851).

FRANKENSTEIN, 1818. With Mary Shelley's own Preface. 616

Shorter Novels.

Vol. I: ELIZABETHAN. Introduction by *George Saintsbury* and Notes by *Philip Henderson*. Contains: Deloney's 'Jack of Newberie' and 'Thomas of Reading'; Nashe's 'The Unfortunate Traveller'; Green's 'Carde of Fancie.' 824

Voltaire, François Marie Arouet de (1694–1778).
 CANDIDE, AND OTHER TALES. Smollett's translation, edited by *J. C. Thornton.* 936
(*See also* History.)
Walpole, Hugh Seymour (1884–1941).
 MR PERRIN AND MR TRAILL, 1911. 918
Wells, Herbert George (1866–1946).
 ANN VERONICA, 1909. Introduction by *A. J. Hoppé.* 997
 THE WHEELS OF CHANCE, 1896; and THE TIME MACHINE, 1895. 915
Wilde, Oscar.
 THE PICTURE OF DORIAN GRAY, 1891. (*See* Poetry and Drama.)
Woolf, Virginia (1882–1941).
 TO THE LIGHTHOUSE, 1927. Introduction by *D. M. Hoare,* PH.D. 949
Zola, Émile (1840–1902).
 GERMINAL, 1885. Translated, with an Introduction, by *Havelock Ellis.* 897

HISTORY

Anglo-Saxon Chronicle. Translated and Edited by *G. N. Garmonsway,* F.R.HIST.SOC.
 Foreword by *Prof. Bruce Dickins.* 624
Bede, the Venerable (673–735).
 THE ECCLESIASTICAL HISTORY OF THE ENGLISH NATION. Translated by *John Stevens,* revised by *J. A. Giles,* with notes by *L. C. Jane.* Introduction by *Prof. David Knowles,* O.S.B., M.A., LITT.D., F.B.A., F.S.A. 479
Carlyle, Thomas (1795–1881).
 THE FRENCH REVOLUTION, 1837. Introduction by *Hilaire Belloc.* 2 vols. 31–2
(*See also* Biography, Essays.)
Chesterton, Cecil (1879–1918). A HISTORY OF THE U.S.A., 1917. Edited by *Prof. D. W. Brogan,* M.A. 965
Creasy, Sir Edward (1812–78).
 FIFTEEN DECISIVE BATTLES OF THE WORLD, FROM MARATHON TO WATERLOO, 1852. With Diagrams and Index. New Introduction by *Audrey Butler,* M.A. (OXON.). 300
Gibbon, Edward (1737–94).
 THE DECLINE AND FALL OF THE ROMAN EMPIRE, 1776–88. Notes by *Oliphant Smeaton.* Intro. by *Christopher Dawson.* Complete text in 6 vols. 434–6, 474–6
Green, John Richard (1837–83).
 A SHORT HISTORY OF THE ENGLISH PEOPLE, 1874. Introduction by *L. C. Jane.* English history from 607 to 1873. Continued by: 'A Political and Social Survey from 1815 to 1915,' by *R. P. Farley,* and revised to 1950. 727–8
Holinshed, Raphael (*d.* 1580?).
 HOLINSHED'S CHRONICLE AS USED IN SHAKESPEARE'S PLAYS, 1578. Introduction by *Prof. Allardyce Nicoll* and *Josephine Nicoll.* 800
Joinville, Jean de. See Villehardouin.
Lützow, Count Franz von (1849–1916).
 BOHEMIA: AN HISTORICAL SKETCH, 1896. Introduction by *President T. G. Masaryk.* H. A. Piehler covers events from 1879 to 1938. 432
Macaulay, Thomas Babington, Baron (1800–59).
 THE HISTORY OF ENGLAND. The complete text in four volumes, which together contain 2,450 pages. Introduction by *Douglas Jerrold.* 34–7
(*See also* Essays.)
Maine, Sir Henry (1822–88).
 ANCIENT LAW, 1861. Introduction by *Prof. J. H. Morgan.* 734
Mommsen, Theodor (1817–1903).
 HISTORY OF ROME, 1856. Translated by *W. P. Dickson,* LL.D. Introduction by *Edward A. Freeman.* 4 vols. (Vols. III and IV only.) 544–5
Motley, John (1814–77).
 THE RISE OF THE DUTCH REPUBLIC, 1856. Intro. by *V. R. Reynolds.* 3 vols. 86–8
Paston Letters, The, 1418–1506. 2 vols. A selection. 752–3
Prescott, William Hickling (1796–1859).
 HISTORY OF THE CONQUEST OF MEXICO, 1843. 2 vols. 397–8
Stanley, Arthur (1815–81).
 LECTURES ON THE HISTORY OF THE EASTERN CHURCH, 1861. Introduction by *A. J. Grieve,* M.A. 251
Thierry, Augustin (1795–1856).
 THE NORMAN CONQUEST, 1825. Introduction by *J. A. Price,* B.A. 2 vols. (*Vol. I temporarily out of print.*) 198–9
Villehardouin, Geoffrey de (1160?–1213?), and Joinville, Jean, Sire de (1224–1317).
 MEMOIRS OF THE CRUSADES. Translated, with an Introduction, by *Sir Frank T. Marzials.* 333
Voltaire, François Marie Arouet de (1694–1778).
 THE AGE OF LOUIS XIV, 1751. Translation by *Martyn P. Pollack.*
(*See also* Fiction.) 780

ORATORY

British Orations. The 1960 edition of this selection of British historical speeches contains selections from four of the most famous of Sir Winston Churchill's World War II speeches. 714

Burke, Edmund (1729–97).
SPEECHES AND LETTERS ON AMERICAN AFFAIRS. New Introduction by the *Very Rev. Canon Peter McKevitt*, PH.D. (*See also* Essays and Belles-Lettres.) 340

Demosthenes (384–322 B.C.).
THE CROWN, AND OTHER ORATIONS. Translated with an Appendix on Athenian economics by *C. Rann Kennedy*. Introduction by *John Warrington*. 546

Lincoln, Abraham (1809–65).
SPEECHES AND LETTERS, 1832–65. A new selection edited with an Introduction by *Paul M. Angle*. Chronology of Lincoln's life and index. 206

POETRY AND DRAMA

Anglo-Saxon Poetry. English poetry between A.D. 650 and 1000, from 'Widsith' and 'Beowulf' to the battle-pieces of 'Brunanburh' and 'Maldon.' Selected and translated by *Prof. R. K. Gordon*, M.A. Reset, and revised by the translator, 1954. 794

Arnold, Matthew (1822–88).
COMPLETE POEMS. Introduction by *R. A. Scott-James*. 334

Ballads, A Book of British. Introduction and Notes by *R. Brimley Johnson*. Ballads from the earliest times to those of Yeats and Kipling. 572

Beaumont, Francis (1584–1616), and **Fletcher, John** (1579–1625).
SELECT PLAYS. Introduction by *Prof. G. P. Baker*. 'The Knight of the Burning Pestle,' 'The Maid's Tragedy,' 'A King and No King,' 'The Faithful Shepherdess.' 'The Wild Goose Chase,' 'Bonduca,' with a glossary. 506

Blake, William (1757–1827).
POEMS AND PROPHECIES. Edited, with special Introduction, by *Max Plowman*. 792

Brontë, Emily.
POEMS. (*See* Fiction.)

Browning, Robert (1812–89).
POEMS AND PLAYS, 1833–64. With a new Introduction by *John Bryson*, M.A., dealing with the four-volume Everyman Browning set. 2 vols. Volume III, containing *The Ring and the Book*, Browning's long dramatic poem (No. 502), is temporarily out of print. 41–2
POEMS, 1871–90. Introduction by *M. M. Bozman*. 964

Burns, Robert (1759–96).
POEMS AND SONGS. A very full selection and a very accurate text of Burns's copious lyrical output. Edited and introduced by *Prof. James Kinsley*, M.A. 94
(*See also* Biography.)

Byron, George Gordon Noel, Lord (1788–1824).
THE POETICAL AND DRAMATIC WORKS. 3 vols. Edited with a Preface by *Guy Pocock* (*See also* Biography.) 486–8

Century. A CENTURY OF HUMOROUS VERSE, 1850–1950. Edited by *Roger Lancelyn Green*, M.A., B.LITT. 813

Chaucer, Geoffrey (*c.* 1343–1400).
CANTERBURY TALES. New standard text edited by *A. C. Cawley*, M.A., PH.D., based on the Ellesmere Manuscript, with an ingenious system of glosses, page by page. 307
TROILUS AND CRISEYDE. Prepared by *John Warrington* from the Campsall Manuscript. 992

Coleridge, Samuel Taylor (1772–1834).
THE GOLDEN BOOK. (*See also* Essays, etc.) 43

Cowper, William (1731–1800).
POEMS. Intro. by *Hugh I'Anson Fausset*. (*See also* Biography.) 872

Dante Alighieri (1265–1321).
THE DIVINE COMEDY, first printed 1472. H. F. Cary's Translation, 1805–14. Edited, with Notes and Index, by *Edmund Gardner*. Foreword by *Prof. Mario Praz*. 308

De la Mare, Walter (1873–1956). (*See* Essays.)

Donne, John (1573–1631).
COMPLETE POEMS. Edited, with a revised Intro., by *Hugh I'Anson Fausset*. 867

Dryden, John (1631–1700).
POEMS. Edited by *Bonamy Dobrée*, O.B.E., M.A. 910

Eighteenth-century Plays. Edited by *John Hampden*. Includes Gay's 'Beggar's Opera,' Addison's 'Cato,' Rowe's 'Jane Shore,' Fielding's 'Tragedy of Tragedies, or, Tom Thumb the Great,' Lillo's 'George Barnwell,' Colman and Garrick's 'Clandestine Marriage,' and Cumberland's 'West Indian.' 818

English Galaxy of Shorter Poems, The. Chosen and Edited by *Gerald Bullett*. 959

English Religious Verse. Edited by *G. Lacey May*. An anthology from the Middle Ages to the present day, including some 300 poems by 150 authors. 937

Everyman, and Medieval Miracle Plays. New edition edited by *A. C. Cawley*, M.A., PH.D. Forewords to individual plays. 381

Fitzgerald, Edward (1809–83). *See* 'Persian Poems.'

Palgrave, Francis Turner (1824–97). *See* 'Golden Treasury of English Songs and Lyrics, The.'   96

Persian Poems. Selected and edited by *Prof. A. J. Arberry*, M.A., LITT.D., F.B.A.   996

Poe, Edgar Allan (1809–49).
  POEMS AND ESSAYS. Introduction by *Andrew Lang.*   (*See also* Fiction.) 791

Poems of our Time. An Anthology edited by *Richard Church*, C.B.E., *M. M. Bozman* and *Edith Sitwell*, D.LITT., D.B.E. Nearly 400 poems by about 130 poets.   981

Pope, Alexander (1688–1744).
  COLLECTED POEMS. Edited with Intro. (1956) by *Prof. Bonamy Dobrée*, O.B.E., M.A.   760

Restoration Plays. Introduction by *Edmund Gosse*. Includes Dryden's 'All for Love,' Wycherley's 'The Country Wife,' Congreve's 'The Way of the World,' Otway's 'Venice Preserved,' Farquhar's 'Beaux-Stratagem,' Vanbrugh's 'Provoked Wife.' Etherege's 'Man of Mode.'   604

Rossetti, Dante Gabriel (1828–82).
  POEMS AND TRANSLATIONS. Introduction by *E. G. Gardner.*   627

Shakespeare, William (1564–1616).
  A Complete Edition, based on Clark and Wright's Cambridge text, and edited by *Oliphant Smeaton*. With biographical Introduction, Chronological Tables and full Glossary. 3 vols.
      Comedies, 153; Histories, Poems and Sonnets, 154; Tragedies, 155

Shelley, Percy Bysshe (1792–1822).
  POETICAL WORKS. Introduction by *A. H. Koszul.* 2 vols.   257–8

Sheridan, Richard Brinsley (1751–1816).
  COMPLETE PLAYS. Introduction and notes by *Lewis Gibbs.*   95

Silver Poets of the Sixteenth Century. Edited by *Gerald Bullett*. The works of Sir Thomas Wyatt (1503–42), Henry Howard, Earl of Surrey (1517?–47), Sir Philip Sidney (1554–86), Sir Walter Ralegh (1552–1618) and Sir John Davies (1569–1626.)   985

Spenser, Edmund (1552–99).
  THE FAERIE QUEENE. Introduction by *Prof. J. W. Hales*, and Glossary. 2 vols. The reliable Morris text and glossary are used for this edition.   443–4
  THE SHEPHERD'S CALENDAR, 1579; and OTHER POEMS. Introduction by *Philip Henderson.*   879

Stevenson, Robert Louis (1850–94).
  POEMS. A CHILD'S GARDEN OF VERSES, 1885; UNDERWOODS, 1887; SONGS OF TRAVEL, 1896; and BALLADS, 1890, Introduction by *Ernest Rhys.*   768
      (*See also* Essays, Fiction, Travel.)

Swinburne, Algernon Charles (1837–1909).
  POEMS AND PROSE. A selection, edited with an Intro. by *Richard Church.*   961

Synge, J. M. (1871–1909).
  PLAYS, POEMS AND PROSE. Introduction by *Michaél Mac Liammóir.*   968

Tchekhov, Anton (1860–1904).
  PLAYS AND STORIES. 'The Cherry Orchard,' 'The Seagull,' 'The Wood Demon,' 'Tatyana Riepin' and 'On the Harmfulness of Tobacco' are included, as well as 13 of his best stories. The translation is by *S. S. Koteliansky*. Introduction by *David Magarshack.*   941

Tennyson, Alfred, Lord (1809–92).
  POEMS. A comprehensive edition (1950), with an Introduction by *Mildred Bozman.* 2 vols.   44, 626

Twenty-four One-Act Plays. Enlarged edition, new Introduction by *John Hampden*. Contains plays by T. S. Eliot, Sean O'Casey, Laurence Housman, W. B. Yeats, James Bridie, Noel Coward, Lord Dunsany, Wolf Mankowitz and others.   947

Webster, John (1580?–1625?), and Ford, John (1586–1639).
  SELECTED PLAYS. Introduction by *Prof. G. B. Harrison*, M.A., PH.D. In one volume: 'The White Devil,' 'The Duchess of Malfi,' 'The Broken Heart,' ''Tis Pity She's a Whore.'   899

Whitman, Walt (1819–92).
  LEAVES OF GRASS, 1855–92. New edition (1947) by *Dr Emory Holloway.*   573

Wilde, Oscar (1854–1900).
  PLAYS, PROSE WRITINGS, AND POEMS. Edited, with Introduction, by *Hesketh Pearson*. Including the two plays, 'The Importance of Being Earnest' and 'Lady Windermere's Fan'; his novel, 'The Picture of Dorian Gray'; the poem, 'The Ballad of Reading Gaol'; the essay, 'The Soul of Man,' etc.   858

Wordsworth, William (1770–1850).
  POEMS. Edited, with Introductory study, notes, bibliography and full index, by *Philip Wayne*, M.A.   203, 311, 998

REFERENCE

Reader's Guide to Everyman's Library. Compiled by *A. J. Hoppé*. This volume is a new compilation and gives in one alphabetical sequence the names of all the authors, titles and subjects in Everyman's Library and its supplementary series, Everyman's Reference Library and the Children's Illustrated Classics.   889
  Many volumes formerly included in Everyman's Library reference section are now included in Everyman's Reference Library and are bound in larger format.

ROMANCE

Aucassin and Nicolette, with other Medieval Romances. Translated, with Introduction, by *Eugene Mason*.　　　　497

Boccaccio, Giovanni (1313–75).
DECAMERON, 1471. Translated by *J. M. Rigg*, 1903. Introduction by *Edward Hutton*, 2 vols. Unabridged.　　　　845–6

Bunyan, John (1628–88).
PILGRIM'S PROGRESS, Parts I and II, 1678–84. Reset edition. Introduction by *Prof. G. B. Harrison*, M.A., PH.D.　　　　(*See also* Theology and Philosophy.) 204

Cervantes, Saavedra Miguel de (1547–1616).
DON QUIXOTE DE LA MANCHA. Translated by *P. A. Motteux*. Notes by *J. G. Lockhart*. Introduction and supplementary Notes by *L. B. Walton*, M.A., B.LITT. 2 vols.　　　　385–6

Chrétien de Troyes (fl. 12th cent.).
ARTHURIAN ROMANCES ('Erec et Enide'; 'Cligés'; 'Yvain' and 'Lancelot'). Translated into prose, with Introduction, notes and bibliography, by *William Wistar Comfort*.　　　　698

Kalevala, or The Land of Heroes. Translated from the Finnish by W. F. Kirby. 2 vols.　　　　259–60

Mabinogion, The. Translated with Introduction by *Thomas Jones*, M.A., D.LITT., and *Gwyn Jones*, M.A.　　　　97

Malory, Sir Thomas (fl. 1400?–70).
LE MORTE D'ARTHUR. Introduction by *Sir John Rhys*. 2 vols.　　　　45–6

Marie de France (12th century), LAYS OF, AND OTHER FRENCH LEGENDS. Eight of Marie's 'Lais' and two of the anonymous French love stories of the same period translated with an Introduction by *Eugene Mason*.　　　　557

Njal's Saga. THE STORY OF BURNT NJAL (written about 1280–90). Translated from the Icelandic by *Sir G. W. Dasent* (1861). Introduction (1957) and Index by *Prof. Edward Turville-Petre*, B.LITT., M.A.　　　　558

Rabelais, François (1494?–1553).
THE HEROIC DEEDS OF GARGANTUA AND PANTAGRUEL, 1532–5. Introduction by *D. B. Wyndham Lewis*. 2 vols. A complete unabridged edition of Urquhart and Motteux's translation, 1653–94.　　　　826–7

SCIENCE

Boyle, Robert (1627–91).
THE SCEPTICAL CHYMIST, 1661. Introduction by *M. M. Pattison Muir*.　　　　559

Darwin, Charles (1809–82).
THE ORIGIN OF SPECIES, 1859. The sixth edition embodies Darwin's final additions and revisions. New Introduction (1956) by *W. R. Thompson*, F.R.S.　　　　811
(*See also* Travel and Topography.)

Eddington, Arthur Stanley (1882–1944).
THE NATURE OF THE PHYSICAL WORLD, 1928. Introduction by *Sir Edmund Whittaker*, F.R.S., O.M.　　　　922

Euclid (fl. c. 330–c. 275 B.C.).
THE ELEMENTS OF EUCLID. Edited by *Isaac Todhunter*, with Introduction by *Sir Thomas L. Heath*, K.C.B., F.R.S.　　　　891

Faraday, Michael (1791–1867).
EXPERIMENTAL RESEARCHES IN ELECTRICITY, 1839–55. With Plates and Diagrams, and an appreciation by *Prof. John Tyndall*.　　　　576

Harvey, William (1578–1657).
THE CIRCULATION OF THE BLOOD. Introduction by *Ernest Parkyn*.　　　　262

Howard, John (1726?–90).
THE STATE OF THE PRISONS, 1777. Intro. and Notes by *Kenneth Ruck*.　　　　835

Marx, Karl (1818–83).
CAPITAL, 1867. Translated by *Eden* and *Cedar Paul*. 2 vols. Introduction by *Prof. G. D. H. Cole*.　　　　848–9

Mill, John Stuart (1806–73). See Wollstonecraft.

Owen, Robert (1771–1858).
A NEW VIEW OF SOCIETY, 1813; and OTHER WRITINGS. Introduction by *G. D. H. Cole*.　　　　799

Pearson, Karl (1857–1936).
THE GRAMMAR OF SCIENCE, 1892.　　　　939

Ricardo, David (1772–1823).
THE PRINCIPLES OF POLITICAL ECONOMY AND TAXATION, 1817. Introduction by *Prof. Michael P. Fogarty*, M.A.　　　　590

Smith, Adam (1723–90).
THE WEALTH OF NATIONS, 1766. Intro. by *Prof. Edwin Seligman*. 2 vols. 412–13

White, Gilbert (1720–93).
A NATURAL HISTORY OF SELBORNE, 1789. New edition (1949). Introduction and Notes by *R. M. Lockley*.　　　　48

Wollstonecraft, Mary (1759–97), THE RIGHTS OF WOMAN, 1792; and **Mill, John Stuart** (1806–73), THE SUBJECTION OF WOMEN, 1869. New Introduction by *Pamela Frankau*.　　　　825

THEOLOGY AND PHILOSOPHY

TRAVEL AND TOPOGRAPHY

angegeben werden. In der ersten Sendung wurden u.a. Transistor-Radios sehr ausführlich behandelt, und das Modell, das unter Dutzenden als "der beste Kauf" erklärt wurde, gelangte zu einem in der heutigen Werbung neuartigen Vorsprung über seine Rivalen.

Überhaupt werden vielfach neue Verhältnisse geschaffen, und an vielen Abschnitten des Konkurrenzkampfes verschieben sich die Fronten. Die neuen Konsumentenschützer bekennen sich als Anhänger des freien Wettbewerbs, der schon selbst weitgehend dafür sorge, daß der Käufer von Markenartikeln nicht kraß und schon gar nicht beharrlich übers Ohr gehauen werde; sie wollen den Käufer nur behutsam durch das Gestrüpp und manchmal den Dschungel einer Unzahl von Waren derselben Gattung und besonders der vielen Haushaltneuheiten führen.

Man könnte nun glauben, daß sie durch ein solches Vorhaben in einen scharfen Konflikt mit der bestimmten Interessen dienenden Berufsreklame geraten. Gewiß ist der sehr wichtige Wirtschaftszweig der englischen Reklamebranche über den eigenartigen Nebenbuhler nicht entzückt, ohne daß es bisher zu offenen Angriffen oder Zusammenstößen gekommen wäre. Die einzigen Kampfhandlungen bestanden darin, daß die eine oder andere Zeitschrift Inserate ablehnte, welche der selber sehr reklamefreudige Konsumentenverband im ganzen Land placiert. Er gab im letzten Jahr fast halb so viel für Eigenpropaganda wie für Warenprüfung aus. Jedenfalls haben seine Begutachtungen den Regeln gegen unlauteren Wettbewerb und vor allem den gesetzlichen Fallstricken standgehalten,

READINGS FROM HEINRICH HEINE